# Identification G

## to Eu

## Non-Pa

# Identification Guide to European Non-Passerines

by

Kevin Baker

British Trust for Ornithology
Field Guide Number 24

*Published by*
*The British Trust for Ornithology*
*The National Centre for Ornithology*
*The Nunnery*
*Thetford*
*Norfolk IP24 2PU*

Baker, K. (1993). Identification Guide to
European Non-Passerines: BTO Guide 24.
British Trust for Ornithology, Thetford.
© BTO1993
ISBN 0-903793-18-0

Printed in Great Britain by
Page Bros, Norwich

# Contents

# FOREWORD

**This work is primarily designed to aid ringers working in the field to identify species, and in some cases subspecies, and to determine the age, and sex of birds in the hand.** It will, no doubt, also prove useful to museum workers studying skins and, because non-passerine species more often exhibit manifestly different plumage traits between ages than do passerines, it will also be used by expert field ornithologists.

This book is the culmination of many years of work spent studying skins and handling live birds, as well as gleaning information from experienced field workers. Journals and books have been searched for relevant material. There has been a wealth of information flow from British and Irish ringers and from overseas colleagues in response to my earlier published works on non-passerine ageing and sexing. The first of them appeared in the December 1979 issue of the *Ringers' Bulletin*, and the last in 1984 following a nine-part series covering some 35 common non-passerine species (Baker 1979 to 1984).

This guide now contains details of over 119 species. I have attempted to select from the enormous list of European non-passerine species those which are likely to be caught, either incidentally during normal mist-netting routines, or, perhaps more commonly, by design. I have probably failed to predict either category with any degree of success! To those workers who find I have not dealt with an 'obvious' species, I humbly apologize. An obvious omission in the list of groups dealt with in the book is the waders *Charadriiformes*. This is because the BTO already has a guide devoted to this Order: *Guide to the identification and ageing of Holarctic Waders* by Tony Prater, John Marchant and Juhani Vuorinen (1977), BTO Guide 17, is available from the BTO (details and price from The National Centre for Ornithology, The Nunnery, Thetford, Norfolk, IP24 2PU). Classification, sequence and scientific nomenclature in this book follow Voous (1977), except where modifications have been adopted by the British Ornithologists' Union Records Committee (BOU 1992).

Since this guide is essentially aimed at the serious ornithologist, it assumes that the user is moderately conversant with basic skills of bird identification. Therefore, no basic material will be found under the heading 'Identification' for those species whose identification is relatively straightforward. However, references may be found to rare European birds or even to vagrants, though they may not themselves be dealt with in the text as individual species. They are included because of their similarity to more common species, and because it is important to identify positively closely related species, rare or otherwise. They are, more often than not, referred to under the species they most resemble.

This book is a guide. The science of ageing and sexing birds is forever developing. Like all technical guides it quickly becomes out of date once it is published. The scope for learning much, much more about ageing and sexing methods in non-passerines is enormous. Periodic revision of such a guide is therefore essential if ringers are to keep abreast of techniques. It is my intention to continue collecting material, with a view to publishing revised editions when, and if, the need arises. Users are urged to pass on information about ageing and sexing methods which are not covered in this guide, or those techniques which need modifying, or those which do not appear to work!

# Acknowledgements

Since I first become interested, and published material in 1979 on the theme of ageing and sexing birds, a very large number of people have been instrumental in helping piece together information for the guide and giving valuable help and advice. Firstly, I must thank Bob Spencer who, at the start of this project, was Head of the Ringing Scheme. It was he who first suggested publishing my findings in the *Ringers' Bulletin*. This guide was written while I was a member of staff of the BTO Ringing Unit, much of whose work is supported through a long term contract from the Joint Nature Conservation Committee on behalf of English Nature, the Countryside Council for Wales and Scottish Natural Heritage and through separate contracts from the Department of the Environment for Northern Ireland and the National Parks and Wildlife Service of the Republic of Ireland. I hope that it will contribute to increasing the conservation value of the ringing data and to JNCC's specific remit for monitoring high common standards of data gathering in Britain and Northern Ireland. The work undertaken would not have been possible had not the staff of the sub-department of ornithology of the British Museum (Nat.Hist.) allowed me unlimited access to the skin collection. In particular Iain Bishop, Graham Cowles, Derek Read, Peter Colston and Michael Walters all helped and advised with some aspect of my work.

There are too many people to thank who have contributed information contained in the pages of this book. To the many ringers and other ornithologists I have talked to, whether out in the field, at conferences or over a pint in some remote forgotten land, I offer my gratitude: Ian Alexander, Colin Bibby, Mike Boddy, Hugh Brazier, Mike Brooke, the late Adrian Cawthorne, Steve and Tim Christmas, Nigel Cleere, John Coulson, Tony Crease, Peter E. Davis, Brian Dudley, George Dunnet, Peter Fearon, Mark Fletcher, Tony Fox, Steve Gale, David Gibbons, the late Peter J. Grant, Geoffrey Gush, Tim Hallchurch, Mike P. Harris, P. Herroelen, Alan Hilton, Peter Hope Jones, Jon Hornbuckle, Barry Hughes, David Jardine, Nigel Jarrett, Roy King, Tom Kittle, G.H.J. de Kroon, Peter Lack, Kate Lessells, Andy Lowe, Sean McMinn, Mick Marquiss, Eric Meek, Ian Newton, Gabriel Noonan, Dave Okill, Steve Ormerod, Myrfyn Owen, Adrian Parr, David Paynter, Steve Petty, Eileen Rees, Nick Riddiford, Derek Scott, Robin Sellers, Trevor Squire, Tim Stowe, John Turner, Andy Village, K. Walkling, John Walmsley, Sarah Wanless, Ian Wyllie, Bernie Zonfrillo. There are countless people that I have forgotten to acknowledge: to them I apologize most sincerely.

There are three major reference works which must be acknowledged since a very substantial part of the information in this book is based on their material. They are 1. *Identification and ageing Raptors by Dick Forsman* (1984), 2. *Identification and ageing of Wildfowl* by Aarno Salminen (1983), and 3. *Identification and ageing of Gulls, Terns and Skuas* by Martti Hario (1986). They are not cited after the species text under Reference; nor are other major works which were consulted, these being *Duck Wings* by H. Boyd, J. Harrison and A. Allison

(1975), *Birds of Europe the Middle East and North Africa: the birds of the Western Palearctic*. Vols I, II, III, IV by Cramp & Simmons (1977, 1980, 1983; Cramp 1985), *Gulls: a guide to identification* by Peter Grant (1982), and the *Handbook of North American Birds*. Vol 1 by R.S. Palmer (1976). Additional material on wildfowl was also provided by Malcolm Ogilvie and Carl Mitchell. Some of these guides, and many published papers also, required translating into English, tasks which were undertaken by Brigitt Baker, Eva Irving, Tarja Armitage, and Agi Peach. To all of them I extend my sincere thanks.

Finally, I am indebted to Chris Mead, David Norman and John Marchant for reading through the manuscript and making useful suggestions to an earlier draft. The staff at the BTO have lent their support over the years during the production of this guide. Special thanks must go to Stephen Baillie who bullied me into finishing the work, and to Jacquie Clark who, for the last year, has helped steer this guide to its finished product.

Thetford, June 1993                                                         Kevin Baker

# Detailed use of this Guide

**IMPORTANT:** Successful ageing and sexing of birds is dependent on the user having a thorough knowledge and understanding of moult and wear of feathers. Please spend some time reading through this section before making use of the main species accounts.

## Species accounts

Each species account is set out in a standard way - Identification (where necessary), Sexing, Ageing, Moult, Geographical Variation, and Biometrics. A summary of what each of these sections describes is set out below.

### Identification

It is assumed that users of this guide have a basic skill in species identification, especially of birds in the hand. There is, therefore, no account given to identification points for species which should present little or no problem to the average ringer, or other users of this guide. However, for those species which can easily be confused with another, common or rare, there is a brief description of the key pointers to use to aid positive identification. Only the most obvious and useful features are highlighted. Where difficulties occur between species the section is enlarged and a combination of pointers may have to be used. In some species it may be necessary to take 'unusual' biometrics to determine identification. In such cases it is important that users are fully conversant with the methods for taking standard biometrics (see section under Biometrics): most of those termed 'unusual' are only variants of those described.

### Sexing

Where obvious plumage differences exist between sexes these are duly recorded in the species accounts under this heading. Not all features are necessarily described, just those which determine, beyond doubt, the sex of the species in question. Sexual characters, in the context of plumage, often become more developed and distinctive with age. Thus, adults show a greater degree of sexual dimorphism than do juvenile or immature birds. In the species accounts it may be necessary to refer to age before determining sex. In such cases the user should find that consideration to this matter is addressed under the one heading of Age, which thus avoids the reader having to switch between two sections.

Sexual discriminants using biometrics are recorded only in those species which exhibit well-defined differentiation, with little or no overlap in measurements. Users should, of course, be fully conversant in taking standard biometrics but may also be asked to take atypical anatomical measurements too. The Biometrics section at the end of each species account should not be used to determine the sex of a bird without reference to other supporting characters, unless, of course, the biometrical evidence is so overwhelming as to give a clear judgement beyond reasonable doubt.

## Ageing

Throughout Europe a standard numbering code is used by ringing schemes to denote age classes in birds. Ringers, of course, will be familiar with this code. The EURING code, as it is known, is used extensively in this guide. The numbering code itself has many advantages over the other ageing terminologies in common use. However, many large non-passerines are long-lived and take several years to reach adulthood. In such birds ageing is still possible after five or six years of life. The EURING code, in these circumstances, can become complex or difficult to work out since codes change with age groups as revealed by plumage change, as well as altering at the end of each calendar year! To complement this code therefore I have resorted to using a well tested method which describes basic plumage sequences, which, of course, are age-related: Juvenile (**Juv**), 1st-winter (**1w**), 1st-summer (**1s**), 2nd-winter (**2w**), 2nd-summer (**2s**) 3rd-winter (**3w**) etc. Summer plumage is synonymous in this context with breeding plumage and winter plumage with non-breeding plumage. The use of seasonal terminology, however, may cause some confusion in the southern hemisphere since the southern winter occurs during the northern summer and vice versa. The following table may help to clarify the meanings of both systems.

## Plumage Terminology and Ringing Codes used in this Guide

```
June July A S O N D J F M A M J J A S O N D J F M A M J J
Pullus---Juv---1w------------------1s-------------2w--------------------2s---------
1----------3J-----3------------5-----------------------------------------7---------------------
```

```
A S O N D J F M A M J J A S O N D J F M A M J J A S O N D
2s-3w------------------3s-------------Ad (w)----------Ad (s)---------Ad (w)---etc
7----------------9-----------------------8-------------10----------------------------------8
```

Euring code used for adults of unknown age:

```
J J A S O N D J F M A M J J A S O N D J F M A M J J A S O
4------------------6--------------------------------------8 only if immatures
  are ageable as 3w,
  otherwise back to 6.
```

Euring code used for birds of unknown age (including current calendar year):

```
J J A S O N D J F M A M J J A S O N D J F
2--------------------4------------------2--------------------4----
```

# Moult

The sections describing moult cycles and timing in each of the species accounts are essential reading for the user to understand the text on ageing and, to a lesser degree, sexing. Moult cycles and moult strategies can be extremely complex in many non-passerine species. Only with knowledge of the moult strategy options available to a species and the timing can the user reach a valid conclusion about the true age of a bird. Moult details are sketchy or unsubstantiated for a number of species dealt with in this guide. In such cases the text will clearly state the deficiencies in our knowledge, though there may be speculative remarks if tentative evidence exists.

Moult terminology follows Ginn & Melville (1983). The numbering of primaries and secondaries (Fig. 14), therefore, follows the normal replacement pattern - i.e. in primaries from the inside to out (descendant), and in secondaries from outside to in (ascendant). The rectrices or tail feathers are numbered in pairs from the centre outwards (centrifugally). Body feathers generally refer to contour feathers, unless otherwise stated.

# Geographical variation

Many non-passerine species which have a large or discontinuous geographical range often show variation in size and plumage. Such differences frequently enable the species to be divided into subspecies or races. Morphological differences in species which have a continuous breeding range tend to be gradual (clinal), and therefore many individuals cannot be ascribed to a particular subspecies with any degree of certainty. Individuals from populations at opposite ends of the species' clinal ranges are easier to separate, though, of course, it is rare to encounter together individuals of the same species from either end of its breeding range! Those species whose breeding ranges are discontinuous, on the other hand, may be relatively easy to separate.

This guide mostly addresses subspecies, or clinal variations, within Europe. However, those that are outside this range (extralimital) may be referred to if there is a probability of their occurrence in western Europe.

Ringers rarely go to the lengths of ascribing races to the birds that they catch. Nevertheless, racial discrimination is useful to those researchers interested in migration studies, and it may be desirable to be able to separate one population of birds from another for many other studies. It must be stressed, however, that positive identification of a subspecies, without having considerable experience, or having additional reference material to hand, can be very subjective. Caution should, therefore, be exercised when considering subspecific identification.

## Biometrics

All linear measurements are given in millimetres, and weights are in grams. As a rule the biometrics listed are: Wing length (maximum chord, unless otherwise stated), Tail (root to tip of longest rectrix), Bill (feathering to bill tip), Tarsus (intertarsal joint to distal end of last complete scale before toes). Two sets of measurements are given, one for each sex, listing a mean, followed in brackets by standard deviation and sample size, then overall range. These and other methods sometimes used are detailed under a later section entitled Measurements.

The sources of biometrical information cited at the end of each species account are given in brackets just after the heading. Generally, those which have been taken from *Birds of the Western Palearctic* (Cramp & Simmons 1977, 1980, 1983; Cramp 1985) are almost exclusively taken from skins, while those taken by individuals are from live, and usually wild, bird populations. The exceptions to this rule are those listed under my name, which were taken using skins. When comparing measurements from live birds to those taken using museum skins, it is important to remember that some shrinkage will have occurred in skins, mostly affecting wing length. Because of this, users should be cautious when comparing their own data with measurements from skins. As has already been mentioned under the heading Sexing, often a measurement cited in this section may appear to offer a definite sex. However, unless discriminant measurements feature under Sexing, it is inadvisable to assign a bird to a particular sex unless a combination of two or three other measurements taken indicate, without question, one sex.

Unless otherwise stated all measurements given are for adults.

# Topography

External areas and features of plumage and bare parts of a bird play an important part in ageing and sexing. The basic feather tracts and body features are illustrated in Fig. 1. The majority of the terms used apply to all species but there are some characteristics which are specific to certain groups or families of birds. Those used in this guide are illustrated and include:

**speculum** - a bar or patch of distinctive colour (usually metallic) found on secondaries in wildfowl
**cere** - a fleshy covering found at the proximal (nearest the body) portion of the upper mandible in birds of prey
**nail** - a horny plate-like feature, shaped like a shield, found at the tip of the upper mandible of all species of wildfowl

**Fig. 1**

Topography

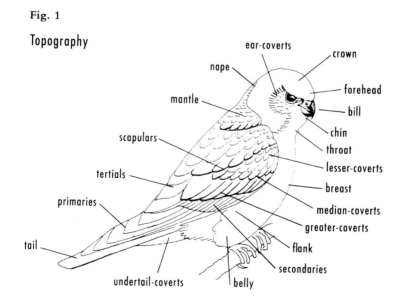

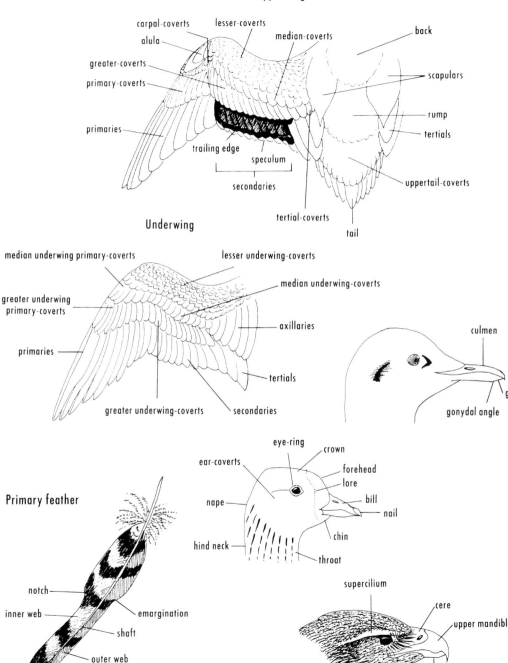

## Upperwing

carpal-coverts
alula
greater-coverts
primary-coverts
primaries
lesser-coverts
median-coverts
back
scapulars
rump
tertials
uppertail-coverts
trailing edge
speculum
secondaries
tertial-coverts
tail

## Underwing

median underwing primary-coverts
lesser underwing-coverts
median underwing-coverts
greater underwing
primary-coverts
primaries
axillaries
tertials
greater underwing-coverts
secondaries

culmen
gonydal angle
g

## Primary feather

eye-ring
crown
ear-coverts
forehead
lore
nape
bill
nail
hind neck
chin
throat

notch
inner web
emargination
shaft
outer web

supercilium
cere
upper mandibl
lower mandible

# Terminology of feather types

In the species accounts standard terms are used to describe certain types of feather pattern. Fig. 2 illustrates those used in this guide.

**Fig. 2   Nomenclature of feather patterning.**

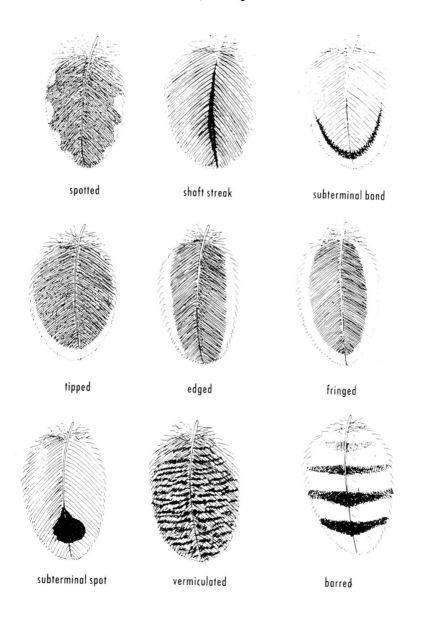

spotted

shaft streak

subterminal band

tipped

edged

fringed

subterminal spot

vermiculated

barred

# Measuring

There are many different ways of measuring birds. There are, however, standard sets of measurements which ringers and museum workers normally take. Unfortunately different measuring techniques exist even within this restricted set of people, for example four different techniques are currently in use to measure wing length. To clarify which of the methods may generally be accepted as 'standard' ones, it is necessary to describe in some depth the techniques used. These are all illustrated in the following section.

Any part of the body or feather being measured must be in good condition and not mis-shapen or abnormal. The moulting and wear of plumage influences, amongst other things, the length of wing and tail, and broken or overgrown claws and bills also give misleading results.

### Wing

The wing length is the distance between the outer bend of the carpal joint and the tip of the longest primary, as measured on the closed wing. There are three different techniques of taking this measurement:

### a. Unflattened wing or minimum wing chord

Using a standard butted wing rule the bend of the carpal joint is pushed up to the butt. The wing is allowed to maintain a natural shape when folded as close to the body of the bird as possible. At a point when the line between the carpal joint and the wing point is parallel to the edge of the ruler, take a reading of the longest primary tip against the scale of the ruler. (Fig. 3).

### b. Flattened wing

This method is similar to measuring the unflattened wing except that, instead of letting only the wing tip touch the ruler, the primaries are flattened downwards against the ruler by applying gentle pressure on the primary-coverts with a thumb, or in the case of large birds, the palm of the hand. No straightening or stroking of the primaries is allowed with this method.

### c. Maximum wing chord

The wing should be flattened as described in method B, then the primaries straightened out longways. Gently push the edge of the wing in the region of the alula inwards (towards the body of the bird) and the outermost part of the

## Fig. 3 Wing length (min)

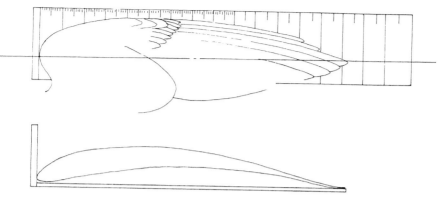

primaries outwards from the body to eliminate the natural curvature of the wing. Stroke the primary tips with a thumb longways and take the maximum reading against the scale (Fig. 4). The longest feather is as straight as possible along the rule as well as close to (and parallel with) the axis of the body.

It is very important that the primaries should not be pulled when stroking the primary tips, nor too much pressure applied to the carpal in attempting to straighten the wing curve - such practice might damage wing bones.

Method C is perhaps the most commonly employed technique now used by ringing schemes. Although it is a measure which gives the most reproducible and comparable one between ringers, it is, without doubt, the most difficult one to learn as a novice. There is no question that, when it comes to medium or large birds, that this method becomes difficult to use and the measurements less reproducible. There is also an increased inherent danger of damaging a very large bird in attempting to flatten out the convex bow of the wing, as well as trying to straighten out the curve along the primaries. In addition, it also requires at least two people to measure a large bird in this way, unlike the unflattened method which can generally be carried out by one person.

## Primary length

A further method, which has recently been developed, takes as its measure the length of the 3rd outermost primary, from a point where the base of the shaft

### Fig. 4  Wing length (max)

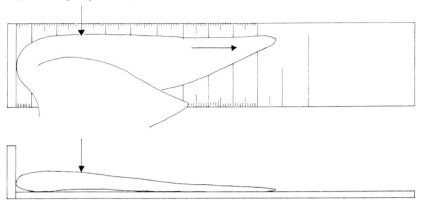

meets the skin follicle to the tip of the primary. To do this it is necessary for the butt of a wing rule to be replaced by a small vertical blunt pin. The gap between the 2nd and 3rd outermost primaries is placed over the pin as far into the base of the primaries as possible and is then gently manoeuvered up the wing to a point where the pin comes into contact with the very base of the primaries, where it comes to a natural halt.

This technique has been tested very much more on passerine than non-passerine species and is swift to execute and is quickly learnt by beginners. Jenni & Winkler (1989) have shown it to be very highly repeatable between different measurers. It is a method likely to gain popularity in years to come. Eventually it may also prove to be an easier and more accurate technique for use on large non-passerine species.

### Tail

As in the wing, the tail length can be measured in a number of ways. The method accepted by most ringers and museum workers to obtain maximum tail length is illustrated in Fig. 5. A square-ended (at zero measurement) flat ruler is required. Place the zero end of the ruler under the tail between the rectrices and the undertail-coverts and slide it gently up towards the body until it reaches the root of the central pair of rectrices (it will become obvious to the measurer when this point has been reached since the ruler should come to a natural halt). It is important not to push too hard against the root of the rectrices since damage can easily be caused.

It is sometimes necessary to measure the distance between the longest and

Fig. 5  Tail length

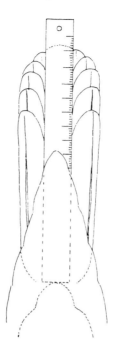

shortest rectrix - most commonly to determine identification of a species or to sex or age an individual. The graduation or fork is measured from the tip of the longest feather to the tip of the shortest when the tail is closed (Fig. 6).

Fig. 6  Tail difference

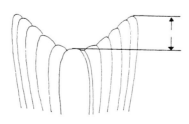

## Bill length

Several standard techniques are used to measure bill length. The method used will largely be dictated by the type of bird being processed. In near-passerine species such as woodpeckers, kingfishers, swifts, etc. It is usual to measure from the base of the skull, where it meets the upper mandible, to the tip of the bill (Fig. 7). In species where the feathering forms a well-defined line at the centre of the upper mandible e.g. divers, grebes, wildfowl, etc. then the measurement is taken from the tip of the bill to the start of the feathering (Fig. 8). The acute downcurve on bills of birds of prey presents another problem. These birds have fleshy shields covering the proximal portion of the upper mandible and it is from the distal end of this fleshy shield along the top edge of the bill to the tip that the measurement is taken (Fig. 9).

In addition to the above standard techniques, a variant sometimes used is the nalospi which is the distance from the anterior edge of the nostril opening to the tip of the bill.

## Bill length

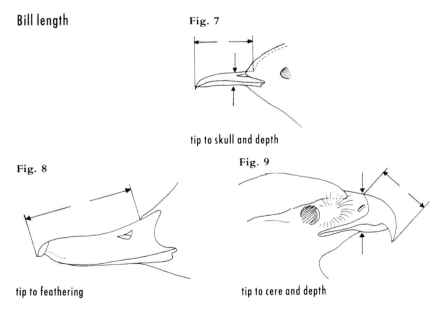

Fig. 7

tip to skull and depth

Fig. 8

tip to feathering

Fig. 9

tip to cere and depth

All the above methods for recording bill length are in regular use today. It is not particularly important which of the methods is employed so long as the measure taken is noted.

Bill measurements are best taken using vernier or dial callipers: with care dividers may be used. In very long-billed species wing rules can be used.

## Bill depth

Vernier or dial callipers are best for taking this measurement. A problem with taking a measurement of bill depth is deciding where to measure from. There can be no general fixed point which could be recommended for all species since bill shapes and sizes vary so greatly. Just as for taking bill length, the important point is for the measurer to make a note of where it has been measured, e.g. proximal end of nostril, at feathering etc. Many groups of non-passerines have a well-defined angle at the tip of the lower mandible called the gonys (see Fig. 1). The point where the angle starts on the lower mandible forms an obvious point of reference from which to take a measurement. Many of the divers, gulls, skuas, auks, and others have a discernible gonydeal angle.

## Bill width

As with bill depth, there is no single recommended method of taking bill width. It is advised to take the largest measurement possible, but avoid soft corners of mouths. Use a reference point and record what this is.

## Head and bill

A combined measure using head and bill length is frequently used by wader and gull ringers. It is a highly repeatable measure. Vernier callipers should be used. Care should be taken to position the callipers so as to measure from the centre of the back of the skull (nape) to the bill tip i.e. the calliper should form a right angle to an imaginary line from the bill tip to the centre rear of the skull. Do not exert excessive pressure when closing the calliper.

## Tarsus

Tarsus length is measured using vernier or dial callipers, or dividers. Measure from the notch at the back of the intertarsal joint to the distal edge of the last large complete scale at the front of the foot, just before the toes diverge (Fig. 10). This is the standard measure used by museum workers and has been generally adopted by ringers.

Another method now being used with greater frequency, which has the advantage of being easy and repeatable between ringers, measures the distance from the rear of the tibia to the last complete scale. To do this requires the use of a butted wing rule. The intertarsal joint is placed up against the butt of the wing rule with the tarsus lying parallel to the edge of the rule, against the scale. The foot is

Fig. 10

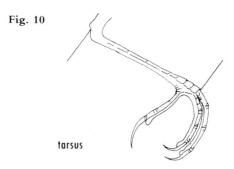

tarsus

gently bent down at right angles to the tarsus to expose the last large scale to enable the measurer to take a reading.

A method of recording tarsus length using the above described method plus the length of the toe (excluding claw) is seen in Fig. 10a.

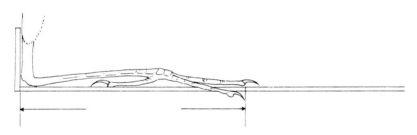

Fig. 10a    **Tarsus and toe**

## Toe

Usually refers to the middle toe. Measure from the middle point of the joint between tarsus and middle toe in front of the leg to the tip of the claw.

## Claws

The measure is best undertaken using callipers or dividers. The measurement is from the top of the claw where the skin meets the horn, to the tip of the claw (Fig. 11).

Fig. 11

hind claw

# Colours

Describing colours, with any degree of accuracy, is a difficult art. The problem is that each individual has his or her image of what might be 'blue-grey' or 'olive-brown'. There have been many attempts to standardize colour codes in the natural history world but few, if any, have succeeded. Colour charts are, without doubt, the single most useful standard but reference to them is useless to someone who does not use one, or who uses a different colour chart. Thus, most ringers and museum workers still describe colours using general terms. For the most part these descriptions are broadly meaningful and certainly relay to the reader the principal colours or shades of primary colours being discussed. Students undertaking very detailed studies, such as age-related colour changes in eye or tarsus colour, must use a reference source or take photographs in standard conditions. Users of this guide who are interested in this subject are advised to consult the *Naturalist's Colour Guide*, by Frank B. Smithe (1975, 1981), which lists over 180 selected colours with definitions and comments.

# General Techniques for Ageing and Sexing

Ageing and sexing techniques described in this guide are, of course, detailed under each species account. There are, however, many basic methods which can be applied to assist in ageing and sexing birds. It is very important for ringers, and other users of this guide, to know what these principles are, for, without them, it is likely that some aspects of ageing mentioned in the species accounts will not be fully understood.

## Juveniles

The Juvenile plumage is the first in which contour feathers are present; it is preceded by the nestling down. Usually the growing juvenile feathers bear the preceding natal, or nestling, down on the tip, but this quickly falls off.

In some non-passerine species e.g. grebes and owls, the natal down may be retained and found on certain parts of the body some weeks after fledging. In those species which assume an adult-looking plumage immediately it is worth looking for downy remains. Juvenile feathers are simpler in structure, generally weaker and looser than later generations (fewer barbs per unit length, fewer barbules with hooklets, etc. (Göhringer 1951)). In many cases juvenile body feathers are easily distinguishable from those that succeed them.

Juvenile feather covering is sparser than later stages of feather growth. Bare patches are normally evident around the underwing-coverts, on the abdomen, and sometimes in the breast area too.

In many instances where juveniles retain some or all of their juvenile flight feathers through the first winter, and beyond, the difference in shape between first-generation feathers (juvenile) and second or later generations is a useful ageing guide. Juvenile feathers, mostly detectable in outer primaries, secondaries, tertials and greater-coverts, are narrower and the tips are more angled and pointed (Fig. 12). Determining subtle differences in feather shape between juvenile and later-generation feathers is often difficult and requires a high degree of practical skill. Many birds are intermediate but the extremes should be possible to determine. Unless the handler is very experienced, this ageing criterion should not be used without reference to other supporting age-related methods. In many large and long-winged species, particularly raptors, the adult-type remiges differ in length considerably from the juvenile ones. The difference is perhaps best illustrated in those raptors, namely Buzzard *Buteo buteo* and White-tailed Eagle *Haliaeetus albicilla*, where juvenile remiges are several centimetres longer (White-tailed Eagle) or 1-2cm shorter (Buzzard) than the corresponding adult

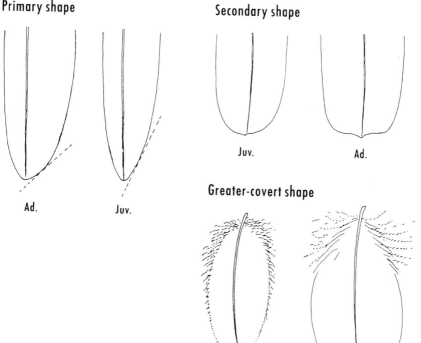

Fig. 12

Primary shape

Secondary shape

Ad.                    Juv.

Juv.                    Ad.

Greater-covert shape

Juv.                    Ad.

Fig. 13    Tail shape in wildfowl

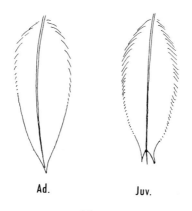

Ad.                    Juv.

feathers. Interpretation of this ageing character should, therefore, be approached with some caution and must be taken on a species-by-species basis.

Most juvenile wildfowl have distinctively shaped tail feathers. In the early stages down is visible on the tips of the rectrices, forming a visible 'bobble'. This eventually falls off leaving a distinct V-shaped notch right at the tip of the tail with the bare shafts showing, best noted towards the central feathers (Fig. 13).

Because the tails are frequently retained through to the following spring or summer, this feature is a useful and quick ageing guide. Some caution should be exercised when very worn tails are encountered. Adults with abraded and broken tail feathers frequently show V-shaped gaps on the tips as well. However, they do not show the characteristic bare shafts as found in juvenile tails.

Colours of bare parts in juveniles are usually different from those of older birds. In many raptors, for example, the feet, the waxy facial skin and eye-ring usually becomes a more striking yellow with age. However, this rule must be used with caution since colours often vary between individuals within species. Such features are nonetheless helpful, but much more research is required before the finer points are fully appreciated and become reliable for ageing and sexing. Ringers are therefore urged to keep detailed notes about bare-part colours, particularly iris colour, when processing live birds, especially those of known age. One word of warning is necessary, however, when considering eye colour in relation to age: it has been noted in some species, perhaps especially those with a pale iris, that stress due to handling can temporarily change the colour of the eye.

Legs of juveniles tend to be fleshier and 'spongy' in texture. The scales, particularly on the front edge of the tarsus, near to the feet, are less well-developed. Older birds have leaner and harder-textured legs, with well-defined scales.

Bills of most juvenile birds are not fully grown for several weeks, or even months in some species, after fledging. Bill length is often, therefore, a good indicator of age and there are several examples of the use of bill development for ageing in this guide (e.g. auks).

Skull development is used frequently as an indicator of age in many passerine species. In juvenile birds the roof of the skull is often poorly developed with just a single layer of translucent bone. Such areas are referred to as 'windows' and can easily be detected when compared to the other parts of the skull which already have a second layer of bone grown on the inside, separated from the first by a layer of air. The growth of this feature is called pneumatization. When the skull is fully developed it is said to be fully ossified. Pneumatization of the skull roof in relation to age is well documented (Winkler 1979) and is an established and proven means of ageing for young birds in late summer and autumn. Research into skull ossification in relation to age has been carried out mostly on passerine species. The subject appears to be more complicated in the non-passerine groups, and less predictable. In divers, herons and auks, for example, skulls are weakly or not at all pneumatized. By contrast the skulls of pigeons, doves and nightjars, are strongly or near-fully pneumatized at a very early age. Quite a varied development of pneumatization occurs in wildfowl, raptors, gulls and woodpeckers. Owls and passerines are the only two orders in which the skulls become completely pneumatized. Clearly, the examination of skull ossification for ageing purposes in non-passerine species is not yet advanced enough to be of practical use for most species.

# Moult and wear

A full understanding of the principles of moult and wear of feathers is <u>essential</u> for the purposes of ageing and sexing birds. A useful introduction to this subject is *Moult in Birds*, BTO Guide 19 by H.B. Ginn & D.S. Melville (1983). More detailed information about individual species can be found in *Birds of the Western Palearctic* (Cramp & Simmons 1977, 1980, 1983; Cramp 1985) and in this guide. Because moult patterns can vary greatly between different groups of non-passerines, an introductory section precedes each of the families or genera, giving basic information common to the group, including moult strategy, sequence, timing, frequency, and details of structure.

## Moult

Moult is the principal factor affecting the appearance of a bird's plumage over time. Contour feathers form the outer covering of the head and body of a bird. In larger non-passerine species it is generally the head and smaller body feathers (including the coverts on tail and wings) which help ringers to identify juvenile and immature-plumaged birds. Later, once birds attain sub-adult plumage, it is the flight feathers, principally primaries and secondaries, which provide the essential clues to ageing. For many non-passerine species, even families, moult patterns are so complex, compared with the simpler sequential strategy of most passerines, that the moult section must be read and understood before proceeding. Only in this way is it possible to appreciate and understand the mechanics of feather replacement and wear in relation to ages of birds.

Readers must bear in mind, when consulting the sections on moult, that there is considerable individual variation in the timing and sequence within many species. Such variations may be exaggerated between different populations, especially in species which are widely distributed. Thus, the information on moult should be interpreted with care.

Of course all birds need to moult. Some moult more frequently than others and at different times of the year, depending on their annual life strategy. Some undergo a partial moult in one place, then stop, to enable them to migrate, and then continue in another. Moult strategies, though predictable in some species are very varied in others. Such strategies operate under overall endogenous control but they are also highly adaptive and affected directly by seasonal and environmental forces. Broadly speaking, most non-passerine species moult twice annually. A complete moult, involving replacement of head, body and flight feathers, takes place after breeding and is normally referred to as post-breeding or post-nuptial moult. A second, partial moult, is undertaken prior to breeding and called pre-breeding or pre-nuptial moult. Typically, this involves some or all of the head and body feathers, a number of wing-coverts, and perhaps variable number of tertials, inner secondaries and tail feathers. These principal moult cycles are summarized in the introductory section on families or genera as:

W = Winter
S = Summer
p = partial moult
C = complete moult

## Sequence and duration of moult

The numbering of primaries and secondaries follows Ginn & Melville (1983). Thus primary 1 is the innermost, primary 10 the outermost; different species have different numbers of secondaries but secondary 1 is the outermost, the rest are numbered towards the innermost (Fig. 14).

**Fig. 14**

## Primary and secondary numbering

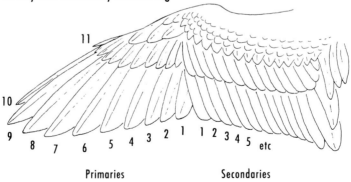

Primaries                    Secondaries

Many species of non-passerines, and nearly all European passerines, follow a very similar sequence of moult - the 'basic sequence'. They begin at the mid-wing point by dropping the innermost primary (p1), then the adjacent primary (p2) and so on in sequence and in an outward direction - this is termed descendant primary moult. The secondaries start from the mid-wing point too by shedding of the outermost feather (s1) roughly at about the time the 6th primary falls though this is subject to considerable variation both between and within species. Secondary moult is less predictable in the sequence in which feathers are dropped but they progress in an inward direction - termed ascendant secondary moult. The basic moult sequence in many of the larger non-passerine species, however, may deviate from this. For example, the interval between shedding of feathers may vary, and the frequency of moult cycles may be such that one wave of moult does not reach the outermost primary before a new moult wave begins again at the innermost primary. The sequence of feather replacement may be irregular in that it does not progress in sequence along the wing, some feathers being passed by and renewed later. In such cases two growing feathers may be separated by one or more old or new feathers - a term called 'transilient' moult (Stresemann & Stresemann 1961). In species such as the Cuckoo *Cuculus canorus* there is a regular alternation of growing and non-growing feathers in the outer primaries, a term called 'alternating' moult. In some groups (e.g. falcons) the primaries moult from the middle of the primary tract at p4 or p5 and proceed centrifugally, i.e. inwards and outwards at the same time. Wildfowl, divers, grebes, rails and auks have evolved a sequence involving simultaneous shedding of all, or most, of their flight feathers, rendering them flightless for several weeks.

The moult of secondaries and, even more so the tail, is substantially more varied and less predictable than the primary moult. Secondaries frequently show several 'blocks' or centres of moult from which replacement spreads, particularly in species with large numbers of secondaries. Tail feathers may be moulted singly, in pairs, in 'blocks' or simultaneously. In many species there may be no discernible pattern of feather replacement. Others have strongly developed patterns which follow one of the more traditional moult sequences: centrifugal - where the moult progresses from the central pair outwards, and centripetal - the opposite of centrifugal where the tail moult starts from the outer pair and finishing with the central pair.

The sequences of moult described above fall into one of six different types of wing moult strategy:

## a. Basic or conventional moult

This is where moult starts at the mid-wing point with p1 and then s1 and progresses sequentially in a descendant direction (i.e. outwards) in primaries, and ascendantly (i.e. inwards) in secondaries. The innermost secondaries (tertials) usually moult separately from the main secondary tract, and in a somewhat irregular sequence. The tail feathers are dropped and replaced in pairs starting from the centre and progressing outwards (centrifugally). Primary-coverts are usually moulted at the same time as their corresponding primaries - an exception being in woodpeckers *Picidae*. Other wing-coverts do not conform to any particular pattern though in juvenile birds unmoulted greater-coverts are generally found at the outer (distal) end of the tract.

### b. Descendant and ascendant moult from one centre

There is a similar sequence to basic moult pattern except that moult starts in the middle of a tract (e.g. p4 and s5) and progresses both descendantly and ascendantly. Such moult can be found in many species of falcon.

### c. Serially descendant and ascendant moult from more than one centre.

A new moult cycle starts before the preceding one has reached the outermost primary (or innermost secondary) so that there are two or more active moult centres in the wing which have started at the same time and are following the same sequence - sometimes referred to as *Staffelmauser* or 'step-wise moult'. Such a strategy can be found in Gannet *Morus bassanus*, Cormorant *Phalacrocorax carbo*, Shag *Phalacrocorax aristotelis* and some terns.

### d. Suspended moult

Moult is interrupted (stopped temporarily) and is subsequently resumed at the point at which it stopped. This strategy was thought to be widespread, particularly among passerines, but recent work has shown this to occur in only a small percentage of birds. Normally it involves individuals in late breeding attempts having to interrupt their normal moult cycle in order to breed and/or migrate (e.g. Harper 1984, Norman 1990). In non-passerines suspended moult has been reported in a number of species (e.g. Bee-eater *Merops apiaster*, Nightjar *Caprimulgus europaeus*, Turtle Dove *Streptopelia turtur*, Woodpigeon *Columba palumbus*, and others). However, it is very difficult to distinguish a true pattern of suspended moult from that of arrested moult (see below) unless a bird is subsequently retrapped having resumed its moult after the interruption. In view of this, and recent findings and re-evaluation of this strategy (Norman 1991), the term suspension should not be taken too literally. In well-tested moult studies, e.g. in Tawny Owl *Strix aluco*, it has been shown that replacement of primaries follows the rule of suspended moult but, because the replacement is so slow, it takes several seasons for all the primaries to be renewed and they are frequently replaced from two or more active moult centres! Some species of tern *Sternidae* exhibit suspended moult too in that moult starts on the breeding grounds, is suspended just prior to migration, and is resumed at the point of interruption in winter quarters. However, there is only a short interval, if any, before a second new wave starts so that two active moult centres are then present in the primary or secondary tract.

### e. Arrested moult

Unfortunately, the term suspended moult is often used synonymously with arrested moult by many workers! This perhaps stems from the fact that the moult sequence has stopped, in both cases, before the full cycle has been completed. Here the similarity ends since in arrested moult it starts again, not at the point of interruption, but back at the point where the moult was first started. Thus a bird which has moulted p1 to p5 and has then arrested would resume the moult at p1, leaving p6 to p10 unmoulted. This moult strategy is probably more commonly used by migrant species than is generally appreciated. The extent to which the moult cycle is completed before arresting seems to be determined largely by environmental factors such as food availability, timing of breeding,

**Fig. 15   Wing moult**

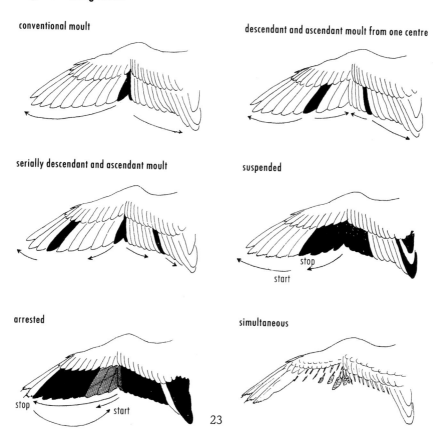

conventional moult

descendant and ascendant moult from one centre

serially descendant and ascendant moult

suspended

arrested

simultaneous

23

onset of migration and so on. Arrested moult is commonly found in Swift *Apus apus*, Stock Dove *Columba oenas*, Wryneck *Jynx torquilla*, and some species of tern *Sternidae*.

## f. Simultaneous moult

Some groups of non-passerines lose the power of flight during moult because a major proportion or all of the flight feathers are shed at the same time. In some species (e.g. Fulmar *Fulmarus glacialis*) large centres of secondaries and primaries are lost and replaced in rapid succession, sometimes resulting in flightlessness for several days. Many waterbirds have evolved a strategy of moulting all their flight feathers simultaneously, often making special moult migrations to undertake this. They can be rendered flightless for four or five weeks: examples are ducks, geese, swans, divers, grebes, rails and auks.

Examples of all the moult strategies described above are illustrated in Fig. 15.

## Wear

Feather wear provides essential clues to ageing. It is important, therefore, that readers appreciate the different kinds of mechanical and natural sorts of wear to which feathers are subjected. Examples are the less robust feathers of the juvenile plumage exposed to ultra-violet light (sunlight) which has the effect of fading the true colour of the feather (compared to those under the closed wing which are protected from direct sunlight and tend to keep their natural colours). This bleaching effect is common in species which live in hot, sunny climates; feathers subject to greater mechanical wear on the distal parts of the wing; feathers where the strengthening effect of melanin can be compared with the weaker white areas e.g. white 'mirror' areas on many gull wings.

Unless a bird has recently undergone a complete moult it will normally be apparent that some feathers are more worn than others. This does not happen by chance but is more likely to be due to (1) some feathers having been more exposed than others; (2) some feathers remaining unmoulted from last moult period; (3) some feathers having been grown early in a moult cycle, others late, this is particularly relevant in slow moulting species e.g. large raptors; (4) certain feathers being more delicate than others; (5) certain colours being 'weaker' than others.

Feather tracts more prone to wear and discoloration are (1) the rectrices, especially the longest, and central pair; (2) inner secondaries or tertials; (3) the distal ends of longest outermost primaries; (4) upper wing-coverts, especially the inner greater-coverts; (5) mantle; (6) crown feathers.

24

The disparity in wear found between different feather tracts can lead to confusion when attempting to distinguish one generation of feathers from another, even amongst experienced workers. This is because certain feathers are well protected and hidden from 'the elements'. In the folded wing these would include, for example, the secondaries (except the innermost), inner primaries, alula, greater- and primary-coverts (except inner greaters). Thus a bird with the same generation of flight feathers might show very abraded and bleached outer primaries, inner secondaries and worn tips to the longer tail feathers but have fresh-looking outer secondaries, inner primaries and shorter tail feathers. Taking factors such as these into consideration is important when using the state of moult to age birds.

In non-passerines, as compared to passerine species, especially careful consideration should be given to wear of feathers. Unlike passerines, many of the larger non-passerine species can take several years to replace all of their primaries and secondaries. Those remiges that are last in the cycle to be replaced might show very considerable abrasion and discoloration, even though they are often in positions where wear is not normally rapid. Judging up to two or three different age-groups in the wing of, say, a Little Tern *Sterna albifrons* takes some experience. In this guide four basic feather-wear categories have been used throughout the text to describe different degrees of abrasion (Fig. 16).

**Fig. 16**

## Primary wear

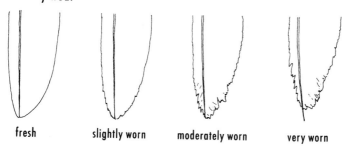

fresh        slightly worn        moderately worn        very worn

Of course feathers change colour with age - they usually get lighter, but each colour behaves differently. In their fresh condition black feathers often have a purple sheen, which gets worn away quite quickly. In species which might retain feathers for three or even four years (e.g. eagles), the transition from black to brown-black to dark brown to pale matt brown is a slow but obvious one. In an equivalent manner brown feathers become duller, bordering onto grey, and grey feathers become brownish. Rust-brown colours become yellowish while rust-yellow becomes white. White areas of feathers, however, become slightly yellow. Substances adhering to the surface of the feathers, and described by Berthold (1967) as "Haftfarben", "adherent colours", is a relatively common occurrence. Discoloring of feathers in this way is due to a number of factors, the most common perhaps being the effects of oil from the preen gland. This often appears as a pinkish suffusion on many of the gulls *Laridae* (Stegmann 1956). A purplish coloration can sometimes be found on the lower parts of Mallard *Anas platyrhynchos*, in the Teal *A. crecca* and the Garganey *A. querquedula*, which is due to a colour of a leaf-louse. More artificial forms of discolouring occur as a consequence of feather contact with industrial waste such as soot or chemicals. The most frequently recorded adherent colour is iron oxide (rust) which has been recorded in more than 120 species. It is mostly found in ducks *Anatidae* and they pick it up from iron-oxidized water, and it does not adhere to the feather surface, but penetrates thin hollow spaces of the barbs, barbules, hooklets, etc.

In considering wear it must also be borne in mind that certain colours of feathers are weaker than others and, therefore, more prone to wear. The action of sunlight will weaken white parts of feathers much more quickly than black, for example. In this context the term wear, which is normally associated with rubbing or contact of feathers with solid objects, is misleading since it involves only the process of photo-degeneration. In feathers which contain both black and white colours this mechanism of 'wear' can alter the overall plumage pattern measurably. For example, summer-plumage Black-throated Divers *Gavia arctica* have a predominantly black-and-white pattern to the upperparts. Towards the end of the breeding period and just before the onset of moult, the white patches on the black feathers are considerably reduced in extent from their original size. In extreme cases the white areas, particularly edging, to some feathers may have 'worn' away completely. Such examples show that plumage patterns can alter greatly due to the effects of sunlight. It is important to take such factors into account when using wear as a guide to ageing (Fig. 17).

**Fig. 17**

## Colour wear

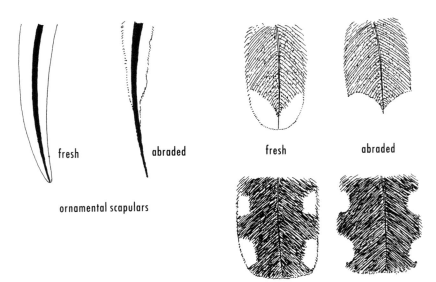

fresh     abraded          fresh          abraded

ornamental scapulars

# Growth bars

Growth bars are commonly found on both rectrices and remiges and appear as numerous bands of a different darkness across each feather. These bars appear as a consequence of metabolic changes between day and night during the growth of the feathers (Wood 1950). The distance between the bars and the width of each bar can vary, determined by daily (or nightly) growth conditions. When all the feathers of, for example, the tail or the secondaries are grown simultaneously the pattern of bars on each feather will be repeated across the entire feather tract, appearing as continuous lines of similarly spaced bars. This simultaneous growth of flight feathers means that either (1) feathers were grown as a part of the juvenile plumage; (2) feathers were replaced at the same time as a consequence of normal moult strategy (i.e. simultaneous moult); or (3) feathers were replaced at the same time as a consequence of accidental loss. Similarly spaced growth bars which form continuous lines across the tail or wing provide information which might help to distinguish juveniles, except in those species which undergo simultaneous moult. In older birds flight feathers are renewed feather by feather, in pairs or in small groups over a long period. The consequence of this is that adjacent feathers are grown at different times. Growth bars are found at different places on adjacent feathers and do not, therefore, form continuous lines across the feather tract.

It must be remembered when studying a rounded tail or the curve of the wing formed by the primaries that, in the case of juveniles, these bands will always occur at approximately the same distance from the tip of each feather (Fig. 18).

## Growth barring

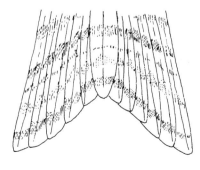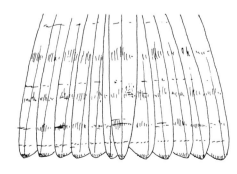

**Fig. 18**

27

It is important to check that bars right across a feather tract are truly in step. It is very easy to miss one or two pairs of feathers which do not fit the juvenile pattern.

Growth bars on tails may only be used to support other ageing characters - the technique employed in isolation on the tail should not be used to determine age. This is because the moult of tail feathers is highly variable, many adults moulting the whole tail simultaneously. Perhaps a more predictable set of feathers to use are the secondaries since they are rarely lost accidentally. Unfortunately, growth bars are less obvious on these feathers. Whichever feather tract is examined it is best that the surface of the feathers is tilted at an angle towards strong light to make any growth bars more easily visible.

# Cloacal examination

In monomorphic species it is sometimes possible to determine the sex according to the shape of the cloacal area - most readily during the period when birds are sexually active. In males the cloacal region shows up as a bulbous protuberance. Its prominence differs between species and, of course, on the stage of the breeding season. In females the cloacal region tapers off gradually to the vent (Fig. 19). The orifice may also be dilated after egg laying.

**Fig. 19**

## Cloacal region - variations

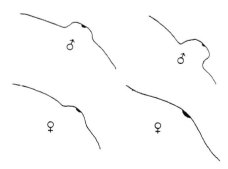

The drawback in using this technique is that it is generally only useful for a limited part of the year. Also, because there is much variation in cloacal shape between species, it relies on the observer having considerable experience. It is, however, a valuable indicator and is especially helpful when used in conjunction with incubation patch (see below).

The sexing of wildfowl, even at nestling stage, using cloacal shape is reliable and useful (Fig. 20). However, it is a technique that requires experience and great care. It is recommended that before practising the method it should be learnt from a ringer familiar with the procedure.

**Fig. 20**

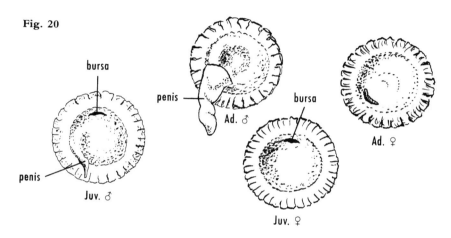

# Incubation patch

Nearly all European non-passerine species develop brood patches of one kind or another just prior to incubating the egg(s). The down feathers on the ventral surface are shed leaving a bald patch whose surface veins become engorged, appearing as a wrinkled, swollen and reddish area. Well-developed incubation patches are, as a rule, found only in females but, in species where males take an active part in incubation, the male too will develop a brood patch, though rarely as marked as in the female. Some days after the young have hatched, the patch will in females will start to change back to the normal condition. The patch will generally become only finely wrinkled, somewhat scaly and less transparent. Once the young have fledged the patch will still be bare of feathers but the skin normal unless there is to be a second brood. Those species whose fledging period is prolonged may have the incubation patch feathered before the young leave the nest. Clearly, during the period that females incubate, this technique is an excellent sexing criterion. The method should be used with caution however since there are relatively few published studies on this topic.

# ABBREVIATIONS & SYMBOLS

| | |
|---|---|
| ad. | adult bird (fully mature adult plumage, repeated year after year). |
| av. | average (mean) |
| bill (F) | measurement taken from feathering to tip of bill (see also F below) |
| BWP | "Birds of the Western Palearctic" (Cramp & Simmons 1977, 1980, 1983; Cramp 1985). |
| (C) | cere |
| ca. | *circa* (approximately) |
| cf. | compare |
| (D) | depth |
| e.g. | *exempli gratia* (for example) |
| etc. | *et cetera* (and the rest) |
| (F) | feathering |
| FG | full-grown |
| fig | figure |
| (Fig) | figure |
| *in litt.* | *in litteris* (through correspondence) |
| i.e. | *id est* (that is) |
| juv | juvenile (fledged young bird in its first plumage of true feathers) |
| p | primary feather e.g. p1 = innermost primary |
| s | secondary feather e.g. s1 = outermost secondary |
| (S) | skull |
| SC | summer complete |
| Sp | summer partial |
| sp., spp. | species (singular, plural) |
| t | tail feather e.g. t1 = innermost tail feather. |
| unpubl. | unpublished |
| WC | complete winter moult |
| Wp | partial winter moult |
| 1s | 1st-summer plumage |
| 2s,3s etc. | 2nd-summer plumage, 3rd-summer etc. |
| 1w | 1st-winter plumage |
| 2w,3w etc. | 2nd-winter plumage, 3rd-winter etc. |
| ♂, ♂♂ | male, males |
| ♀, ♀♀ | female, females |
| = | equals |
| = 5/6 | equals between fifth and sixth (primaries) |
| > | greater than |
| < | less than |

# Systematic list

## Divers *Gaviidae*

Medium to large, foot-propelled diving birds. Body elongated. Wings narrow, relatively small, and strongly pointed. Feet set far back. Predominantly dark plumages to upperparts, finely or strongly speckled white in summer plumage. White below. Browner and more subdued non-breeding plumage.

**Feather structure**
Primaries = 11 (p10 longest, p11 minute).
Secondaries = 23 +
Tail = 18 (16-20)

**Sexes**
Similar in plumage. ♂ ♂ average larger.

**Moult**
Strategy: simultaneous.
Sequence: simultaneously.
Frequency: twice annually; Sp (SC,Wp in *Gavia stellata*) WC. Rectrices replaced at each moult cycle. Body feathers slow and protracted, perhaps continuous.
Timing: late summer finishing early winter; late winter finishing early spring.

### RED-THROATED DIVER *Gavia stellata*

**Identification** In winter plumage from Black-throated Diver by bold white spots on upperparts forming speckling (adult & 1st-winter) or whitish V-shaped speckling (juveniles) (Fig).

Red-throated Diver    Black-throated Diver

Back feathers

Juvenile

**Sexing**

Use this 3 measurement variable discriminant score: (0.167 x Wing) − (0.133 x Bill) + (1.39 x Tarsus).

♂              If score >144.7mm.*

♀              If score <144.7mm.*

\* Measurements taken from Shetland (Scotland) population.

**Autumn/Winter**

3              Upperparts dark grey with dark bottle-green wash to feathers of mantle and rump with white V-shaped subterminal band, more evident on mantle and scapulars (Fig). Head and back of neck plain dove-grey.

1w (3/5)       Possible retention of some juvenile feathers on upperparts, otherwise once moulted similar to adult except smaller, less distinct, white spotting on mantle and back, and with very little on rump.

Adult (4/6)    Dark brown upperparts with conspicuous white spots.

**Back feathers**

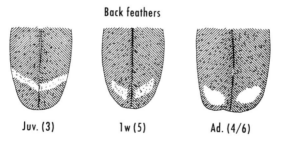

Juv. (3)          1w (5)          Ad. (4/6)

**Spring/Summer**

1s (5)         As adult but red throat-patch duller and not very glossy. Upperparts have mixture of new and 1st-winter feathers. Wing feathers bleached pale brown and abraded.

Adult (6)      Ash-grey head with dark glossy chestnut-red throat. Upperparts uniform dark brown, often with some white spotting on wing-coverts.

## Moult

**3/5** Partial post-juvenile moult confined to head, body, tail and some wing-coverts, from December.

**5** Partial moult of head and body starting before end of juvenile moult, May-July. In autumn moult then as adult though flight feathers moulted slightly earlier, summer rather than autumn.

**Adult** Complete post-breeding moult (August) September-December. Simultaneous moult of flight feathers. Pre-breeding moult partial and confined to head, body, tail and some wing-coverts, March-April.

**Geographical variation** Negligible, but birds from Spitsbergen and Franz Joseph Archipelago have greyish fringes to mantle in breeding plumage and are paler on hindneck (recognized by some as a subspecies *squamata*) but this character highly variable.

**Biometrics** Adult (Okill, unpubl. data).

| | | | | | | |
|---|---|---|---|---|---|---|
| Wing | ♂296 | (5.00;28) | 283-320 | ♀286 | (7.00;33) | 274-305 |
| Bill | 54.9 | (2.40;28) | 50-61 | 53.2 | (2.40;33) | 49-61 |
| Tarsus | 76.7 | (1.80;28) | 73-82 | 71.6 | (1.90;33) | 68-75 |

**References** Baker (1983a), Appleby, Madge & Mullarney (1986), Okill, French & Wanless (1989).

# BLACK-THROATED DIVER *Gavia arctica*

**Identification** Smaller than Great Northern and White-billed Diver (see Biometrics). In summer by grey on back of head and neck. Adults in winter by absence of grey fringes on upperparts with retention of black and white breeding feathers on wing-coverts and parts of mantle. Juveniles resemble Red-throated Diver but latter shows characteristic white V-shaped subterminal bars on mantle and back (see identification under that species).

## Autumn/Winter

**3** Dark brown upperparts with grey terminal fringes giving overall scalloped effect. Lacks white spots on upper wing-coverts.

| 1w (3/5) | Many juvenile feathers retained on upperparts but some replaced with darker, adult-type feathers. |
|---|---|

| 2w (5/7) | Similar to 1st-winter but lacks juvenile grey feathers on upperparts, replaced completely by dark brown feathers with suggestion of dull white subterminal spots. Lacks white spots on upper wing-coverts. |
|---|---|

| Adult (6/8) | Dark brown upperparts always with some retained black-and-white breeding feathers on mantle and upper wing-coverts. |
|---|---|

### Spring/Summer

| 1s (5) | Appearance as 1st-winter but upperparts all brownish-black, sometimes with suggestion of white subterminal spots on mantle, as in 2nd-winter. |
|---|---|

| 2s (7) | Assumes adult breeding plumage but throat feathers much browner, often mixed with white, especially on chin. |
|---|---|

| Adult (8) | Uniform deep purple to almost black throat with vertical transverse white streaking to lower throat extending to sides of upper breast. Ash-grey head and nape. |
|---|---|

### Moult

| 3 | Partial post-juvenile moult confined to head and body. Protracted and slow from December through to April or May. |
|---|---|

| 5 | More or less continuous body moult from post-juvenile moult into 2nd-winter darker plumage. |
|---|---|

| 7 | First complete pre-breeding moult from February, completed by May (June). Simultaneous moult of flight feathers from April onwards. |
|---|---|

| Adult | Partial post-breeding moult. Extent and timing highly variable; usually (September) October through to March and confined to body, tail and some upper wing-coverts. Some birds, however, do not moult after breeding (percentage thought to be small), moulting instead in January. Complete pre-breeding moult starting January, simultaneous moult of flight feathers from February, completed by April. |
|---|---|

**Geographical variation** *G.a.viridigularis* (Siberia) differs from nominate *arctica* by green gloss on throat, rather than purple or blue and by slightly larger size; winter plumage indistinguishable. Nearctic *pacifica* (N. America) with paler grey nape and hind neck, averages smaller than nominate; minor differences in winter plumage.

**Biometrics**  Adult. Nominate *arctica* (BWP).

| | | | | | | |
|---|---|---|---|---|---|---|
| Wing | ♂324 | (17.4;10) | 294-343 | ♀309 | (16.3;10) | 282-337 |
| Bill | 60.7 | (5.57;9) | 52-68 | 60.2 | (5.14;10) | 52-68 |
| Tarsus | 82.2 | (6.06;11) | 72-89 | 78.8 | (5.41;10) | 71-87 |

**References**  Appleby, Madge & Mullarney (1986).

# GREAT NORTHERN DIVER *Gavia immer*

**Identification**  Very similar in appearance to White-billed Diver in summer, especially in winter or in juvenile plumages. In full breeding plumage bill is totally black, compared to yellow or yellowish-white in White-billed. Other diagnostic features include black primary shafts (pale in White-billed). Maxillary feathering falls short of nostril. In non-breeding plumage retains dark and distinctive culmen ridge, not pale as rest of bill as in White-billed; white spots on mantle more rounded and smaller (Fig).

**Great Northern Diver**

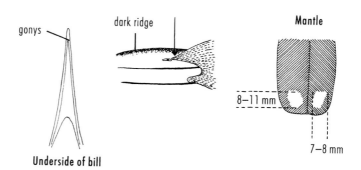

**Autumn/Winter**

3                 Pale brown upperparts which are heavily scalloped, especially on mantle and scapulars due to distinctive grey terminal band. Feathers on upperparts smaller and more rounded in shape (Fig).

1w (3/5)          Some juvenile feathers replaced with darker, more brownish-grey ones, giving less whitish contrast with rest of juvenile feathers. Lacks white rounded terminal spot on innermost secondaries.

2w (5/7)          Upperparts darker than 1st-winter, more like adult but lacks white spotting on black mantle and upper wing-coverts. Innermost secondaries without white terminal spots. Before moult of flight feathers (January-March) old unprotected outer primaries very bleached and abraded.

Adult (6/8)       Upperparts dark blackish-brown with diffuse pale fringe. Retained white spotting from breeding plumage present on upper wing-coverts, scapulars and mantle. Two white terminal spots, sometimes only one, on innermost secondaries.

## Back feathers

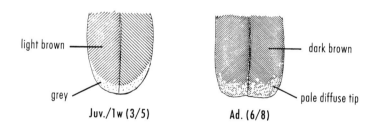

Juv./1w (3/5)          Ad. (6/8)

**Spring/Summer**

1s (5)            Appearance as for 1st-winter.

2s (7)            Like adult breeding but possibly with patches of white feathering on cheeks, neck and throat. Head blackish-brown, not as dark or glossy as adult.

Adult (8)         Jet-black head merging into greenish gloss on neck and throat; lower neck iridescent purple.

**Moult**

5 | Partial post-juvenile moult confined to head, body, tail and innermost wing-coverts from February, finishing June though some moult recorded throughout summer into complete autumn moult, November-early spring (7).

7 | First complete moult (see 5 above) November-March with flight feathers shed simultaneously from January onwards.

Adult | Partial post-breeding moult confined to body, tail and some wing-coverts, usually September or October through to January. Complete pre-breeding moult February-May; simultaneous shedding of flight feathers February-March.

**Biometrics** Adult - sexes combined (BWP).

| | | | |
|---|---|---|---|
| Wing | 366 | (13.4;29) | 331-400 |
| Bill | 80.2 | (3.33;27) | 72-89 |
| Tarsus | 91.4 | (3.39;25) | 83-100 |

**References** Appleby, Madge & Mullarney (1986).


# WHITE-BILLED DIVER *Gavia adamsii*

**Identification** See Great Northern Diver.

Ageing characteristics follow Great Northern Diver. In juveniles the upperparts are paler and the fringes greyer than Great Northern Diver. Method of ageing is, however, the same.

### White-billed Diver

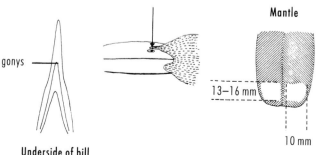

Mantle

gonys

13–16 mm

10 mm

Underside of bill

**Moult**

All ages      Apparently as Great Northern Diver.

**Biometrics**    Adult. Sexes similar and combined (BWP).

| | | | |
|---|---|---|---|
| Wing | 381 | (4.90;7) | 376-402 |
| Bill | 90.4 | (3.20;10) | 83-96 |
| Tarsus | 91.9 | (2.74;11) | 89-97 |

**References**    Burn & Mather (1974), Appleby, Madge & Mullarney (1986), Busching (1987).

# Grebes *Podicipedidae*

Small to medium-large, foot-propelled diving birds. Body elongated or rotund. Wings small and narrow. Feet placed far back. Breeding plumage characterized by display markings on head, especially in *Podiceps*. Non-breeding plumage plainer, dark above, white below.

### Feather structure
Primaries = 12 (p10 longest, p12 minute)
Secondaries = 17-22
Tail = vestigial

### Sexes
Similar in plumage ( ♀ ♀ often duller). ♂ ♂ average larger.

### Moult
Strategy: simultaneous.
Sequence: simultaneously.
Frequency: twice annually; SC, Wp. Rectrices replaced at each moult cycle. Body feathers slow and protracted.
Timing: ♂ usually 2-3 weeks earlier than ♀ in some species of *Podiceps*. Midsummer finishing early winter; midwinter finishing spring.

## LITTLE GREBE *Tachybaptus ruficollis*

**Identification** Smallest of the grebes. In summer by black crown and hindneck, chestnut face, throat, foreneck and upper breast. Distinctive white tip to black bill. In winter from Black-necked Grebe by smaller size, buffish-brown, not greyish-white, cheeks and sides of neck, shorter and stouter bill with diagnostic white tip.

### Autumn/Winter

3 — Usually with remnants of dark brown or white striping on sides of head and neck. White patches or streaks on cheeks or back of neck. Iris dark brown.

1w (3/5) — Plumage similar to adult once post-juvenile moult completed. If there are no downy feathers on the back or remnants of white or dark brown striping on sides of face or neck, ageing on plumage is virtually impossible.

Iris colour also changing to take on reddish appearance but should not yet be brick-red as in adult.

Adult (4/6)    Usually shows traces of chestnut streaking on cheeks and sides of neck in autumn (moulting out, or, in winter, moulting in). During winter there may be a period when birds in full non-breeding plumage are impossible to separate from 1st-winter birds except for iris which is rich brick-red.

## Spring/Summer

Full-grown
(4)    All plumages.

## Moult

3    Partial post-juvenile moult confined to head, body and tail, July-December.

5    More-or-less continuous moult from post-juvenile into pre-breeding plumage, January-April, some later, depending on climate.

Adult    Complete post-breeding moult starting early August, sometimes later, depending on breeding stage, and usually completed by November (December); traces of body moult can be found in some tracts throughout year. Simultaneous shedding of flight feathers at which point birds become flightless for 3-4 weeks, August-November. Pre-breeding moult partial and confined to head and body, tail, some tertials and inner wing-coverts, January-April.

**Geographical variation** White in the secondaries increases from west to east as far as India but then reverses thereafter. *T.r. capensis* (Africa, India, Turkestan) has extensive area of white in the secondaries and even inner primaries. *T.r. poggei* (E. Asia), similar to nominate *ruficollis* but longer bodied and bill more slender. About 6 other races recognized in Old World.

**Biometrics**    Full-grown. Nominate *ruficollis* (BWP).

| | | | | | | |
|---|---|---|---|---|---|---|
| Wing | ♂101 | (2.98;20) | 95-106 | ♀99 | (2.88;20) | 90-102 |
| Bill | 18.9 | (1.24;21) | 16-21 | 17.0 | (0.92;20) | 15-19 |
| Tarsus | 36.0 | (1.23;20) | 34-38 | 34.6 | (1.73;20) | 30-38 |

**References**    Baker (1981 *b*).

41

# GREAT CRESTED GREBE *Podiceps cristatus*

**Identification** Largest of the grebes and distinguished in summer by head ornaments (tippets) and white neck. In winter from Red-necked Grebe by whiter neck and white supercilium.

## Sexing

♂        Bill length (gape to tip) >60mm.
                     (rear of nostril to tip) >40mm.

        Bill depth (proximal point of nostril) >12mm.

♀        Bill length <60mm.
                     <39mm.

        Bill depth <12mm.

## Autumn/Winter

3        Remains of brown striping on head usually very prominent.

1w (3/5)    Scapulars with downy tips, prominent in autumn but often worn off by winter. Inner webs of outer greater-coverts grey-brown, sometimes with white leading edge, but not completely white as in adult (Fig).

Adult (4/6)   Inner webs of outer greater-coverts pure white (Fig).

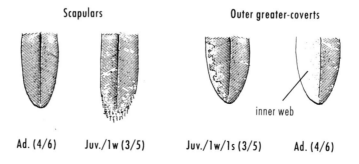

| Scapulars | | Outer greater-coverts | |
|---|---|---|---|
| Ad. (4/6) | Juv./1w (3/5) | Juv./1w/1s (3/5) | Ad. (4/6) |

inner web

## Spring/Summer

1s (5)        Inner webs of outer greater-coverts grey-brown, perhaps with white blotching (Fig). Tufts on head sooty black and under-developed.

Adult (6)      Inner webs of outer greater-coverts pure white (Fig).

## Moult

3        Partial post-juvenile moult confined to some parts of the head and body, and some of the small wing-coverts, July onwards.

5        Partial pre-breeding moult leading to sub-adult breeding plumage in April; somewhat later than moult in adult. Subsequent moult timing as adult.

Adult        Complete post-breeding moult July-December though moult of some feather tracts in the body virtually continuous. Primaries and secondaries moulted simultaneously rendering bird flightless for about 3-4 weeks, August-October. Partial pre-breeding moult of head and body into full breeding plumage, December-late spring.

**Geographical variation** None in western Palearctic but *P.c. infuscatus* (Africa) and *australis* (Australia & New Zealand) both darker and lack white supercilium. *P.c. infuscatus* averages shorter in the wing than nominate *cristatus*.

**Biometrics**    Adult. Nominate *cristatus* (BWP).

| | | | | | | |
|---|---|---|---|---|---|---|
| Wing | ♂195 | (4.2;28) | 175-209 | ♀184 | (5.6;19) | 168-199 |
| Bill | 51.8 | (1.9;22) | 41-55 | 46.1 | (1.9;23) | 38-50 |
| Tarsus | 63.6 | (2.6;23) | 59-71 | 61.6 | (2.4;23) | 57-65 |

**References**    Kop (1971), Baker (1981 *b*), Piersma (1988).

# RED-NECKED GREBE *Podiceps grisegena*

**Identification** From breeding Great Crested Grebe by red neck; also lacks ornamental collar (tippets) and crest. In winter plumage by grey or brown foreneck and lack of white supercilium (black cap extends to or below eye).

## Sexing

♂          Bill length (gape to tip) >51mm.
           Bill depth (proximal point of nostril) >11.5mm.

♀          Bill length <51mm.
           Bill depth <10.5mm.

## Autumn/Winter

3          Assumes plumage reminiscent of breeding adult but brown and white
           striping on head and face apparent from nestling period. Iris yellow.

1w (3/5)   Like adult but longest scapulars unmoulted and show downy tips or
           loose structure to ends (Fig). Iris yellow.

Adult (4/6)  Scapulars well formed showing no broken tips or downy remains (Fig).
             Iris dark brown.

### Scapulars

Ad. (4/6)          Juv./1w (3/5)

## Spring/Summer

1s (5)     Crown browner than adult, not glossy black. Cheeks and chin whiter.
           Iris yellow.

Adult (6)  Crown glossy black (full breeding dress). Cheeks and chin light grey. Iris
           dark brown.

## Moult

3          Partial post-juvenile moult confined to head and body. Timing highly
           variable, September-January.

44

| 5 | Partial body moult into pre-breeding plumage, (January) February-June or even July. |
| --- | --- |

| Adult | Complete post-breeding moult in late summer, July-November though almost continuous moult of some body feathers throughout year. Simultaneous moult of flight feathers usually August-September. Pre-breeding moult confined to head and body, tail and some innermost secondaries and wing-coverts, December-May. |
| --- | --- |

**Geographical variation** None in western Palearctic but *P.g. holboellii* (E. Asia & N. America) is larger in wing and bill. Vaurie gives wing in ♂♂ 187-212mm (20) av. 196.9, and bill 58-71mm (20) av. 62.9, and in ♀♀ 176-204mm (20) av. 189.7, and 52-64mm (20) av. 59.

**Biometrics** Full-grown. Nominate *grisegena* (BWP).

| | | | | | | |
| --- | --- | --- | --- | --- | --- | --- |
| Wing | ♂175 | (8.09;21) | 164-193 | ♀169 | (9.79;23) | 153-182 |
| Bill | 40.0 | (2.47;25) | 34-44 | 37.1 | (2.25;30) | 33-42 |
| Tarsus | 55.9 | (3.36;17) | 51-63 | 53.8 | (2.48;26) | 49-60 |

# SLAVONIAN GREBE *Podiceps auritus*

**Identification** In winter from Black-necked Grebe by diagnostic bill shape (Fig) and also by whiter cheeks. Bill depth useful guide; from distal point of nostril 6.0-8.3mm av. 7.1 (Black-necked Grebe 5.0-6.3mm av. 5.8); proximal point of nostril 6.8-9.1mm av. 8.1 (Black-necked 6.2-7.4mm av. 6.5).

Typical bill shape

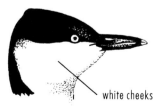

white cheeks

## Autumn/Winter

3            Sometimes with dark downy stripes on sides of head; when these are lost, cheeks white with greyish-brown blotching, sometimes forming indistinct stripe below the eye. Border between brownish-black crown and whiter cheeks is diffuse, unlike clearly defined border on adult. Upperparts browner, usually with remnants of down on back and particularly on the tips of scapulars (Fig).

1w (3/5)     Upperparts admixture of brown (juvenile) and black (1st-winter) feathers. Longest scapulars loosely structured or downy-looking towards tips (Fig).

Adult (4/6)  Clearly defined border between black crown and white sides of the face. White tip to black bill (Fig). Upperparts blacker but with pale feather edges forming scalloped pattern.

### Scapulars

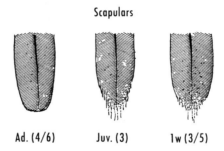

Ad. (4/6)          Juv. (3)          1w (3/5)

## Spring/Summer

Full-grown    Ageing is extremely difficult once breeding plumage is acquired since
(4) or 1s (5)  young birds, although moulting later than adults, take on the full breeding dress of old breeding birds. The dark upperparts may not be so glossy black as adults, having a brownish tinge to them. However, a combination of brownish-black upperparts and evidence of later acquisition of breeding dress (best indication of this is remains of white feathers on chin), sometimes well into May, is indicative of a 1st-summer (5) bird.

## Moult

3            Partial post-juvenile moult confined to head, neck and remainder of upperparts (not wing or wing-coverts) and flanks, October or November, completed by January.

5

Partial pre-breeding moult confined to same areas as 3 (above), acquiring breeding plumage, starting March or April, some still active in May.

**Adult** Complete post-breeding moult starting in June in ♀♀ and July in ♂♂. Completed by September or October though some feather tracts more or less in continuous moult. Flight feathers shed simultaneously rendering bird flightless for 3-4 weeks. Partial pre-breeding moult of head and body from as early as November or December, more usually February or March.

**Geographical variation** Slight: populations from west to east in Palearctic become paler; Atlantic form slightly larger, with heavier bill, and showing white on upper wing-coverts of patagial zone. North American race is greyer above with paler head tufts.

**Biometrics** Full-grown. Nominate *auritus* (BWP).

| | | | | | | |
|---|---|---|---|---|---|---|
| Wing | ♂144 | (5.28;26) | 136-158 | ♀141 | (4.98;22) | 131-153 |
| Bill | 23.3 | (1.07;19) | 21-25 | 22.5 | (1.36;15) | 20-25 |
| Tarsus | 45.9 | (2.67;7) | 42-50 | 44.2 | (2.06;4) | 42-46 |

**References** Fjeldså (1973).

# BLACK-NECKED GREBE *Podiceps nigricollis*

**Identification** In breeding plumage with completely black head, neck and back, interrupted only by long golden-brown feather tufts on sides of head. In winter similar to Slavonian Grebe but with darker face. Bill shape diagnostic (Fig). Bill depth from distal point of nostril 5.0-6.3mm av. 5.8 (Slavonian Grebe 6.0-8.3mm); proximal point of nostril 6.2-7.4mm av. 6.5 (Slavonian Grebe 6.8-9.1mm av. 8.1).

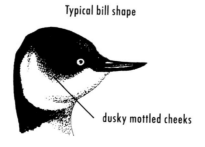

Typical bill shape

dusky mottled cheeks

## Autumn/Winter

3                Upperparts pale brown, often with olive hue; frequently shows loosely structured or downy-looking feathering to scapular tips (Fig).

1w (3/5)      Like juvenile but brown upperparts admixed with black 1st-winter feathers. Late in the season birds moult out all juvenile body feathers and assume adult-type plumage though scapulars and wing-coverts generally retained. Condition of scapular tips useful guide (Fig).

Adult (4/6)    Upperparts uniform black or blackish-brown. Scapular tips rounded and well formed (Fig).

### Scapulars

Ad. (4/6)

Juv./1w (3/5)

## Spring/Summer

1s (5)        Plumage similar to adult but crown not so glossy black and with some brown feathers. Wing-coverts brown and faded. Primaries abraded at the tips and fading brown.

Adult (6)     Head, neck and all upperparts uniform glossy black.

## Moult

3                Partial post-juvenile moult confined to body and tail, late autumn-December.

5                Partial pre-breeding moult March-May (June).

Adult          Complete post-breeding moult early to mid-June completed October (November); some feather tracts in the body in continuous moult. Simultaneous shedding of flight feathers, September. Partial pre-breeding moult confined to head, body and tail, February-April (May).

**Geographical variation** Slight: 2 other races - *P.n. californicus* (N. America) is similar to nominate *nigricollis* but inner primaries lack white. *P.n. gurneyi* (Africa) is paler and smaller, mean wing ♂ ♀ 125mm.

**Biometrics** Full-grown. Nominate *nigricollis* (BWP).

| | | | | | | |
|---|---|---|---|---|---|---|
| Wing | ♂134 | (3.77;20) | 127-139 | ♀130 | (2.82;19) | 124-136 |
| Bill | 23.4 | (1.04;18) | 21-26 | 21.5 | (1.25;15) | 20-24 |
| Tarsus | 43.2 | (1.73;18) | 40-45 | 42.1 | (1.64;18) | 39-45 |

# Fulmars and Shearwaters *Procellariidae*

Large to medium-sized pelagic seabirds. Body ovate, more elongated in shear-waters. Wings long and narrow. Plumage mostly black or grey above and white below; predominantly white and grey in *Fulmarus*. Light and dark morphs occur in *Fulmarus*.

## Feather structure
Primaries = 11 (p10 longest, p11 minute)
Secondaries = 20-29
Tail = 12 (14 in *Fulmarus*)

## Sexes
Similar in plumage. ♂ ♂ average larger.

## Moult
Strategy: primaries descendant. Secondaries descendant and ascendant. Tail irregular.
Sequence: primaries rapidly, almost simultaneously in early part of moult. Secondaries in 4 groups.
Frequency: once annually; SC. Body feathers slow and protracted.
Timing: from early-midsummer finishing winter-spring.


## **FULMAR** *Fulmarus glacialis*

| | |
|---|---|
| **Sexing** | Bill length (from feathers at base of culmen to tip of bill): |
| ♂ | >41mm. |
| ♀ | <38mm. |

### Autumn/Winter

| | |
|---|---|
| 3 | No yellow on neck and head. Plumage fresh. Primaries fresh, outers rather pointed at tip (Fig). |
| 1w (3/5) | Similar to 3 but plumage moderately worn. |
| 2w (5/7) | Before completion of wing moult outermost primaries very faded and heavily abraded; the overall shape of the tip is lost due to wear but is |

very narrow and pointed. After completion of moult appearance as adult but timing different - birds with very fresh and rounded outer primaries in autumn or early winter can thus be aged as 2nd-winter.

Adult (6/8)     Before completion of moult, outer primaries faded and worn, though tips remain comparatively rounded (Fig). Head, neck and upper breast with yellow tinge.

**Primary 9**

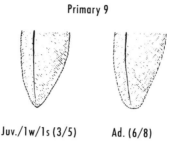

Juv./1w/1s (3/5)          Ad. (6/8)

## Spring/Summer

1s (5)     Before outer primaries are moulted can be aged on shape of these feathers (Fig).

Adult (6)     All other plumages.

Note: Immature Fulmars spend several years at sea before returning to breeding colonies.

## Moult

5     Complete post-juvenile moult starting in May of 2nd calendar year. Completed by September.

Adult     Complete post-breeding moult starting towards later stages of breeding (at chick stage) (June) July or early August when inner primaries are moulted and replaced in rapid succession, sometimes with up to 8 growing simultaneously (more usually 4-5); in final stages outer primaries are replaced and grown at much slower rate, not reaching full length before late February. Body moult starts before wing, June-July.

**Geographical variation** *F.g. rodgersii* (north Pacific) has more slender bill; lightest colour morph lighter, darkest darker than nominate *glacialis*. Variation in Atlantic great with birds averaging darker in high arctic localities than populations from southern, boreal part of Atlantic range, which tend to be overwhelmingly 'double light' morphs.

**Biometrics**   Full-grown. Nominate *glacialis* (Dunnet & Anderson 1961, BWP).

| | | | | | | |
|---|---|---|---|---|---|---|
| Wing | ♂340 | (9.46;18) | 324-355 | ♀323 | (8.13;17) | 309-336 |
| Bill | 40.9 | (1.34;23) | 38-44 | 37.7 | (0.97;26) | 36-39 |
| Tarsus | 53.7 | (1.42;10) | 51-55 | 50.2 | (0.89;14) | 49-52 |

**References**   Dunnet & Anderson (1961), Baker (1981 *b*).


# CORY'S SHEARWATER *Calonectris diomedea*

**Identification** From Great Shearwater *Puffinus gravis* by yellow bill and more uniform ash-brown upperparts. Great Shearwater has diagnostic black or dark brown cap, grey collar and black bill.

### Autumn/Winter

3/5   All parts of plumage fresh. White fringes to upper tail-coverts and edges to inner secondaries fresh and unabraded. Outer primaries fresh and pointed (Fig).

2w (5/7)   Wing moult score more advanced than adult; before completion of wing moult outer primaries still 1st generation (juvenile) and appear very faded and heavily abraded.

Adult (6/8)   Before moult, wing and most feathers on upperparts worn and faded.


**Primary 9**

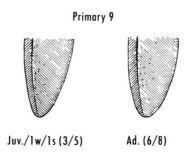

Juv./1w/1s (3/5)          Ad. (6/8)

## Spring/Summer

1s (5)          Primaries moderately worn; shape narrow and pointed (Fig). By late summer likely to be in wing moult.

Adult (6)        Primaries fresh to moderately worn and rounded at tips (Fig).

Note: movements of immature birds are little understood but they are thought to be pelagic for their first 2 or possibly 3 years of life, probably in southern latitudes. It is unlikely, therefore, that birds return to breeding colonies until breeding maturity is achieved.

## Moult

5          Data scarce; complete post-juvenile moult starting in summer (earlier than adults) of 2nd calendar year.

Adult        Complete post-breeding moult soon after leaving breeding colony, (September) October, finished by February or March.

**Geographical variation** Mid-Atlantic *C.d. borealis* very similar to Mediterranean nominate *diomedea*, but averages larger and darker on head and mantle. Vaurie (1965) gives wing and bill measurements as follows: *diomedea* 335-361mm av. 346, 48-58mm av. 52.8; *borealis* 349-372mm av. 363, 54-62mm av. 58. *C.d. edwardsii* (Cape Verde Islands) is smaller than nominate race and darker above with black bill; wing 300-325mm av. 309, bill 40-46.5mm av. 44.3.

**Biometrics**    Full-grown. Nominate *diomedea* (JKB, BWP).

| | | | | | | |
|---|---|---|---|---|---|---|
| Wing | ♂346 | (4.68; 9) | 339-351 | ♀339 | (6.83; 5) | 330-347 |
| Bill | 51.2 | (1.51;17) | 49-55 | 47.3 | (1.78;16) | 45-50 |
| Tarsus | 53.0 | ( ;10) | 51-56 | 51.8 | ( ; 7) | 49-53 |

# MANX SHEARWATER *Puffinus puffinus*

**Identification** Mediterranean Shearwater *Puffinus yelkouan* has shorter tail, browner upperparts, duskier axillaries (Fig) and undertail-coverts, often extending up the side of the body to beneath the wing. The white crescent on the side of the neck so typical of Manx, is usually absent on Mediterranean Shearwater.

## Axillaries

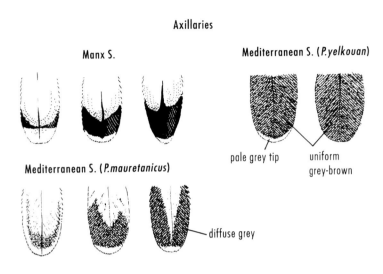

Manx S.

Mediterranean S. (*P.yelkouan*)

pale grey tip    uniform grey-brown

Mediterranean S. (*P.mauretanicus*)

diffuse grey

Variations in pattern of longest axillaries in three Shearwater types.

**Autumn/Winter**

3        Fledglings sometimes have large areas of ventral down and traces of down on nape. Pure black upperparts and wings (young birds may reach South American waters within 10 days of fledging and still show natal down!).

1w (3/5)    Longest axillaries pointed and often with white spot at tip, more extensive black than adult (Fig); reliable in UK probably until June (fledging August-September). Pure black upper body and wings.

Adult (4/6)    Longest axillaries rounded and variably pigmented; black less extensive than juveniles, usually fringed white at tip (Fig). Secondaries usually show some degree of intermittent moult, with one or two brown, worn feathers retained.

## Axillaries

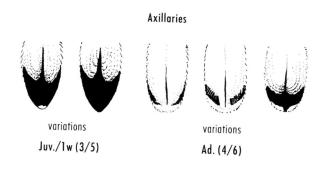

| variations | variations |
|:---:|:---:|
| **Juv./1w (3/5)** | **Ad. (4/6)** |

## Spring/Summer

1s (5)         Axillaries perhaps retained longer than other feathers.

Adult (4/6)    As Autumn/Winter plumage.

Note: very few 1st-summer birds return to breeding colonies, most remaining in southern hemisphere until their 2nd year - some, however, stray and can even be found as far north as European waters.

## Moult

3/5            Poorly known.

Adult          Complete post-breeding moult with body starting in mid-July into August followed by wings in late September; complete by February-April. Main moult thought to be in South American wintering grounds but more information required.

**Biometrics**    Full-grown (BWP).

| | | | | | | |
|---|---|---|---|---|---|---|
| Wing | ♂239 | (3.66;19) | 231-243 | ♀235 | (4.50;14) | 226-242 |
| Bill | 34.9 | (1.30;16) | 33-38 | 34.3 | (1.26;15) | 31-36 |
| Tarsus | 45.6 | (1.46;16) | 43-48 | 44.4 | (0.85;14) | 43-46 |

**References**    Harris (1966a, 1966b), Zonfrillo (1987), Bourne, Mackrill, Paterson & Yésou (1988), Yésou, Paterson, Mackrill & Bourne (1990).

# Storm-petrels *Hydrobatidae*

Small seabirds with black plumage and white rump. Long thin legs and long pointed wings.

## Feather structure
Primaries = 11 (p9 longest, p11 minute)
Secondaries = 14
Tail = 12

## Sexes
Similar in plumage. ♀ ♀ average slightly larger.

## Moult
Strategy: primaries descendant. Secondaries irregular. Often suspends. Tail irregular.
Sequence: primaries slowly over several months. Secondaries even slower, somewhat irregular and complicated.
Frequency: once annually; SC. Body and flight feathers slow and protracted.
Timing: from midsummer slowly through winter. Outer primaries and half secondaries still growing when birds return to breeding grounds.

## STORM PETREL *Hydrobates pelagicus*

**Identification**  From other west Palearctic storm-petrels by smaller size and diagnostic whitish bar or patch on underwing-coverts, sometimes pure white and very prominent. Also narrow whitish line along leading edge of greater-coverts (fresh plumage only).

**Sexing**  Recognition of ♀ possible immediately prior to and after egg laying. The cloaca has several stages of development beginning when roundish vent becomes slightly transverse and the lips swell and thicken. From this point separation of most ♀ ♀ should be straightforward, as cloaca becomes very red and distended. The regression of the swollen cloaca is gradual.

Circular 1st stage

Transverse 2nd stage

## Autumn/Winter

3          White tips to greater-coverts, extending also to tips of tertials and some innermost secondaries.

1w (3/5)     Similar to juvenile but some wear to greater-coverts reduces conspicuousness of white tips. Care should be exercised so as not to confuse these feathers for those of newly moulted adults which also show pale edges and tips to greater-coverts - these though have a more waxy sheen. Uppertail-coverts useful guide (Fig).

Adult (4/6)    Greater-coverts and tertials uniform dark brown, unless newly moulted (see note above under 1st-winter). Uppertail-coverts useful guide (Fig).

Upper tail-coverts

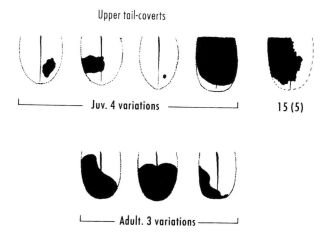

Juv. 4 variations         15 (5)

Adult. 3 variations

## Spring/Summer

1s (5)       Very few, if any, 1st-summer birds visit breeding colonies. Before first complete moult, greater-coverts still show evidence of pale whitish tips.

Degree of conspicuousness is variable, but pale tips are also detectable on tertials and inner secondaries on many birds. Most age 3-type uppertail-coverts will have been replaced during winter but some may still be evident though much worn (Fig). The period over which ageing is reliable extends until August on some birds.

Adult (4/6)   Greater-coverts uniform blackish or blackish-brown. Uppertail-covert pattern useful guide (Fig).

**Moult**

3   Partial post-juvenile moult confined to head and body, begins in nest burrow; down may be visible when bird leaves burrow.

1s   Complete moult in summer, June onwards, finishing October-November. Onset of moult is usually 3-4 weeks earlier than adults.

Adult   Complete post-breeding moult starting with body during 2nd half of incubation period, usually July. Primary moult starts towards end of breeding cycle, though clearly later in some birds. Suspended moult is common, seen mainly in outer primaries in spring. Secondaries also frequently show two ages of feathers.

**Biometrics**   Full-grown (BWP).

| | | | | | | |
|---|---|---|---|---|---|---|
| Wing | ♂120 | (2.95;19) | 116-127 | ♀121 | (2.93;25) | 116-127 |
| Bill | 10.8 | (0.49;20) | 9.5-11.5 | 11.0 | (0.41;24) | 10.8-11.8 |
| Tarsus | 21.5 | (0.68;20) | 19.6-22.3 | 22.1 | (0.87;25) | 20.2-24.3 |

**References**   Scott (1970), Baker (1984).


# LEACH'S PETREL *Oceanodroma leucorhoa*

**Identification** From Storm Petrel by forked tail, 17-23mm (shortest to longest tail feathers, t1-t6). Madeiran Petrel *O. castro* has completely white rump and less deeply forked tail, <13mm (usually 5-8mm).

## Autumn/Winter

1w (3/5)    On leaving nest burrows most birds have some remains of down on the body; otherwise, whitish edges to pale greater-coverts. In late winter pale edges become worn reducing amount of white, sometimes making distinction from adults difficult. Outer primaries comparatively pointed at tip (Fig).

Adult (4/6)    Greater-coverts uniform, without whitish edges. Outer primaries rounded at tip (Fig).

### Primary 9

Juv./1s (3/5)    Ad. (4/6)

## Spring/Summer

1s (5)    Greater-coverts show traces of worn white edges, though often absent due to excessive wear. Primary shape may be helpful if distinct. Any bird in active wing moult (but beware of suspended moult) in spring or early summer will be a bird of this age.

Adult (4/6)    All other plumages.

Note 1: Intermediate primary shape also occurs. Such birds should not be aged without reference to other features.

Note 2: Very few, if any, 1st-summer birds visit breeding colonies, most probably staying in southern hemisphere waters.

## Moult

5    Complete post-juvenile moult starting in April of 2nd calendar year with flight feathers, completed by October-December.

Adult    Complete post-breeding moult starting with body towards end of breeding cycle. Inner primaries and some tail feathers may be moulted October but suspend until winter quarters are reached; moult resumed November onwards, completed by February (March). Non-breeders moult earlier, beginning with body in May or June and flight feathers not until August or September.

**Geographical variation** Within nominate *leucorhoa* negligible; 3 or 4 other subspecies recognized (N. America).

**Biometrics**   Full-grown. Nominate *leucorhoa* (BWP).

| | | | | | | |
|---|---|---|---|---|---|---|
| Wing | ♂158 | (3.76;47) | 148-165 | ♀158 | (3.56;54) | 152-166 |
| Bill | 15.7 | (0.46;50) | 14.2-16.6 | 15.7 | (0.50;56) | 14.7-16.9 |
| Tarsus | 24.0 | (0.58;50) | 22.9-25.5 | 24.1 | (0.70;55) | 22.3-25.5 |

**References**   Ainley, Lewis & Morrell (1976), Baker (1984).

# Gannets *Sulidae*

Medium-large to large seabirds. Body elongated. Wings long, narrow and pointed. Adult plumage predominantly white with black on wings.

## Feather structure
Primaries = 11 (p9 or p10 longest, p11 minute)
Secondaries = 28 (26-31)
Tail = 12

## Sexes
Similar in plumage.

## Moult
Strategy: primaries serially descendant. Secondaries descendant and ascendant. Often suspends. Tail irregular.
Sequence: primaries moult from 3 centres. Secondaries complicated but involves moult from several centres.
Frequency: once annually; SC. Body and flight feathers slow.
Timing: from spring-midsummer finishing mid-late winter.


## GANNET *Morus bassanus*

| Sexing | Only reliable after 3rd calendar year (3W). |
|---|---|
| ♂ | Greenish lines on mid-ridge of toes, continued and fusing on tarsus, tending to yellow. |
| ♀ | Greenish lines on mid-ridge of toes, continued and fusing on tarsus, tending to blue. |

### Autumn/Winter

| 1w (3/5) | Upperparts uniform chocolate-brown (sometimes almost black, others silvery-grey) with rows of small V-shaped spots, most prominent on neck and head. Underparts whitish, feathers tipped brown. No sharp demarcation line between darker upperparts and white underparts. |
|---|---|
| 2w (5/7) | Upperparts much the same as 1st-winter but tend to be browner and without white spots - appearing more uniform. Often shows pale patch below lores and ear-coverts, giving capped appearance. Underparts |

whiter with strong demarcation between brown flanks and thigh patches or brown throat and upper breast. Advanced birds may have white or yellow head and white rump with white leading edge to the wing between the carpal joint and elbow. Some white feathers may be apparent on the mantle, upper back and possibly some wing-coverts.

3w (7/9)      Upperparts admixed blackish or dark brown and white. White areas extensive on scapulars, mantle and upper back. Lesser-coverts and some median-coverts white. Some white secondaries (varies greatly). Small number of black tail feathers.

4w (9/11)     Upperparts wholly creamy-white and much the same appearance as adult. Many, however, with 1 or even 2 black feathers in the tail and outer secondaries. Some inner primary-coverts brown.

5w (11/13)    Plumage as adult. A very small percentage of birds however may have retained a black tail or secondary feather but more commonly 1 or 2 brown inner primary-coverts.

Adult (10/12) Body all white except for black primaries and alula. Head yellow-buff extending to upper neck.

## Spring/Summer

1s (5)        Like 1st-winter but white spotting on upperparts beginning to deteriorate making appearance more uniform brown. Underparts whiter giving strong demarcation line between dark upperparts, flanks, thigh and throat.

2s (7)        Upperparts an admixture of blackish or deep brown and white feathers on rump, back, scapulars and some wing-coverts, with mixture of black and white secondaries and some black tail feathers. Underparts white but sometimes with brown thighs. Variably white suffused yellow on the back of the head and nape. Leading edge of wing broadly white.

3s (9)        Like 3rd-winter but more advanced; areas of white feathering usually quite extensive, greater than areas of black markings. Secondaries with blocks of black and white (old and new) feathers. Most wing-coverts white, retained black ones present only in small numbers. Scapulars usually white. Tail white with 1 or 2 old black feathers.

4s (11)       As for 5w

5s (13)       As for 5w.

Adult (12)    As Autumn/Winter but yellow-buff on head less intensive.

Note: a Gannet may reach full adult plumage a few months before its 4th birthday (4w), i.e. when it is still 3 years old. More normally attainment of adult plumage is during its 5th year (5w), i.e. when it is 4 years old.

## Moult

3/5    Gradual body moult begins as early as November, usually January. Flight feathers begin about 6 or 7 months after fledging, February-May. When birds are about 1 year old up to 6 inner primaries have been replaced. P7 may just be growing out but then p1 (innermost) is replaced again and descendant moult continues from this point. Thus, 3 generations of primaries are quite normal and most easily seen in immatures; the outer primaries belong to the 1st generation; the middle ones to the 2nd and the innermost to the 3rd. Secondaries are moulted in similar manner but the tail is somewhat irregular and asymmetrical. Moult timing thereafter is similar to adult.

Adult    Moult probably continuous but most active in May when body moult is apparent. Flight feathers begin July lasting through to December or January (February). Wing replaced from 3 different moult centres which may represent 3 generations of feathers.

## Biometrics    (BWP).

| Wing | ad. ♂ 491 | (11.0;23) | 460-515 | ♀ 485 | (12.8;23) | 460-520 |
|---|---|---|---|---|---|---|
|  | juv. 474 | (15.1;18) | 445-505 | 479 | (16.6;12) | 450-505 |
| Bill | ad. 99.3 | (2.31;24) | 95-103 | 97.4 | (3.10;22) | 92-101 |
| Tarsus | ad. 60.2 | (1.61;21) | 58–64 | 60.3 | (1.61;22) | 58-64 |

# Cormorants and Shags *Phalacrocoracidae*

Medium-sized to large aquatic birds. Body elongated. Wings with long inner portion (arm) and short tip (hand). Plumage black with metallic sheen.

### Feather structure
Primaries = 11 (p8/9 longest, p11 minute)
Secondaries = 18-19 (17-23)
Tail = 12-14

### Sexes
Similar in plumage.

### Moult
Strategy: primaries serially descendant. Secondaries descendant and ascendant. Often suspends/arrests. Tail irregular but more or less alternating.
Sequence: primaries from 2, rarely 3 centres. Secondaries from several centres.
Frequency: twice annually; SC, Wp. Body and flight feathers slow and protracted.
Timing: from mid-late summer finishing early-midwinter; midwinter finishing early spring.


## CORMORANT *Phalacrocorax carbo*

**Identification** From Shag by longer wing >300mm.

**Sexing**

♂         Wing >352mm; Bill depth* >16mm.

♀         Wing <345mm; Bill depth* <15mm.

        * Bill depth is taken at minimum depth in middle of bill.

        Note: above measurements relate to nominate *P.c. carbo*. The central and southern European race *sinensis* averages smaller: Wing ♂ >340mm ♀ <325mm.

**Autumn/Winter**

1w (3/5)        Upperparts predominantly dark brown tipped glossy blue or brown-black, becoming dull bronze on side of mantle, scapulars and some wing-coverts. Underparts generally white often with some brown streaking or blotching, usually on chin, lower breast, belly and vent (Fig); much individual variation. Tips to outermost primaries and tips of scapulars pointed (Fig). Iris grey-brown to blue-green.

2w (5/7)   Crown and hindneck dark bluish-black edged brown. Remainder of upperparts mostly glossy but with some old brown and worn juvenile feathers. Belly often more mottled appearance due to emergence of sub-adult-type feathers. Old, worn and pale outer primaries retained after arrest of moult, number variable but up to 6, more usually 4. Iris emerald-green, as adult.

3w (7/9)   Advanced birds like adult but some brown feathers remaining on neck. Birds in active wing moult may still have unmoulted outer juvenile primaries - very abraded and pale; such birds usually show 3 ages of primaries and moult from 2 centres; otherwise (in later stages or after moult) 2 ages of primaries. Some may retain long outermost primary (p10) into 4th calendar year.

Adult (8)   Upperparts black glossed metallic blue or bluish-purple except crown and hindneck which are blue-black tinged brown. White feathers of chin and sides of head tipped buff. Lacks white elongated head and neck feathers of breeding plumage. Iris emerald-green.

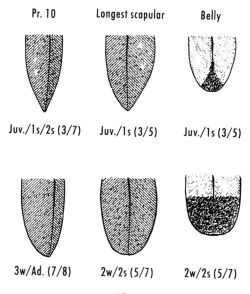

Pr. 10            Longest scapular            Belly

Juv./1s/2s (3/7)     Juv./1s (3/5)     Juv./1s (3/5)

3w/Ad. (7/8)        2w/2s (5/7)        2w/2s (5/7)

## Spring/Summer

1s (5)   Like 1st-winter in early part of spring but gradually moulting out juvenile feathers. By summer admixture of old juvenile feathers and new ones. Outer primary tips and scapulars pointed (Fig). Iris grey-brown, greyish-green, or bluish-green, but not bright emerald-green.

2s (7)   Like 2nd-winter but more glossy on crown and neck. Breast and belly dark blue-black; white feather-bases partly visible still, giving mottled appearance.

3s (9)   Birds showing very abraded and faded outermost primary (p10) can be aged as 3. In normal circumstances this feather is dropped at onset of post-breeding moult (June, July). After moult cannot be aged beyond 4+ calendar years (8).

Adult (8)   Upperparts black glossed metallic blue or bluish-purple. Crown, upper neck and lower throat with variable number of white, elongated feathers - lost by the time eggs have been hatched. Hindneck and centre of nape with black elongated feathers. Underparts as above except for white thigh-patches. Iris emerald-green.

Note: some birds breed for the first time in their second summer (most are breeding by their third). These all acquire white thigh-patches, the size of which seems to increase with age, and usually at least a few white head feathers.

## Moult

3/5   Extent of moult varies greatly but nominate *carbo* undergoes partial moult involving head, neck, mantle and belly, sometimes a few scapulars too, August-December. Subspecies *sinensis* can begin wing moult August-September of 1st calendar year. In *carbo* a complete moult is undertaken during 2nd calendar year; body starts February followed by wings and tail from June onwards, arresting in December when about 4 to 6 outer primaries and a number of tail feathers remain unmoulted. Moult is resumed in the spring of 3rd calendar year, beginning with another new series of innermost primaries (3rd generation). At the same time the old juvenile outer primaries are moulted out giving 2 centres of moult involving 3 ages of primaries. In a proportion of birds (probably small) this moult period may still exclude loss of outermost primary (p10); it is, however, one of the first feathers to be dropped when moult is resumed in June of the 4th calendar year.

Adult   Complete post-breeding moult starting with head and body June; wings and tail July. 2, sometimes 3, active moult centres, serially descendant; tail moult irregular. Partial pre-breeding moult January-April confined to head, neck and some body feathers.

**Geographical variation** *P.c. sinensis* (western continental Europe, east to Japan) is glossy blue-green, not blue-purple as in nominate *carbo,* and averages smaller (see Biometrics). In breeding plumage head and neck generally much whiter, but some adult ♂ *carbo* as white as typical *sinensis*. Two other palearctic subspecies recognized, *lucidus* (W. Africa), *maroccanus* (northwest Africa). In both the white areas extend to upper breast and in *lucidus* sometimes to belly.

**Biometrics**    Full-grown. Nominate *carbo* (JKB).

| | | | | | | |
|---|---|---|---|---|---|---|
| Wing | ♂358 | (5.05;26) | 347-368 | ♀339 | (9.27;20) | 318-352 |
| Bill | 76.4 | (3.68;20) | 73-85 | 70.0 | (2.56;20) | 67-76 |
| Tarsus | 74.0 | (3.02;26) | 66-78 | 70.4 | (2.67;22) | 65-75 |

Full-grown (BWP).

| | | | | | | |
|---|---|---|---|---|---|---|
| Wing | ♂357 | (5.19;6) | 350-363 | ♀339 | (9.27;12) | 318-351 |
| Bill (D)* | 16.3 | (0.92;4) | 16-18 | 14.1 | (0.45;8) | 13-15 |
| Tarsus | 74.0 | (3.18;6) | 68-78 | 70.6 | (2.35;12) | 67-74 |

Breeding adults. *P.c. sinensis* (BWP).

| | | | | | | |
|---|---|---|---|---|---|---|
| Wing | ♂347 | (8.04;38) | 330-364 | ♀325 | (6.49;18) | 311-337 |
| Bill (D)* | 14.0 | (0.82;34) | 13-16 | 11.8 | (0.59;14) | 11-13 |
| Tarsus | 69.4 | (2.33;38) | 66-73 | 66.1 | (1.84;18) | 64-70 |

* Depth at middle of bill.

**References**    Alström (1985), Winkler (1987).

# SHAG *Phalacrocorax aristotelis*

**Identification** From Cormorant by smaller wing <290mm.

**Sexing**

| | |
|---|---|
| ♂ | Wing >272mm; Bill depth* mostly >11.3mm. Usually vocal (croaks and grunts) at nest. |
| ♀ | Wing <258mm; Bill depth* mostly <11.3mm. Usually silent, sometimes hisses at nest. |

\* Bill depth is taken at minimum depth in middle of bill.

**Autumn/Winter**

Juv/1w (3/5)  Underparts pale brown becoming paler towards foreneck; chin is almost white. Upperparts darker, admixed with a few metallic green feathers. Hindneck feathers of 1st-winter (3/5) darker than juvenile showing some metallic green while upperparts have faint green gloss with wing-coverts and scapulars edged dark brown. Iris yellow-white.

2w (5/7)  Underparts darker brown than 1st-winter but still with some feathers on chin. Chin usually shows signs of white feathering. Abdomen to vent pale brown. Upperparts completely metallic green but tend to be duller and browner than adult. Outer juvenile primary (p10) retained in 70% of ♀♀ and 30% of ♂♂, worn and pale. Iris yellow-green.

3w (7/9)  A small percentage of birds (2% of ♂♂, 4% of ♀♀) retain outermost primary (p10) until summer of 4th calendar year; thus, birds with very abraded outer primary (often distal portion of feather with just shaft) can be aged 7/9. Otherwise age 8.

Adult (8)  Whole of body glossy metallic greenish-blue, the only contrast being dark brown primaries and black tail. Bare patch of skin behind lower mandible, and upper chin black, speckled yellow. In late winter, develops distinctive crest on crown. Iris bright emerald-green.

**Spring/Summer**

1s (5)  As for 1st-winter but glossy green feathering on upperparts more advanced. Iris yellow-green.

2s (7)  More advanced than 2nd-winter with more adult-type feathers, especially on upperparts. Wing in active moult and follows one of two patterns: 1. In birds where wing moult was arrested - see 2w; moult from 2 centres - inner primaries starting at p1, and from place where moult was interrupted, normally just the outermost primary, and involving 3 generations of primaries! 2. In birds where wing moult was completed during 1st moult; moult from one centre only and involves just two generations of primaries - 2nd and 3rd. A small percentage of birds however retain the outermost juvenile primary (p10) until summer of 4th calendar year.

3s (9)       Most not ageable but small percentage of birds still with retained outermost primary which is <u>very</u> worn and faded (distal half of feather just with shaft remaining).

Adult (8)    As Autumn/Winter.

**Moult**    Complex and variable.

3/5          Head and neck feathers start moulting from September of the 1st calendar year, followed by mantle in November but then suspended during winter. Resumed in spring of 2nd calendar year along with wing and tail, usually May, sometimes earlier. Completed by December when moult is then arrested at which point about 33% of ♂♂ and 70% of ♀♀ retain the long outermost primary (p10) until summer of 3rd calendar year. About 2% of ♂♂ and 4% of ♀♀ keep unmoulted p10 for a further year (4th calendar year).

Adult        Primaries are moulted from 2, sometimes 3, active centres, serially descendant. Primary cycle active most months but pauses during winter (November-February); thereafter resumed at slower rate than summer, becoming faster after breeding is over. Pre-breeding moult confined to head, neck and parts of body, November-February.

**Geographical variation** Slight in western Europe: *P.a. desmarestii* (Mediterranean & Black Sea) is slightly smaller than nominate *aristotelis*, but bill longer and more slender (length 58-65mm, depth (from middle of bill) 8.2-10.6mm), and with more extensive yellow with only culmen and tip black; crest much reduced. Bare skin on face, legs and webs usually paler and more yellowish. Juveniles with much more white on underparts. *P.a. riggenbachi* (northwest Africa) combines body size and colour of bare parts of *desmarestii* with bill dimensions of nominate *aristotelis*.

**Biometrics**    Full-grown. Nominate *aristotelis* (BWP).

| | | | | | | |
|---|---|---|---|---|---|---|
| Wing | ♂271 | (5.31;12) | 261-278 | ♀258 | (4.78;18) | 251-269 |
| Bill | 58.9 | (1.65;14) | 56-61 | 59.3 | (2.08;11) | 57-63 |
| Bill (D)* | 11.6 | (0.80;15) | 10.4-12.1 | 9.9 | (0.95;10) | 9.1-12.1 |
| Tarsus | 64.7 | (2.07;12) | 62-68 | 62.0 | (1.99;18) | 58-65 |

* Depth at middle of bill (Scottish birds).

Full-grown (JKB).

| | | | | | | |
|---|---|---|---|---|---|---|
| Bill | ♂61.3 | (1.85;20) | 57-65 | ♀61.0 | (1.68;20) | 55-65 |

**References**    Potts (1971), Baker (1981 *b*), Aebischer (1985), Alström (1985).

# Herons and Bitterns *Ardeidae*

Medium-sized to large wading birds. Body slim with long neck and long legs. Wings long and broad. *Ardea* mostly grey upperparts, white below. *Botaurus* cryptic plumage, predominantly brown and buff with blackish vermiculations.

## Feather structure
Primaries: = 11 (p7-p10 longest, p11 minute)
Secondaries = 15-20
Tail = 10 in *Botaurus*, 12 in *Ardea*.

## Sexes
Similar in plumage. ♂ ♂ average larger.

## Moult
Strategy: irregular or inner primaries descendant, outers irregular. Secondaries ascendant and descendant. Tail centripetal. Sometimes suspends.
Sequence: primaries irregular in *Botaurus*; in *Ardea* p10 often moulted before p8 or p9. Secondaries irregular and involving several centres.
Frequency: once (twice?) annually; SC. Body feathers replaced in winter and some ornamental plumes on nape growing in spring.
Timing: midsummer-autumn finishing winter-early spring.


## BITTERN *Botaurus stellaris*

**Identification**  Larger than vagrant American Bittern *B. lentiginosus*, wing >290mm, weight >700g; also by mottled brown primaries and secondaries, not black; black, not rufous crown.

**Sexing**  Wing and toe length useful guide:

♂  Wing >338mm; Toe >120mm; Tail >112mm.

♀  Wing <330mm; Toe <108mm; Tail <110mm.

### Autumn/Winter

3  Crown patch black tinged brown and less extensive, usually not extending to nape. Moustachial streak brown or blackish strongly tinged brown. Upper wing-coverts paler, less buffish and more strongly vermiculated. Outer primaries narrow and pointed (Fig).

1w (3/5)     Gradual change to adult appearance but wing and wing-coverts retained (perhaps some new coverts replaced) (Fig).

Adult (6)    Crown and nape black, latter with wide buff margins. Moustachial streak black. Upper wing-coverts golden-buff, mottled and freckled tawny and black. Outer primaries broad and rounded at tip (Fig). After completion of moult cannot be reliably aged beyond 2+ calendar years (4).

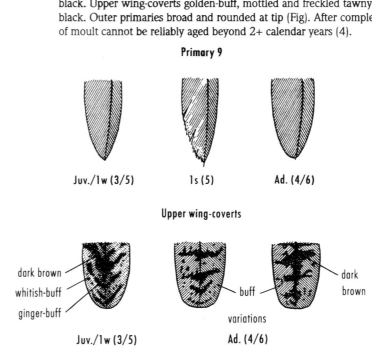

Primary 9

Juv./1w (3/5)          1s (5)          Ad. (4/6)

Upper wing-coverts

dark brown
whitish-buff
ginger-buff
buff
variations
dark brown

Juv./1w (3/5)          Ad. (4/6)

## Spring/Summer

1s (5)       As 1st-winter but primary shape less useful as shape distorted by abrasion.

Adult (6)    As Autumn/Winter.

## Moult

3/5          Partial post-juvenile moult confined to body and tail, starting with head and neck soon after fledging; a percentage replace some wing-coverts and perhaps some flight feathers (number involved and extent of moult poorly known). Apparently head moulted again in midwinter or early spring (needs confirmation).

Adult        Poorly studied due to elusive nature, especially during moulting period.

Complete post-breeding moult July-January, but usually finished November, but some as late as March. Sequence of wing moult irregular. No details on pre-breeding moult.

**Geographical variation** *B.s capensis* (southern Africa) is darker than nominate *stellaris* and with primaries spotted rather than barred. Eastern populations more striped on underparts.

**Biometrics**    Full-grown. Nominate *stellaris* (BWP).

| | | | | | | |
|---|---|---|---|---|---|---|
| Wing | ♂346 | (6.67;21) | 335-357 | ♀311 | (7.34;16) | 296-327 |
| Tail | 117 | (4.40;11) | 112-126 | 104 | (4.87;8) | 96-110 |
| Bill | 69.1 | (3.24;20) | 61-74 | 64.3 | (2.10;16) | 60-68 |
| Tarsus | 102 | (3.53;11) | 97-109 | 91.0 | (2.63;9) | 87-95 |
| Toe | 118 | (5.04;20) | 110-132 | 107 | (5.02;15) | 98-119 |

Full-grown (JKB).

| | | | | | | |
|---|---|---|---|---|---|---|
| Wing | ♂333.4 | (;20) | 310-347 | ♀306 | (;15) | 278-336 |
| Bill | 70.8 | (;20) | 66-75 | 66.4 | (;15) | 60-71 |
| Tarsus | 98 | (;18) | 88-105 | 91.6 | (;14) | 83-98 |

# LITTLE BITTERN *Ixobrychus minutus*

**Identification**    From vagrant Least Bittern *I. exilis* (N. America) by larger size, wing > 130mm (Least range 108-122mm), and from Schrenck's Little Bittern *I. eurhythmus* (central Russia, China, Japan, Indo-China) by black mantle and back (♂) or buff upperparts and wing-coverts, heavily streaked dark brown (♀); in Schrenck's ♂ has dark chestnut upperparts and ♀ has white speckling and spotting on chestnut upperparts and wing-coverts, as does juvenile.

**Sexing**    Adults only:

♂    Crown, mantle, scapulars, back, rump and tail black with green gloss. Greater-coverts white or grey-buff.

♀      Mantle, scapulars, back and rump brown, sometimes strongly tinged rufous, with buff margins to feathers. Wing-coverts buff.

## Autumn

3      Similar to adult ♀ but forehead and crown with wider and paler brown edges. Mantle, scapulars and back blackish-brown with broad buff or gingery-buff margin giving striped effect. Wing-coverts dark brown-grey with wide buff margins.

2w (5)      Some birds retain small number of old gingery (♂) or dark V-shaped centred (♀) wing-coverts, especially outer greater-coverts. Inner secondaries brown, not jet-black. After moult cannot be aged beyond 2+ calendar years (4).

Adult ♂ (6)      Greater-coverts white or grey-buff.

Adult ♀ (6)      Wing-coverts uniform buff.

## Spring/Summer

1s (5)      As 2nd-winter.

Adult (6)      As Autumn.

**Moult**      Poorly known.

3/5      Partial post-juvenile moult confined to body, November-January.

Adult      Complete post-breeding moult starting with body, July, followed by some flight feathers late July, August. Suspends just prior to migration and resumes once in winter quarters; p1-p7 descendant, outers irregular. Some may not moult at all before arrival in Central African winter quarters.

**Geographical variation** Within Europe negligible. Five subspecies recognized. Differences involve colour of upperparts and size.

**Biometrics** Adult. Nominate *minutus* (BWP).

| | | | | | | |
|---|---|---|---|---|---|---|
| Wing | ♂153 | (2.47;15) | 149-157 | ♀148 | (3.42;12) | 142-153 |
| Bill | 48.6 | (1.91;14) | 46-53 | 46.5 | (1.75;11) | 44-49 |
| Tarsus | 46.2 | (2.79;12) | 43-52 | 43.0 | (2.00;8) | 41-47 |
| Toe | 51.8 | (1.48;12) | 50-54 | 50.0 | (2.00;8) | 48-53 |

Full-grown (JKB).

| | | | | | | | | |
|---|---|---|---|---|---|---|---|---|
| Wing | ♂149 | (;23) | 138-160 | ♀144 | (;14) | | 127-152 |
| Bill | 48.5 | (;22) | 44-52 | 47.5 | (;16) | | 44-52 |
| Tarsus | 46 | (;22) | 42-51 | 45 | (;16) | | 41-48 |

# GREY HERON *Ardea cinerea*

**Sexing**     Adults only:

♂          Wing >465mm; Bill >125mm.

♀          Wing <439mm; Bill <109mm.

### Autumn/Winter

3          Forehead, crown and neck grey. Upperparts dark grey without orna-
           mental feathers.

1w (3/5)   Upperparts more blue-grey than juvenile. Crown grey, streaked sooty
           black. Nape sooty black with elongated ornamental feathers, but these
           shorter and less glossy than in adult.

2w (5/7)   Similar in appearance to adult, but forehead grey with some white
           feathers in mid crown.

Adult (6/8)  Sides of upper breast black with long pinkish ornamental feathers. Rest
           of underparts admixed black, white and grey. Upperparts uniform grey,
           with long pale grey ornamental plumes to mid and lower back. Forehead
           and central crown stripe pure white bordered either side by black crown
           feathers which become elongated towards back of head.

           Note: Some adults show 'grey caps' – usually confined to small areas of
           grey feathering in the forehead, but occasionally the whole crown can
           be grey. Such birds, however, usually have white napes.

### Spring/Summer

1s (5)     Neck off-white with some grey feathers. Forehead and mid crown with
           indications of white feathers. Some black feathers to sides of upper
           breast.

| 2s (7) | Possibly some birds with some grey feathers in otherwise white forehead. |
| Adult (8) | As for Autumn/Winter. |

## Moult

| 3/5 | Body moult begins in September and continues into February. Wing and tail retained until the next moult. Subsequent moults similar to adult, though non-breeders probably moult earlier, and there is some evidence to suggest that non-breeders and sub-adults moult flight feathers in a regular centrifugal fashion as opposed to the irregular replacement by adults. |
| Adult | Complete post-breeding moult starting in June, usually completed by November. Inner primaries moulted descendantly, but outer ones replaced in irregular sequence. |

**Geographical variation** Largely clinal in nominate *cinerea:* birds become paler on the neck and upper wing-coverts from west to east. Within Europe differences negligible. Three other races recognized.

**Biometrics** Full-grown. Nominate *cinerea* (BWP).

| | | | | | | |
|--------|------|-----------|---------|--------|-----------|---------|
| Wing | ♂457 | (12.2;20) | 440-485 | ♀443 | (9.77;12) | 428-463 |
| Bill | 120 | (5.76;26) | 110-131 | 112 | (5.06;19) | 101-123 |
| Tarsus | 151 | (8.14;23) | 136-172 | 141 | (5.74;16) | 132-153 |

**References** Milstein, Prestt & Bell (1970), Baker (1982).

# Swans and Geese *Anatidae: Anserinae*

Medium-large to large waterbirds. Body broad and rather elongated. Wings broad and long. Long necks. Webbed feet. All white plumage in *Cygnus*, mostly grey, brown, or black with white in *Anser* and *Branta*.

### Feather structure
Primaries = 11 (p9 longest, p11 reduced)
Secondaries = 17-28 (mostly 22-28 in *Cygnus*, 17-18 in *Anser* and *Branta*)
Tail = 16-24 (mostly 20-24 in *Cygnus*, 16-20 in *Anser* and *Branta*)

### Sexes
Similar in plumage.

### Moult
Strategy: simultaneous.
Sequence: simultaneously.
Frequency: once annually (some moult head and neck again after main moult);
SC. Body and tail slow and protracted.
Timing: early-late summer finishing autumn-winter.


## MUTE SWAN *Cygnus olor*

**Identification**  Juveniles are grey-brown overall, have pointed tails and black at the base of the bill. Juvenile Whooper and Bewick's Swans are pale cinnamon-grey, have rounded tails and lack black at the base of the bill (see Bewick's Swan).

**Sexing**  All ages by cloacal examination, at any season. Size of bill knob in adults only reliable within breeding pair when knob of ♂ virtually always larger than that of ♀. Wing measurement and weight useful guide but much overlap:

♂  Wing >595mm; Weight >11kg.

♀  Wing <570mm; Weight <9kg.

## Autumn/Winter

**3**      Overall grey-brown with variable amounts of white on body. Bill dirty grey-pink.

     Note: beware of rare all-white morph, 'Polish Swan'. Juveniles are all-white with pinkish bills and legs. Adults like ordinary Mute Swan but with pink legs.

**1w (3/5)**      Increasing whiteness but variable in speed of acquisition and extent, though some degree of uniformity among siblings. Greater- and median-coverts remain dirty grey-brown. Tips of primaries sullied brown. Bill pinkish.

**2w (5/7)**      Most, though not all, retain scattered brown feathers on head, wing-coverts and, especially, on the rump. Bill colour variable and unreliable for ageing.

**Adult (6/8)**      White all over. Bill variable from pinkish-orange to orange-red though not reliably distinct enough from advanced 2nd-winter birds.

## Spring/Summer

**1s (5)**      Notched tail feathers and worn juvenile wing feathers retained until flightless period.

**2s (7)**      Similar to 2nd-winter but more advanced with fewer brown feathers; last remnants usually to be found on rump. After moult like adult.

**Adult (8)**      Ageable up to period of moult: as Autumn/Winter. After moult cannot be aged beyond 3+ calendar years (6).

## Moult

**3/5**      Partial post-juvenile moult starting shortly after fledging, mainly of head, neck and upper mantle, spreading to scapulars and sides of body. More-or-less continuous through autumn and winter. Continuation of body moult in June of 2nd calendar year, followed shortly after, July to early August, by wings when birds become flightless for about 6 weeks. This sequence and timing follows similar pattern through to 3rd calendar year (7). Thereafter seemingly as adult.

**Adult**      Complete post-breeding moult. Breeding pair usually stagger moult period starting in ♀ when young are small, followed by ♂ when ♀ is nearing completion; sometimes order reversed or near-simultaneous.

Flightless period 6-8 weeks when wing feathers are moulted out simultaneously; after completion of wing, moult continues with tail and rest of the body.

**Biometrics**   (BWP).

| | | | | | | | |
|---|---|---|---|---|---|---|---|
| Wing | *ad.* | ♂606 | (12.1;12) | 580-623 | ♀562 | (16.3;10) | 533-589 |
| | *juv.* | 582 | (18.2;4) | 552-598 | 556 | (13.1;7) | 540-572 |
| Bill | *ad.* | 80.6 | (3.88;12) | 74-88 | 74.2 | (2.89;13) | 69-79 |
| Tarsus | *ad.* | 114 | (3.49;12) | 107-118 | 104 | (4.69;10) | 99-114 |

**References**   Scott *et al.* (1972).

# BEWICK'S SWAN *Cygnus columbianus*

**Identification** Juvenile from Mute Swan by paler, cinnamon-grey plumage, not grey-brown, and rounded, not pointed tail, and by pinkish base to bill, not black. Adult from Whooper Swan by shorter wing, range 474-570mm, and bill, range 79-110mm; in Whooper wing range 562-635mm, and bill range 92-116mm (cloacal examination of birds in overlap area will reveal whether an isolated bird caught is a large male Bewick's or a small female Whooper). Less yellow in the bill (Fig). Juvenile from Whooper by size and structure: tail <155mm, Whooper >154mm; wing range 445-538mm, Whooper 530-632mm. Becomes whiter much later in winter than Whooper; bill remains grey-brown until spring, whereas in Whooper the bill pattern is like adult, albeit whitish and grey-black rather than yellow and black.

**Sexing**   All ages by cloacal examination, at any season. In adult wing and toe useful guide but much overlap:

♂   Wing >542mm; Toe >130mm.

♀   Wing <480mm; Toe <117mm.

**Autumn/Winter**

3   Pale cinnamon-grey, darker on head. Whiter underparts. Bill sullied pink, often whitish at base. Tail feathers notched at tip, bare shafts projecting.

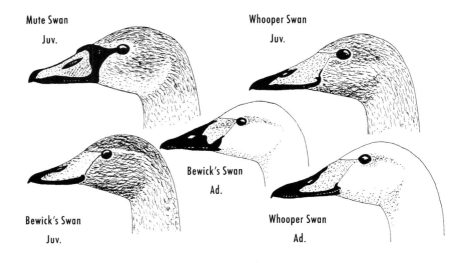

Mute Swan Juv.

Whooper Swan Juv.

Bewick's Swan Ad.

Bewick's Swan Juv.

Whooper Swan Ad.

**1w (3/5)**     Increasing whiteness but variable in speed of acquisition and extent, though often uniformity between siblings. Notched tail feathers. Greater- and median-coverts remain grey. Bill only begins to change in late winter, with dusky areas towards tip which later turn black.

**2w (5/7)**     As adult, but some (probably only small proportion) retain scattered grey feathers on head, neck and wing-coverts, and, less often, on rump. Number of old feathers retained variable but only attempt to age if they are present in quantity since older birds may also retain a few, especially on head and neck. Bill as adult though some show pink or red flush. Sometimes odd juvenile tail feathers retained.

**Adult (6/8)**     All-white plumage. Bill black with yellow basal patch.

### Spring/Summer

**1s (5)**     Retained juvenile tail feathers notched at tip with bare shafts showing (beware since wear obscures the notching on many). Worn juvenile wing feathers retained until flightless period.

**2s (7)**     Scattered grey feathers retained until moult, and occasionally after.

| Adult (8) | White all over. Ageable up to period of moult. Thereafter cannot be aged beyond 3+ calendar years (6). |

**Moult**

| 3/5 | Partial post-juvenile moult starting October with head and neck, spreading to mantle, scapulars, breast and flanks by January, sometimes also a few tertials and tail feathers. Many old feathers retained until summer when flight feathers are moulted simultaneously; birds flightless for about 4-5 weeks, late July-early September. Subsequent moults, while birds remain in immature plumage, follow this routine and timing. |

| Adult | Complete post-breeding moult. Unlike other swan spp. ♂ and ♀ moult at same time, not staggered. Moult starts with simultaneous shedding of flight feathers, late July onwards, after which birds become flightless for 4-5 weeks. Body starts when wings in quill. Completed by December. |

**Biometrics**  *C. c. bewickii* (Evans & Kear 1978).

| | | | | | | | |
|---|---|---|---|---|---|---|---|
| Wing | ad. | ♂529 | (15.4;152) | 480-570 | ♀509 | (13.9;133) | 474-542 |
| | juv. | 500 | (17.1;69) | 468-538 | 482 | (14.0;65) | 445-525 |
| Bill | ad. | 94.5 | (5.54;112) | 81-110 | 91.2 | (4.09;112) | 79-102 |
| Tarsus | ad. | 106 | (5.16;111) | 93-119 | 102 | (5.41;110) | 87-113 |

**References**  Scott *et al.* (1972), Evans & Kear (1978).

# WHOOPER SWAN *Cygnus cygnus*

**Identification** Juvenile from Mute Swan by paler, cinnamon-grey plumage, not grey-brown, rounded not pointed tail, and pinkish base to bill, not black. Adult from Bewick's by longer wing, range 562-635mm, and bill, 92-116mm (cloacal examination of birds in overlap area will reveal whether an individual is a large male Bewick's or a small female Whooper). More extensive yellow on bill (see Bewick's Swan). Juvenile from Bewick's by size and structure: tail >154mm, Bewick's <155mm; wing range 530-632mm, Bewick's 445-538mm. Also becomes whiter earlier in winter than Bewick's and by late winter bill shows pattern of adult, albeit in whitish and grey-black rather than yellow and black,

81

while Bewick's remains grey-brown until spring, when black begins to appear.

**Sexing**          All ages by cloacal examination, at any season. In adult wing and toe useful guide but much overlap:

♂          Wing >618mm; Toe >158mm.

♀          Wing <585mm; Toe <140mm.

**Autumn/Winter**

3          Pale cinnamon-grey, darker on head. Whiter underparts. Bill sullied pink. Tail feathers notched at tip, bare shafts projecting.

1w (3/5)          Increasing whiteness but variable in speed of acquisition and extent, though often uniformity between siblings. Notched tail feathers. Greater- and median-coverts remain grey. Bill gradually becomes like that of adult but whitish instead of yellow and grey-black instead of black.

2w (5/7)          As adult, but some (probably only small proportion) retain scattered grey feathers on head, neck and wing-coverts, and less often on rump. Quantity variable but only age if they are present in quantity since older birds may also retain a few old ones, especially on head and neck. Bill like adult. Sometimes odd juvenile tail feathers retained.

Adult (6/8)          All-white plumage. Bill distally black, basally yellow.

**Spring/Summer**

1s (5)          Retained juvenile tail feathers notched at tip with bare shafts showing (beware of wear obscuring the notching on many). Worn juvenile feathers retained until flightless period.

2s (7)          Scattered grey feathers retained until moult, and occasionally after.

Adult (8)          White all over. Ageable up to period of moult. Thereafter cannot be aged beyond 3+ calendar years (6).

**Moult**

3/5          Partial post-juvenile moult starting October with head and neck, spreading to mantle, scapulars, breast and flanks by January-March; sometimes also a few tertials and tail feathers. Many old feathers retained until summer when flight feathers are moulted simultaneously; flightless for about 5-6 weeks, June to late August. Subsequent moults, while birds remain in immature plumage, follow this routine and timing.

Adult        Complete post-breeding moult. Breeding pair usually stagger moult period starting in ♀ when young are small, followed by ♂ when ♀ is nearly flying again. Flight feathers moulted simultaneously, June to late August; birds flightless for about 5-6 weeks. Body moult starts when wings in quill. Usually completed by December.

**Biometrics**   (BWP).

| | | | | | ♀ | | |
|---|---|---|---|---|---|---|---|
| Wing | ad. | ♂610 | (13.0;17) | 587-635 | 583 | (14.2;14) | 562-615 |
| | juv. | 611 | (17.9;6) | 586-632 | 553 | (23.1;7) | 530-597 |
| Bill | ad. | 106 | (4.7;19) | 98-116 | 102 | (4.4;15) | 92-111 |
| Tarsus | ad. | 123 | (3.9;21) | 116-130 | 113 | (3.8;22) | 104-119 |
| Toe | ad. | 156 | (6.6;21) | 142-172 | 141 | (6.8;22) | 129-155 |

**References**   Scott *et al.* (1972).

# BEAN GOOSE *Anser fabalis*

**Identification**   Black bill with orange band near tip of upper mandible and variable orange along sides of bill distinguish this species from other grey geese (see White-fronted Goose). Orange legs.

**Sexing**   All ages by cloacal examination, at any season. In breeding season soon after start of incubation, breeding ♀ has obvious brood patch. By hatching, new feathers are growing on brood patch, but these are normally distinct from and often paler than surrounding feathers. Within a pair, ♂ almost always larger than ♀. Wing length useful guide but much overlap:

♂        Wing >490mm.*

♀        Wing <450mm.*

        * nominate *fabalis* only.

**Autumn/Winter**

3        Wing-coverts grey-brown with pale whitish-brown tips giving scaly appearance; rather narrow and tapering (Fig). Orange of bill and legs dull.

| 1w (3/5) | Similar to juvenile but with some replaced adult-type feathers admixed. |
|---|---|
| 2w (5/7) | A small proportion of birds retain a few worn, faded, rather blunt juvenile median-coverts, contrasting sharply with broader, unabraded new ones (Fig). |
| Adult (4/6) | Wing-coverts dark grey-brown with clear white tips, tending to form parallel barring; feathers broad and blunt- or square-ended (Fig). |

### Median-coverts

| | | worn | | new | worn |
|---|---|---|---|---|---|
| | new | | | | |

| Juv. (3) | ⌐ Immature (5–7) ¬ | ⌐ Adult (4–6) ¬ |
|---|---|---|

## Spring/Summer

| 1s (5) | Some juvenile feathers retained until flightless period, especially very worn and narrow median-coverts (Fig). |
|---|---|
| Adult (6) | As Autumn/Winter. After moult cannot be aged beyond 2+ calendar years (4). |

## Moult

| 3/5 | Partial post-juvenile moult, more-or-less continuous from October, starting with head and neck, flanks and mantle, continuing in midwinter with tail. By late January, the most advanced birds have renewed all body feathers, central tail feathers and some median-coverts, but other birds not until several weeks later. Subsequent moults as adult. |
|---|---|
| Adult | Complete post-breeding moult starting with simultaneous shedding of wing feathers, July- August, at which point birds become flightless for about 1 month. Body and tail moulted when wing half-grown, completed late September or October. Partial pre-breeding moult of head and neck, midwinter. |

**Geographical variation** 5 subspecies recognized; 4 of these are extralimital, though at least one, *rossicus,* occurs in Europe in winter. Races fall into 2 distinct groups, both of which increase in size clinally from west to east: 1. those found in tundra which have heavy bills and shorter neck, tarsus and toes, and 2. those inhabiting taiga, with slender bills, longer wings, neck, tarsus and toes. Tundra subspecies include *rossicus* (Kanin to Taymyr Peninsula) to larger *serrirostris* (eastern Siberia) both with relatively dark bills. On taiga, smaller nominate *fabalis* (taiga of northern Europe to Urals) with mainly orange bill grades to large, dark-billed *middendorffii* (Siberian highlands).

**Biometrics**   Adult. Nominate *fabalis* (BWP).

| | | | | | | |
|---|---|---|---|---|---|---|
| Wing | ♂481 | (14.0;87) | 452-520 | ♀460 | (13.7;73) | 434-488 |
| Bill | 63.6 | (2.96;93) | 57-70 | 60.0 | (2.73;75) | 55-66 |
| Tarsus | 82.2 | (3.61;21) | 76-90 | 76.7 | (3.57;11) | 73-80 |
| Toe | 88.6 | (3.38;12) | 82-94 | 82.7 | (5.09;11) | 78-84 |

Adult. *A.f. rossicus* (BWP).

| | | | | | | |
|---|---|---|---|---|---|---|
| Wing | ♂454 | (9.97;144) | 430-478 | ♀433 | (10.8;133) | 405-458 |
| Bill | 57.7 | (2.32;142) | 52-63 | 54.6 | (2.24;134) | 49-60 |
| Tarsus | 75.2 | (3.84;13) | 70-81 | 73.9 | (3.22;13) | 69-79 |
| Toe | 76.4 | (3.90;12) | 67-81 | 74.7 | (3.12;9) | 70-81 |

# PINK-FOOTED GOOSE *Anser brachyrhynchus*

**Identification**   Small compact bill with pink band near tip of upper mandible (see White-fronted Goose). Pink feet.

**Sexing**   All ages by cloacal examination, at any season. In breeding season soon after start of incubation, breeding ♀ has obvious brood patch. By hatching, new feathers are growing on brood patch, but these are normally distinct from and often paler than surrounding feathers. Within a pair, ♂ almost always larger than ♀. Wing length useful guide but much overlap:

♂          Wing >440mm.

♀          Wing <420mm.

## Autumn/Winter

| | |
|---|---|
| 3 | Wing-coverts grey-brown with pale whitish-brown tips giving scaly appearance; rather narrow and tapering (see fig. under Bean Goose). Pink of bill and legs greyish-pink or yellow-ochre. Breast and upper belly unevenly mottled. |
| 1w (3/5) | Similar to juvenile but some replaced adult-type feathers admixed. |
| 2w (5/7) | As adult, but some birds retain a few old, worn and faded median-coverts, contrasting with broader, blunt-ended new ones (see fig. under Bean Goose). |
| Adult (4/6) | Upperparts more slaty (less brownish) than juvenile. Wing-coverts grey with broad white tips, tending to form parallel barring; rather broad and blunt- or square-ended. Underparts uniform. |

## Spring/Summer

| | |
|---|---|
| 1s (5) | Some juvenile feathers retained until flightless period, especially very worn and narrow median-coverts, also, in some birds, belly and mantle feathers. |
| Adult (6) | As Autumn/Winter. After moult cannot be aged beyond 2+ calendar years (4). |

## Moult

| | |
|---|---|
| 3/5 | Partial post-juvenile moult, more-or-less continuous from October, starting with head and neck, lower scapulars and lower flanks, then mantle and breast in November-December, and belly, back, rump and some tail feathers in January-February. Some individuals retain juvenile feathering on mantle and belly until summer moult in 2nd calendar year, others only some wing feathers. Subsequent moults as adult. |
| Adult | Complete post-breeding moult starting with simultaneous shedding of wing feathers, July-August, at which point birds become flightless for about 25 days. Body and tail moult once wing feathers are fully grown. Moult completed by October. |

**Biometrics** (BWP, Salminen 1983).

| | | | | | | | |
|---|---|---|---|---|---|---|---|
| Wing | *ad.* ♂ | 443 | (11;12) | 421-458 | ♀ 423 | (7;9) | 411-434 |
| | *juv.* | 423 | (7;11) | 412-435 | 406 | (14;12) | 377-425 |
| Bill | *ad.* | 45.9 | (2.6;12) | 41-51 | 43.5 | (1.7;9) | 41-46 |
| Tarsus | *ad.* | 75.4 | (2.31;16) | 72-80 | 70.3 | (2.66;16) | 65-74 |
| Toe | *ad.* | 75.6 | (1.77;16) | 72-78 | 70.1 | (2.03;16) | 66-73 |

# WHITE-FRONTED GOOSE *Anser albifrons*

**Identification** Eurasian race, nominate *albifrons*, has pink bill, slightly orange towards base, and grey-brown plumage. Greenland race, *flavirostris* has orange bill, slightly pink just behind nail, and dark brown plumage with heavier belly bars in adult than on *albifrons*. Juveniles more similar. Bill of Eurasian race can be yellowish, but plumage always paler, with less marked dark-capped appearance on head and nape. Combination of white forehead and black belly bars of adult of both races unmistakable, though beware small flecking around the base of the bill in a few adult Bean and Pink-footed Geese, and small black belly bars on adult Greylag Geese. 1st-autumn birds, before first white forehead feathers appear, confusable with juvenile Bean and Greylag but, unlike Bean, bill lacks any black except for dark horn nail which goes whitish by midwinter, and is much less deep than Greylag's; also Greylag's pale wing-coverts are lacking. Distinct on measurements, especially bill and skull, from Lesser White-fronted Goose at all ages (Fig).

Greylag                    White-fronted Goose

Ad.                    Ad.                    Juv.

Lssr. White-fronted Goose          Pink-footed Goose

Ad.                    Juv.

Bean Goose

*fabalis*                    *rossicus*

| **Sexing** | All ages by cloacal examination, at any season. In breeding season soon after start of incubation, breeding ♀ has obvious brood patch. By hatching, new feathers are growing on brood patch, but these are normally distinct from and often paler than surrounding feathers. Within a pair, ♂ almost always larger than ♀. Wing length useful guide to determine ♂ ♂ only: |
|---|---|
| ♂ | Wing >440mm.* |
| | *nominate *albifrons* |

## Autumn/Winter

| 3 | No white forehead or bars on belly. Wing-coverts narrow and tapering, grey-brown with buff tips giving scaly appearance (see fig. under Bean Goose). Bill duller and yellower with dark nail. |
|---|---|
| 1w (3/5) | Gradual change to adult plumage but some juvenile feathers always present, especially on wing-coverts. Majority have white forehead by March, black feathers at front, but belly bars usually absent. |
| 2w (5/7) | Like adult, but some birds retain a few old, worn and faded median-coverts, contrasting with broader blunt-ended new ones. |
| Adult (4/6) | Wing-coverts broad and rounded, broadly tipped white, tending to form parallel barring (see fig. under Bean Goose). Belly and sides of body with varying amounts of black feathers (edged white when fresh), forming irregular patches or transverse bars. Nail white. |

## Spring/Summer

| 1s (5) | Usually lacks belly bars of adult. Some juvenile feathers retained until flightless period, especially very worn and narrow median-coverts, also occasional tail feathers. |
|---|---|
| Adult (6) | As Autumn/Winter. After moult cannot be aged beyond 2+ calendar years (4). |

## Moult

| 3/5 | Partial post-juvenile moult starting with head and neck in November, forehead from December-March, scapulars and flanks from November onwards. Extent of body moult variable; some complete by February, others not until summer moult. Subsequent moults as adult. |
|---|---|

| Adult | Complete post-breeding moult starting with simultaneous shedding of wing feathers, end of July-late August, when birds become flightless for about 25 days. Body moult begins when flight feathers fully grown, mostly finished before reaching winter quarters. Partial pre-breeding moult of head, neck and some body feathers, midwinter to spring. |

**Geographical variation** In Europe 2 subspecies winter and are normally separable: Greenland population *flavirostris* characterized by long orange-yellow bill; mantle and scapulars black-brown with narrower white edging than nominate *albifrons* (Tundra of northern Russia and Siberia - wintering western and southern Europe); breast darker brown; belly and vent more heavily barred black. 3 extralimital races recognized, all larger and darker than nominate.

**Biometrics**  Nominate *albifrons* (Beer & Boyd 1962, BWP).

| | | | | | | | |
|---|---|---|---|---|---|---|---|
| Wing | *ad.* ♂ | 423 | (14;73) | 377-464 | ♀ 400 | (14;60) | 379-438 |
| | *juv.* | 399 | (15;15) | 375-419 | 388 | (18;18) | 359-410 |
| Bill | *ad.* | 47.1 | (2.8;74) | 43-53 | 44.9 | (2.6;64) | 40-51 |
| Tarsus | *ad.* | 72.8 | (2.9;49) | 68-80 | 69.3 | (2.7;34) | 64-76 |
| Toe | *ad.* | 74.2 | (3.76;26) | 69-82 | 68.4 | (3.43;26) | 63-75 |

*A.a. flavirostris* (O.J. Merne, BWP).

| | | | | | | | |
|---|---|---|---|---|---|---|---|
| Wing | *ad.* ♂ | 426 | (14.4;232) | 389-463 | ♀ 423 | (14.5;261) | 389-461 |
| | *juv.* | 410 | (13.4; 94) | 370-441 | 405 | (15.6;149) | 361-439 |
| Bill | *ad.* | 52.7 | (2.61;326) | 46-60 | 52.0 | (2.84;410) | 44-60 |
| Tarsus | *ad.* | 74.9 | (4.27;326) | 65-84 | 74.4 | (3.91;410) | 63-83 |

**References**  Beer & Boyd (1962).

# LESSER WHITE-FRONTED GOOSE *Anser erythropus*

**Identification** Small size and, especially, small, almost triangular bill (see White-fronted Goose) distinguish all ages from other geese. Yellow eye-ring and wing tips extending beyond tail also diagnostic.

**Sexing**  All ages by cloacal examination, at any season. In breeding season soon after start of incubation, ♀ has obvious brood patch. By hatching, new feathers are growing on brood patch, but normally these are distinct from and often paler than surrounding feathers. Within a pair ♂ almost always larger than ♀.

## Autumn/Winter

3
Wing-coverts grey-brown with pale buff tips giving scaly appearance; narrow and tapering (see fig. under Bean Goose). Bill and legs dull. Nail brown.

1w (3/5)
Gradual change to adult plumage but some juvenile feathers always present, especially on wing-coverts. Majority get white forehead by March, but belly bars always absent.

2w (5/7)
As adult, but some birds retain a few old, worn median-coverts, contrasting with broader blunt-ended new ones.

Adult (4/6)
Wing-coverts broad and rounded, grey with clear white tips, tending to form parallel barring (see fig. under Bean Goose). Belly and sides of body have varying amounts of black feathers (edged white when fresh), forming irregular patches or transverse bars. Nail white.

## Spring/Summer

1s (5)
Lacks belly bars of adult. Some juvenile feathers retained until flightless period, especially very worn and narrow median-coverts, also occasional tail feathers.

Adult (6)
As Autumn/Winter. After moult cannot be aged beyond 2+ calendar years (4).

**Moult**
In all respects like White-fronted Goose though flight feathers apparently moulted some 1-2 weeks earlier.

**Biometrics**
(Salminen 1983, BWP).

| | | | | | | | |
|---|---|---|---|---|---|---|---|
| Wing | ad. ♂ | 387 | (10;17) | 370-407 | ♀ 363 | (16;16) | 342-392 |
| | juv. | 367 | (9;6) | 350-376 | 344 | (12;4) | 331-359 |
| Bill | ad. | 33.1 | (1.6;12) | 29-35 | 31.2 | (2.2;10) | 28-35 |
| Tarsus | ad. | 63.7 | (2.20;13) | 59-68 | 61.0 | (2.49;15) | 57-65 |
| Toe | ad. | 62.5 | (2.24;13) | 59-67 | 59.7 | (1.91;19) | 56-63 |

# GREYLAG GOOSE *Anser anser*

**Identification** Heavy, deep bill, orange-pink or pink with whitish nail (see White-fronted Goose); very pale blue-grey wing-coverts diagnostic. For hybrids, see Canada Goose.

**Sexing** All ages by cloacal examination, at any season. In breeding season soon after start of incubation, ♀ has obvious brood patch. By hatching, new feathers are growing on brood patch, but these are normally distinct from and often paler than surrounding feathers. Within a pair, ♂ almost always larger than ♀. Wing length and, especially, weight useful guides but some overlap:

♂　　　　　　 Wing >467mm; Weight >4kg.

♀　　　　　　 Wing <445mm; Weight <2.6kg.

## Autumn/Winter

3　　　　　　 Wing-coverts pale grey with buffish tips giving scaly appearance; narrow and tapering (Fig). Bill and legs dull.

1w (3/5)　　 Gradual change to adult plumage but some juvenile feathers always present, especially on wing-coverts. Belly bars absent. Eye-ring dull.

2w (5/7)　　 As adult, but some birds retain a few worn median-coverts, contrasting with broader blunt-ended new ones. Lack of any black belly bars probably indicator of 2nd-winter bird but needs confirmation.

Adult (4/6)　Wing-coverts broad and rounded, pale blue-grey with white tips, tending to form parallel barring (Fig). Small black bars develop on belly, probably increasing with age, but needs confirmation. Eye-ring pink or yellow.

**Median-coverts**

Immature (3–7)　　　　Adult (4–6)

**Spring/Summer**

1s (5)    Some juvenile feathers retained until flightless period, especially very
          worn and narrow median-coverts, also occasional tail feathers, and
          sometimes on belly and mantle.

Adult (6)   As Autumn/Winter. After moult cannot be aged beyond 2+ calendar
            years (4).

**Moult**

3/5    Partial post-juvenile moult, more-or-less continuous from September,
       beginning with head and neck, flanks and sides, followed by tail,
       underparts, back and some wing-coverts. By late November the most
       advanced birds have renewed all body feathers, central tail feathers and
       some median-coverts, but others still moulting in January and February.
       Moult thereafter apparently as adult.

Adult    Complete post-breeding moult starting with simultaneous shedding of
         wing feathers rendering bird flightless for about 1 month, mid-May to
         mid-August. Body and tail moult when growth of wings complete,
         underparts first, followed by back, mantle, neck and head. Tail moult
         prolonged. No information on pre-breeding moult.

**Geographical variation** *A.a. rubrirostris* (south-east and east Europe, west and central
          Asia) is paler grey-brown above with broad light edges to scapulars and
          mantle feathers and with pink bill.

**Biometrics**    Nominate *anser* (Matthews & Campbell 1969, BWP).

| Wing | *ad.* ♂ | 465 | (10.6; 7) | 448-480 | ♀ 442 | (14.4;16) | 412-465 |
|------|---------|-----|-----------|---------|-------|-----------|---------|
|      | *juv.*  | 450 | (13.3;122) | 418-482 | 433 | (15.2;119) | 390-466 |
| Bill | *ad.* | 66.6 | (3.16;32) | 59-74 | 61.5 | (2.10;24) | 58-65 |
| Tarsus | *ad.* | 84.7 | (3.80;32) | 78-93 | 78.8 | (3.51;24) | 71-87 |
| Toe | *ad.* | 91.6 | (3.84;32) | 84-102 | 85.7 | (3.93;24) | 80-97 |

**References**    Matthews & Campbell (1969).

# SNOW GOOSE *Anser caerulescens*

**Identification**   Two races, Lesser, nominate *caerulescens* (north-east Siberia, N. America), and Greater, *atlanticus* (north-east Canada, north-west Greenland), which is less numerous. Mostly separable on measurements; bill length is best, though wing length and tarsus may help, but considerable overlap. Two colour morphs recognized: dark morph (Blue Snow Goose) virtually always Lesser, indeed apparent Greater dark morph may in fact be intergrades with Lesser, which occur. White morph of both races unmistakable, as is adult Blue Snow Goose.

**Sexing**   All ages by cloacal examination, at any season. In breeding season soon after start of incubation, ♀ has obvious brood patch. By hatching, new feathers are growing on brood patch, but these are normally distinct from and cleaner than surrounding feathers in white morph, and paler in dark morph. Within a pair, ♂ almost always larger than ♀. Wing length useful guide but much overlap:

*A.c. caerulescens*

♂         Wing >440mm.

♀         Wing <394mm.

*A.c. atlanticus*

♂         Wing >475mm.

♀         Wing <430mm.

## Autumn/Winter

3         Wing-coverts narrow and tapering, buffish tips giving scaly appearance. In white morph, grey or grey-brown feathering, usually fringed buff to white, over most of head, neck and upperparts. In dark morph, greater-coverts not elongated nor white-tipped. Bill and leg colour dull.

1w (3/5)   Gradual change to adult plumage but juvenile feathers always present, especially wing-coverts and tail.

2w (5/7)   Like adult, but a small proportion of birds may retain a few old, worn and dark median-coverts, contrasting with broader blunt-ended new ones.

93

| Adult (4/6) | White morph all-white except for black outer wings. In dark morph elongated greater-coverts, tertials, scapulars and inner secondaries brown-black with broad white edgings. |

**Spring/Summer**

| 1s (5) | Some juvenile feathers retained until flightless period, especially very worn and narrow median-coverts, also occasional tail feathers, and sometimes on belly and mantle. |

| Adult (6) | As Autumn/Winter. After moult cannot be aged beyond 2+ calendar years (4). |

**Moult**

| 3/5 | Partial post-juvenile moult, more-or-less continuous from October, beginning with head and neck, flanks and sides, followed by tail, underparts, back and some wing-coverts. Progress of moult as variable as other *Anser* geese. Thereafter moult apparently as adult. |

| Adult | Complete post-breeding moult starting with simultaneous shedding of wing feathers rendering bird flightless for about 3 weeks, late July to late August. Moult of body, tail etc. probably the same as other tundra *Anser.* |

**Geographical variation** See under identification of species.

**Biometrics** Adult. Nominate *caerulescens* (BWP).

| Wing | ♂430 | (45) | 395-460 | ♀420 | (43) | 380-440 |
| Bill | 58 | (45) | 51-62 | 56 | (40) | 50-61 |
| Tarsus | 84 | (35) | 78-91 | 82 | (37) | 75-89 |

Adult. *A.c. atlanticus* (BWP).

| Wing | ♂450 | (20) | 430-485 | ♀445 | (10) | 425-475 |
| Bill | 67 | (20) | 59-73 | 62 | (10) | 57-68 |
| Tarsus | 92 | (20) | 86-97 | 86 | (10) | 80-92 |

# CANADA GOOSE *Branta canadensis*

**Identification** Unmistakable combination of white chinstrap and black stocking neck, plus overall brown plumage, quite distinct from white cheeks, black neck and chest and grey plumage of Barnacle Goose, which is much smaller than all but smallest races of Canada. Hybrids with other geese, perhaps especially Greylag but also Barnacle, not infrequent. Those with grey geese invariably have pink or orange legs, those with Barnacle quite often have Barnacle-type face, neck and chest markings, but dark brown, not grey, body plumage.

**Sexing**    All ages by cloacal examination, at any season. In breeding season soon after start of incubation, breeding ♀ has obvious brood patch. By hatching, new feathers are growing on brood patch, but normally distinct from and often paler than surrounding feathers. Within a pair, ♂ almost always larger than ♀. Wing length useful guide but much overlap:

♂    Wing >530mm.*

♀    Wing <480mm.*

* nominate *canadensis* only.

## Autumn/Winter

3    Wing-coverts narrow but with rounded tips, not broad and square. Breast feathers narrow with dark shaft-streak and lacking white subterminal band. Primaries very pointed. Carpometacarpus (wrist) feathered (Fig).

1w (3/5)    Quite rapid change to adult plumage but some juvenile feathers always present, especially wing-coverts and breast, and usually but not always some tail feathers.

2w (5/7)    As adult, but carpometacarpus remains feathered until about midwinter (Fig). A minority of birds retain a few worn wing-coverts, contrasting with broader blunt-ended new ones.

Adult (4/6)    Wing-coverts broad and blunt-tipped; some worn feathers can remain after wing moult! Breast feathers broad, lacking dark shaft-streaks but with wide white subterminal bars. Primaries rounded and blunt-tipped. Carpometacarpus partly bare in at least some birds, probably more usually ♂ ♂ but uncertain sex guide (Fig).

### Carpometacarpus

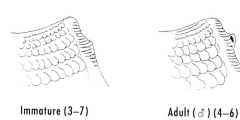

Immature (3–7)          Adult ( ♂ ) (4–6)

## Spring/Summer

1s (5)    Some juvenile feathers retained until flightless period, especially very worn median-coverts, but not always in tail as in other geese, and certainly not as distinct in this plumage from adult as in other geese. Outer primaries tend to have worn tips by spring, contrasting with new black tail feathers.

Adult (6)    As Autumn/Winter. After moult cannot be aged with certainty beyond 2+ calendar years (4).

## Moult

3/5    Partial post-juvenile moult, more-or-less continuous from September, beginning with head and neck, flanks and shoulders, continuing in midwinter with tail. By late January, most birds have renewed bulk of body feathers, often most or all tail feathers and majority of wing-coverts. Subsequent moults as adult.

Adult    Timing markedly dependent on latitude and climate. Complete post-breeding moult starting with simultaneous shedding of flight feathers rendering bird flightless for about 3-4 weeks. Body feathers moulted when wing and tail completed. Partial pre-breeding moult in spring confined to head and neck, but probably not body.

**Geographical variation** Considerable and very complex, giving rise to different opinions on subspecies and even specific distinctions within this group (up to 4 subspecies sometimes recognized in Europe). Variation concerns mostly body size; proportion of neck, bill, tarsus, and foot; also darkness and barring of plumage, amount of white on lower neck and pattern of cheek patch. There is much intergrading making distinction more diffi-cult. Only the most optimistic or incautious will attempt to put racial names to individuals! Nominate *canadensis* (south-east Canada, north-east USA) introduced to parts of north-west Europe but possibly wild populations involving 3 or perhaps 5 other North American subspecies occur in western Europe.

**Biometrics** Nominate *canadensis* (Palmer 1976, BWP).

| Wing | *ad.* ♂ |  |  | 485-566 ♀ |  | 470-525 |  |
|------|---------|--|--|-----------|--|---------|--|
|      | *juv.* |  |  | 461-537 |  |  | 463-520 |
| Bill | *ad.* | 56.5 | (;36) | 50-63 | 53.7 | (;41) | 49-58 |

# BARNACLE GOOSE *Branta leucopsis*

**Identification** Only possible confusion with Canada Goose or hybrids (see that species).

**Sexing**    All ages by cloacal examination, at any season. In breeding season after start of incubation, breeding ♀ has obvious brood patch. By hatching, new feathers are growing on brood patch, but these are normally distinct from and often paler than surrounding feathers. Within a pair, ♂ almost always larger than ♀. Wing length useful guide but much overlap:

♂    Wing >420mm.

♀    Wing <365mm.

## Autumn/Winter

3    Wing-coverts grey-brown with dark brown subterminal band and narrow brownish-white tips; narrow with rounded tips (Fig). Black of breast dull, white of face sometimes slightly obscured by blackish feather tips. Tail feathers notched at tip, bare shafts projecting.

1w (3/5)    Quite rapid change to adult plumage but some juvenile feathers usually present, especially median-coverts. Notched juvenile tail feathers moulted through the winter. By January a good proportion of birds have all-new tail feathers.

2w (5/7)    As adult, but some birds retain a few old worn inner median-coverts into the autumn, contrasting with broader blunt-ended new ones.

Adult (4/6)    Wing-coverts ash-blue with broad black or very dark brown subterminal bands and white tips, forming parallel bars across wing; broad and blunt-tipped (Fig). Breast glossy black. At least into early autumn, some birds may retain unmoulted and therefore worn wing-coverts, but not restricted to inner median-coverts as 2nd-winter.

### Median-coverts

|  |  | worn | new |
| Juv. | Immature (3–7) | └─────── Adult (4–6) ───────┘ |

97

## Spring/Summer

1s (5)    Sometimes juvenile feathers retained until flightless period, especially very worn median-coverts and perhaps one or two tail feathers.

Adult (6)    As Autumn/Winter. After moult cannot be aged with certainty beyond 2+ calendar years (4).

## Moult

3/5    Partial post-juvenile moult, more-or-less continuous from October, beginning with head, neck, mantle and chest, then scapulars and lower flanks, continuing midwinter with at least central tail feathers. By spring most birds have renewed bulk of body feathers, most tail feathers and majority of wing-coverts. Subsequent moults as adult.

Adult    Complete post-breeding moult starting with simultaneous moult of wing feathers, mid-July to mid-August, rendering bird flightless for 3-4 weeks. Moult of body, head and tail starts when wing almost fully grown; completed about October-November.

## Biometrics    (BWP).

| | | | | | | |
|---|---|---|---|---|---|---|
| Wing ad. | ♂410 | (10.8;23) | 388-429 | ♀392 | (8.60;19) | 376-410 |
| juv. | 389 | (8.79;9) | 374-399 | 372 | (9.76;9) | 362-393 |
| Bill | 29.6 | (1.43;32) | 28-33 | 28.6 | (1.28;28) | 27-32 |
| Tarsus | 72.1 | (3.55;560) | 60-81 | 68.2 | (3.26;541) | 64-72 |
| Toe | 62.6 | (2.45;24) | 57-68 | 58.2 | (2.39;22) | 54-63 |

Full-grown (Owen & Ogilvie 1979, Myrfyn Owen unpubl.data).

| | | | | | | |
|---|---|---|---|---|---|---|
| Wing | ♂412 | (11.7;300) | 370-444 | ♀389 | (16.4;281) | 353-414 |
| Tarsus | 72.1 | (3.55;560) | 60-81 | | 68.2 | (3.26;541) | 58-81 |

# BRENT GOOSE *Branta bernicla*

**Identification**  Three races, Light-bellied *hrota* (arctic Canada east to Spitzbergen and Franz Joseph) has white or very pale grey belly, pale brown flanks with white edgings, and buff edgings to grey mantle and scapulars. Dark-bellied, nominate *bernicla* (tundra USSR), has dark grey belly and upperparts, and grey-brown flanks with white edgings. Black Brant *nigricans* (tundra USSR, north Alaska, north-west Canada) has very dark slate-grey belly, differing only slightly from black breast, and broad white edgings to flanks. Adult Black Brant has deeper white neck-patches usually meeting in front. Adult Light-bellied with worn plumage and juvenile may have light brown belly, close to colouring of Dark-bellied, but back always paler and browner. Intergrading occurs between Dark-bellied and Black Brant and between Light-bellied and Black Brant. Species not confusable with any other goose.

**Sexing**

All ages by cloacal examination, at any season. In breeding season soon after start of incubation, breeding ♀ has obvious brood patch. By hatching, new feathers are growing on brood patch, but these are normally distinct from and often paler than surrounding feathers. Within a pair, ♂ almost always larger than ♀. Wing length useful guide but much overlap (*bernicla* & *hrota* only):

♂          Wing >343mm.

♀          Wing <320mm.

## Autumn/Winter

3          Wing-coverts narrow but with rounded tips (Fig). Greater- and median-coverts with broad grey-white tips. Secondaries tipped white. Flanks lack white tips. Black of head, neck and chest dull.

1w (3/5)          Quite rapid change to adult plumage but some juvenile feathers always present, especially median-coverts and tail. White neck-patches appear during autumn and winter, but very variable between individuals. A few may already have them on arrival in winter quarters.

2w (5/7)          Like adult, except some birds retain a few old worn inner median-coverts into the autumn, contrasting with broader blunt-ended new ones, and often with remnants of pale tips (Fig).

Adult (4/6)          Wing-coverts broad and blunt-tipped, lacking whitish tips (Fig). No white tips to secondaries. In early autumn, some birds have unmoulted and therefore worn wing-coverts.

## Median-coverts

|  | new | worn | new | worn |

Juv. (3)  └────── Immature (5–7) ──────┘  └────── Adult (4–6) ──────┘

### Spring/Summer

1s (5)  Some juvenile feathers retained until flightless period, especially very worn median-coverts and tail.

Adult (6)  As Autumn/Winter. After moult cannot be aged with certainty beyond 2+ calendar years (4).

### Moult

3/5  Partial post-juvenile moult, more-or-less continuous from October, beginning with head, neck, mantle and chest, then scapulars and lower flanks during winter. By spring, most birds have renewed bulk of body feathers, most of tail feathers and majority of wing-coverts, but much individual variation. Subsequent moults as adult.

Adult  Complete post-breeding moult starting with simultaneous shedding of wing feathers, mid-July to mid-August, rendering bird flightless for about 3 weeks. Body moult starts when wing fully grown, first on underparts, ending with tail. Sometimes entire plumage replaced before autumn migration. Partial pre-breeding moult in spring confined to head and neck.

**Geographical variation** See under identification of species.

**Biometrics**  Nominate *bernicla* (Salminen 1983).

| | | | | | | | |
|---|---|---|---|---|---|---|---|
| Wing | ad. ♂ | 337 | (7;43) | 323-355 | ♀ 324 | (7;22) | 313-337 |
| | juv. | 323 | (9;24) | 308-342 | 307 | (9;16) | 291-326 |
| Bill | ad. | 34.4 | (1.6;42) | 30-38 | 32.7 | (1.6;23) | 30-36 |
| | juv. | 32.7 | (1.7;22) | 29-36 | 30.6 | (2.0;12) | 28-34 |

Adult (BWP).

| | | | | | | |
|---|---|---|---|---|---|---|
| Wing | ♂340 | (5.93;18) | 330-353 | ♀324 | (4.60;13) | 317-335 |
| Bill | 34.9 | (1.80;17) | 32-38 | 31.7 | (1.11;14) | 29-33 |
| Tarsus | 63.7 | (2.27;17) | 60-67 | 58.1 | (1.34;13) | 56-61 |
| Toe | 58.4 | (1.94;16) | 55-62 | 54.3 | (1.42;13) | 51-57 |

*B.b. hrota* (BWP).

| | | | | | | |
|---|---|---|---|---|---|---|
| Wing *ad.* | ♂344 | (;3) | 338-348 | ♀329 | (3.22;7) | 323-333 |
| *juv.* | 326 | (4.33;7) | 321-332 | 316 | (6.52;4) | 308-325 |

# RED-BREASTED GOOSE *Branta ruficollis*

**Sexing**

All ages by cloacal examination, at any season. In breeding season soon after start of incubation, breeding ♀ has obvious brood patch. By hatching, new feathers are growing on brood patch, but these are normally distinct from and often paler than surrounding feathers. Wing length useful guide (adults only):

♂      Wing >355mm.

♀      Wing <350mm.

## Autumn/Winter

3

Overall, a duller version of adult. Wing-coverts narrow, tipped brown (Fig), can be brownish-white and can be quite distinct. Russet breast feathers tipped black. Black areas dull.

1w (3/5)

Quite rapid change to adult plumage but some juvenile feathers always present, especially median-coverts and tail.

2w (5/7)

Like adult, but some birds retain a few old worn inner median-coverts into the autumn, contrasting with broader blunt-ended new ones.

| Adult (4/6) | Wing-coverts broad and blunt-tipped, with broad white tips (Fig). Black areas glossy. |
|---|---|

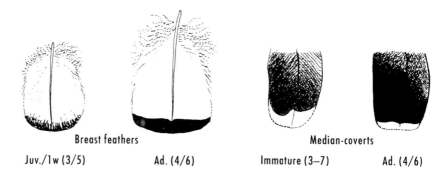

| Breast feathers | | Median-coverts | |
|---|---|---|---|
| Juv./1w (3/5) | Ad. (4/6) | Immature (3–7) | Ad. (4/6) |

## Spring/Summer

| 1s (5) | Some juvenile feathers retained until flightless period, especially very worn median-coverts and tail. |
|---|---|
| Adult (6) | As Autumn/Winter. After moult cannot be aged with certainty beyond 2+ calendar years (4). |

## Moult

| 3/5 | Partial post-juvenile moult, more-or-less continuous from September, beginning with head, neck, mantle and chest, continuing through winter so that by spring, most birds have renewed bulk of body feathers, most of tail feathers and majority of wing-coverts. Subsequent moults as adult. |
|---|---|
| Adult | Complete post-breeding moult starting with simultaneous shedding of flight feathers between mid-July and late August, rendering bird flightless for about 15-20 days. Body moult starts when flight feathers fully grown. |

**Biometrics**  Adult (BWP).

| | | | | | | |
|---|---|---|---|---|---|---|
| Wing | ♂367 | (7.12;8) | 355-379 | ♀343 | (6.09;7) | 332-352 |
| Bill | 24.9 | (1.02;9) | 23-27 | 24.2 | (0.95;8) | 22-26 |
| Tarsus | 61.3 | (2.50;8) | 58-65 | 57.1 | (2.03;8) | 54-61 |
| Toe | 54.2 | (2.36;9) | 50-59 | 51.4 | (1.11;8) | 49-53 |

# EGYPTIAN GOOSE *Alopochen aegyptiacus*

**Sexing**  All ages by cloacal examination, at any season. In breeding season soon after start of incubation, breeding ♀ has obvious brood patch. By hatching, new feathers are growing on brood patch, but normally distinct from and often paler than surrounding feathers. Within a pair, ♂ almost always larger than ♀.

## Autumn/Winter

3  Dull overall. Lacks chestnut markings on head, neck and breast. Greater-coverts grey-brown, with black subterminal bar and white tips with black mottling. Median- and lesser-coverts narrow and tipped pale grey-brown.

1w (3/5)  Quite rapid change to more adult plumage through winter, but juvenile lesser- and median-coverts retained.

2w (5)  A few birds retain some old and worn wing-coverts into autumn.

Adult (4/6)  Chestnut markings on head, neck and breast. Greater-coverts white with black subterminal bar, other wing-coverts white.

## Spring/Summer

1s (5)  Juvenile wing-coverts and some tail feathers retained until summer moult.

Adult (6)  Like Autumn/Winter. After moult cannot be reliably aged beyond 2+ calendar years (4).

## Moult

3/5  Little-studied but begins soon after fledging and continues through autumn and winter.

Adult  In Britain, probably complete summer moult during and after flightless period, but not studied. In Africa, moult timing related to variable breeding season, itself dependent upon rains.

**Biometrics**    Adult (BWP).

| | | | | | | |
|---|---|---|---|---|---|---|
| Wing | ♂392 | (12.1;6) | 378-406 | ♀375 | (14.5;7) | 352-390 |
| Bill | 49.6 | (3.18;7) | 46-54 | 47.9 | (2.87;10) | 43-52 |
| Tarsus | 85.5 | (5.14;7) | 80-95 | 80.2 | (4.39;10) | 73-85 |
| Toe | 76.9 | (3.44;7) | 72-82 | 72.4 | (3.66;10) | 67-76 |

# Ducks *Anatidae: Anatinae*

Medium-sized to fairly large wildfowl. Body rotund in most, rather elongated in some. Wings rather narrow and pointed in most, broader and more rounded in *Tadornini* (sheldgeese and shelducks). Plumage sexually dimorphic and highly varied. Elaborate and colourful in spring/summer in most ♂ ♂, more cryptic in eclipse plumage and in ♀ ♀.

## Feather structure
Primaries = 11 (p9 longest, p11 reduced)
Secondaries = 12-18 (mostly 16-18)
Tail = 14-20 (mostly 14-18)

## Sexes
Sexually dimorphic.

## Moult
Strategy: simultaneous.
Sequence: simultaneously.
Frequency: twice annually (some almost continuous though);SC, Wp.
Timing: ♂ usually 3-4 weeks later than ♀. Spring-summer finishing early-mid autumn; autumn-early winter finishing late winter-early spring.


# RUDDY SHELDUCK *Tadorna ferruginea*

**Identification** Beware confusion with escaped Cape Shelduck *Tadorna cana*. ♂ ♂ differ from Ruddy Shelduck by ash-grey, not buff, head and breast. ♀ ♀ have obvious slate-grey head with whitish facial patches.

**Sexing** All ages by cloacal examination, at any season. Plumage characters in adults as follows:

♂ Black collar in breeding season (ca.February to August or September). Thereafter black collar thin or absent; if latter, like ♀ except feathers at base of upper mandible cinnamon-buff, not white. Bill black.

♀ No black collar. White feathering at base of upper mandible and around and behind the eye, though amount is individually variable. Base of bill flesh with black spotting.

### Autumn/Winter

3      Crown and hindneck dark grey-brown. Cinnamon-buff tips to grey-brown body feathers, especially mantle and scapulars, also rump and some outer tail feathers. Wing-coverts lack buff or yellow tinge. Greater-coverts ash-grey, medians- and lessers- white with grey tips, though these wear off later in the season. Notched tail feathers with bare shafts showing.

1w (3/5)      Moults quite rapidly into adult-type plumage, but retains juvenile wing, especially grey greater-coverts, though tertials and some inner coverts may moult to adult.

Adult (4/6)      Crown and hindneck bright cinnamon-buff, other areas of body rufous-cinnamon to deep chestnut. Upper wing-coverts white apart from black primary-coverts, washed pink-buff or creamy-yellow on tips when fresh. Much bleaching and fading overall in worn plumage.

**Greater-coverts**

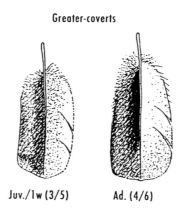

Juv./1w (3/5)        Ad. (4/6)

### Spring/Summer

1s (5)      Some juvenile wing feathers present until summer moult.

Adult (6)      As Autumn/Winter, except ♂ usually with conspicuous black collar in early part of summer. After moult cannot be reliably aged beyond 2+ calendar years (4).

## Moult

**3/5**     Partial post-juvenile moult of head, neck and body, beginning early July, completed by December. A pre-breeding moult of head and most of body sometime in spring of 2nd calendar year.

**Adult**    Complete post-breeding moult. ♂ moults into non-breeding plumage about June, losing black collar, ♀ a little later. Simultaneous shedding of wing feathers renders bird flightless for about 4 weeks; body moult starts with scapulars and flanks, then head and rest of body, finishing September, except for tail which may not finish until November. A pre-breeding moult involving most of head and body, also tertials, again into breeding plumage from September-October, though often suspended/arrested during December to February. Full breeding plumage attained March-April.

**Biometrics**    (Salminen 1983, BWP).

| | | | | | | | |
|---|---|---|---|---|---|---|---|
| Wing *ad.* | ♂368 | (16;30) | 333-402 | ♀340 | (12;36) | 321-371 |
| *juv.* | 340 | (12;4) | 325-352 | 326 | (18;3) | 313-346 |
| Bill | 44.1 | (2.1;31) | 40-49 | 40.1 | (2.4;36) | 35-44 |
| Tarsus | 61.5 | (1.69;11) | 59-64 | 54.6 | (1.51;10) | 52-57 |


# SHELDUCK *Tadorna tadorna*

**Sexing**    All ages by cloacal examination, at any season. In breeding season soon after start of incubation, breeding ♀ has obvious brood patch. By hatching, new feathers are growing on brood patch, but these are normally distinct from and often paler than surrounding feathers. Plumage characters in adults as follows:

**♂**    Bill bright red (especially spring & summer), and with fleshy knob at base. Black nail and often spot by nostrils. Head and neck glossy greenish-black. Chest- and belly-bands broad and glossy. In non-breeding plumage black mottling on breast and central belly. Outer web of outermost tertial strongly chestnut-brown (Fig). 1st-winter/spring birds develop black feathering on breast and central belly. Knob at base of bill. Outer web of outermost tertial strongly chestnut-brown.

**♀**    Bill dull red, usually with black round tip as well as black nail; no fleshy knob at base of bill. Feathers of head and neck dull black, tinged brown on face and throat. Chest- and belly-bands narrower and duller. Outer web of outermost tertial light chestnut-brown with greyish-brown longitudinal stripe to inner web (Fig). In non-breeding plumage dark on underparts restricted to sides of breast. 1st-winter/spring birds have buff and sooty-brown on breast and central belly. Absence of knob at base of bill no guarantee that bird is ♀.

## Tertials

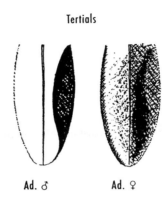

**Ad. ♂**          **Ad. ♀**

## Autumn/Winter

| | |
|---|---|
| 3 | White tips to secondaries and all but 4 outermost primaries. Greater-coverts grey. All plumage dull and mottled with buff or whitish edgings. |
| 1w (3/5) | Gradual change to more adult-like plumage, but juvenile wing retained until full summer moult. |
| 2w (5/7) | Some birds with grey spots on tips of greater- and median-coverts. |
| Adult (4/6) | Primaries and secondaries all-black; no white at tips as in juvenile wing. Black areas dull or glossy; chestnut breast-band bright. |

## Spring/Summer

| | |
|---|---|
| 1s (5) | Juvenile wing retained until full summer moult. |
| Adult (6) | Pre-breeding as Autumn/Winter. After moult cannot be reliably aged beyond 2+ calendar years (4); black areas become edged with dark |

brown, whitish feathering around base of bill. Breast-band obscured by buff fringes. Upper and underparts with fine grey barring. Some ♀♀ become similar in appearance to juveniles on body, but wing pattern remains adult, i.e. no white tips to secondaries or primaries.

## Moult

3/5        Partial post-juvenile moult soon after fledging, almost continuous from late July and early October, finishing midwinter involving head, breast, and belly, and variable amount of chest, flanks, scapulars, and mantle. Subsequent moults as adult.

Adult      Complete post-breeding moult starting with body shortly after hatching of young (June), starting with underparts and head, followed by mantle and scapulars; body feathers arrested once wing and tail moult starts, early July to mid-October, when birds become flightless for about 25-31 days. Partial pre-breeding moult confined to head and body (some overlap with post-breeding moult) starting when wings fully grown, completed August-December.

## Biometrics    (BWP).

| | | | | | | |
|---|---|---|---|---|---|---|
| Wing *ad.* | ♂334 | (8.75;33) | 312-350 | ♀303 | (7.83;28) | 284-316 |
| *juv.* | 315 | (12.2;13) | 291-334 | 290 | (9.18;13) | 277-307 |
| Bill | 53.0 | (1.82;37) | 50-58 | 47.3 | (1.70;36) | 44-50 |
| Tarsus | 55.8 | (1.64;34) | 52-60 | 50.1 | (1.86;36) | 46-54 |

# WIGEON *Anas penelope*

**Identification** Breeding ♂ unmistakable. Size and shape distinguish eclipse ♂, ♀ and immatures from all except American Wigeon but that species has clear or lightly marked white axillaries and central underwing whereas in Wigeon these areas are whitish but extensively and closely marked with grey, appearing light grey. Small grey bill and blackish-brown speculum, usually slightly glossed green. Breeding ♀ has 4 morphs of 2 colours (grey and rufous, plain or barred). Upperparts of grey-barred morph olive-sepia on mantle, broadly edged olive-grey and barred pink-buff subterminally;in rufous-barred morph, feathers of mantle and back sepia, with many pink-buff bars and narrow buff or white edges. In plain morphs, upperparts show fewer and usually incomplete subterminal bars, edges of feathers pink-buff or olive-grey;in rufous morphs, chest and sides of breast sepia, feathers broadly tipped cinnamon-buff and barred pink-buff or white subterminally;feathers of chest sometimes cinnamon-buff with faint sepia subterminal bars;in grey morphs, chest pale pink-buff, feather variably tipped vinaceous-grey, flanks pale cinnamon, tips washed white.

**Sexing**          All ages by cloacal examination, at any season. Plumage characters as follows:

♂          Head and neck reddish-brown, with buff-yellow centre to crown and forehead. Green patch behind eye. Breast greyish-pink. Undertail and sides of undertail-coverts black. Eclipse ♂ like ♀ but forewing white, not pale grey-brown with vermiculations as in ♀. Immatures not always separable from ♀ on plumage as upperwing, in particular, extremely variable; median-coverts greyish-white forming uniform light area, most prominent towards outermost coverts. Greater-coverts typically with black tips but much variation (Fig): also white tips to secondaries tapered unlike ♀ which show broader, more bar-like pattern. Speculum with green gloss. Outer web of innermost secondary white, narrowly margined black. From October onwards check for adult-type feathers in moulting birds, especially on head.

♀          Forewing uniform pale grey-brown or brown, not white as in ♂. Greater-coverts typically grey or smoky-grey with whitish subterminal bar and black terminal bar, or with pale edges to tips, but much variation (Fig). White tips of secondaries broader and bar-like. Secondaries rarely with any green sheen and usually outer web of innermost secondary suffused grey.

## Autumn/Winter

3          Median-coverts narrow and tapered, with rounded tips. Greater-coverts narrow, with tapering tips. Tertial-coverts narrow, tapered and fringe-tipped. Tertials narrow, short and pointed, dark brown with narrow pale and frayed outer margin; worn and frayed tips. Speculum brown to blackish. White belly lightly mottled dusky. Tail feathers narrow, notched at tip, bare shaft projecting.

3 ♂          Median-coverts greyish-brown or greyish-white with narrow buff edges to posterior rows, or with dusky margins and barring. Greater-coverts generally greyish-brown with darker subterminal bar, sometimes dirty white with dull black subterminal bar, but much variation (Fig).

3 ♀          Median-coverts brown or brownish-grey with poorly defined pale

110

margin. Greater-coverts smoky-grey with pale edges and tips, sometimes speckled or blotched blackish on pale tips (Fig).

1w (3/5)  Very variable change to adult plumage but most of immature wing feathers retained. Beware some or all of tertials may be replaced. Some or most immature tail feathers retained until summer moult.

Adult (4/6)  Wing-coverts broad and round-tipped. Greater-coverts with broad (squarish) tips (Fig). Tertials long and lanceolate (longer in ♂♂), outer web black with well-defined smooth white or buff margins. Belly white, in ♀ sometimes finely speckled grey.

**Greater-coverts**

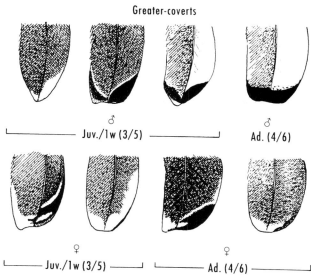

♂

— Juv./1w (3/5) — ♂ Ad. (4/6)

♀

— Juv./1w (3/5) — ♀ Ad. (4/6)

## Spring/Summer

All ages  As Autumn/Winter.

## Moult

3/5  Partial post-juvenile moult. Timing and extent of moult highly variable. Usually starts September and mainly involves head and body. Tertials may be moulted any time from September to May. Tail mostly from October to May, sometimes not until following July-August. Partial pre-breeding moult involving body, tertials and tail from October in ♂, December in ♀, completing any time between April and May.

Adult  Complete post-breeding moult starting in ♂ or unsuccessful breeding ♀ with body, May-July. Wing feathers replaced between end of June and early September, when birds become flightless for about 4 weeks. Partial pre-breeding moult involving body, tertials, and central tail feathers starts soon after wing moult is finished, ♂ generally earlier than ♀; most in breeding plumage by December though some (ca.15%) of ♂♂ retain eclipse plumage tertials, central tail feathers and other scattered feathers to March-April.

**Biometrics**  (BWP).

| | | | | | | |
|---|---|---|---|---|---|---|
| Wing *ad.* | ♂267 | (6.37;45) | 252-281 | ♀250 | (4.54;19) | 242-262 |
| *juv.* | 257 | (4.92;42) | 246-266 | 244 | (6.54;32) | 228-261 |
| Tail | 106 | (3.84;19) | 102-119 | 90.7 | (2.50;13) | 86-95 |
| Bill | 34.7 | (1.29;84) | 32-38 | 33.8 | (1.48;51) | 31-37 |
| Tarsus | 39.5 | (1.47;49) | 37-44 | 38.6 | (1.42;40) | 35-41 |

# AMERICAN WIGEON *Anas americana*

**Identification** Breeding ♂ unmistakable. Eclipse ♂, ♀ and immatures very similar to Wigeon, but have white axillaries and median underwing-coverts, often slightly speckled dusky on tips, while in Wigeon axillaries are more extensively speckled grey and median underwing-coverts are grey-brown edged white.

**Ageing and Sexing** Not known to differ significantly from Wigeon.

**Moult**  Apparently does not differ from Wigeon.

**Biometrics**  Like Wigeon but adult tail significantly longer (BWP).

Tail ♂ 116   (7.23; 6)   101-126  ♀96.3  (;3)      96-97

# GADWALL *Anas strepera*

**Identification** Adult and eclipse ♂ unmistakable, latter retaining adult wing with inner third of speculum white, outer two-thirds black. Adult ♀ from Mallard by white inner third of speculum, often reduced, whitish belly and

112

orange sides to smaller brown bill. Immature speculum may have little or no white at first, but never has green/blue sheen of Mallard.

**Sexing**   All ages by cloacal examination, at any season. Plumage characters in adults as follows:

♂   Ventral region, uppertail-coverts and rump black. Median-coverts maroon-chestnut, some with black tips. Outer two-thirds grey with black on outer webs, or all-black at tip with inner third white. Inner greater-coverts deep black. Tertials long, lanceolate and pointed, silvery-grey. Eclipse ♂ from ♀ by larger speculum, more extensive chestnut on median-coverts. Outer webs of middle secondaries black, not grey bordered black.

♀   Ventral region, uppertail-coverts and rump grey-brown mottled and fringed blackish, giving strong scalloping effect. Median-coverts with pale terminal tips forming strong pale traverse barring across the wing, with only small traces of chestnut. Tertials shorter than ♂ ♂, brownish-grey with pale buff tips. Outer two-thirds grey with black outer margins, inner third off-white or grey or hardly any different from other secondaries.

## Autumn/Winter

3   Tail notched at tip, edged white, bare shafts projecting - retained until about September. Median- and greater-coverts narrow and tapered (Fig). Tertials short, brownish-grey with paler tips becoming worn and frayed. Greater tertial-coverts sooty-brown, worn and frayed.

3 ♂   Median-coverts with light wavy horizontal stripes and chestnut tips.

3 ♀   Median-coverts with more regular barring and paler tips, chestnut, if present, only on outer covert tips.

1w (3/5)   New tertials appear during December and presence of growing tertials in midwinter good indicator of 1st-winter bird. Gradual acquisition of other adult characters on head and body but most juvenile wing feathers, other than tertials, retained.

Adult (4/6)   Wing-coverts wide and round-tipped (Fig). Tertials long, smooth and pointed, pale silvery grey in ♂, olive-brown or brownish-grey with pale buff tips in ♀.

113

**Greater-coverts**　　　　　**Median-coverts**

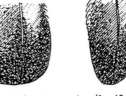

Ad (4/6) ♂　　Juv./1w (3/5) ♀　　Ad. (4/6) ♀　　Juv./1w (3/5) ♂

## Spring/Summer

All ages　　　As Autumn/Winter.

## Moult

3/5　　Partial post-juvenile moult confined to head, body, and some or all of tail, August-October. ♂♂ generally moult all of tail and tertials by midwinter while ♀♀ retain some or all of both feather groups until spring. Partial pre-breeding moult of body, tertials and tail September-December.

Adult　　Complete post-breeding moult starting with head and body in May-July (♂) and June-August (♀). Flight feathers follow after completion of body, in ♂♂ end of June-September, ♀♀ later, sometimes into October. Birds flightless for about 4 weeks. Partial pre-breeding moult involving body, tertials and most or all of tail, complete by September (♂) or October (♀), but tertials and some greater- and median-coverts of ♀♀ not until spring.

**Biometrics**　　(BWP).

| | | | | | | |
|---|---|---|---|---|---|---|
| Wing *ad.* | ♂269 | (5.85;24) | 261-282 | ♀252 | (5.24;14) | 243-261 |
| *juv.* | 264 | (5.52;37) | 251-274 | 246 | (6.58;32) | 233-262 |
| Bill | 42.4 | (1.63;60) | 39-46 | 39.8 | (1.60;48) | 37-43 |
| Tarsus | 40.3 | (1.01;42) | 38-42 | 38.8 | (1.24;34) | 36-42 |

# TEAL *Anas crecca*

**Identification**  Adult ♂ unmistakable. Eclipse ♂ retain adult wing characters, i.e. with inner speculum metallic green, outer half to two-thirds black. Smallest west Palearctic duck (see Biometrics). Adult ♀ from Garganey by overall mottled brownish plumage with whitish belly, bright green speculum, dark crown and eye-stripe, and grey bill with fleshy base. Immatures as ♀, but green speculum reduced in area. Only adult ♂ of American race *A.c. carolinensis* distinguishable (see Geographical variation). See also Blue-winged Teal.

**Sexing**  All ages by cloacal examination, at any season. Plumage characters in adult as follows:

♂  Head bright chestnut, with broad green patch, curving back from eye to nape. Yellow-buff patch on either side of black undertail-coverts. Rich cream breast with blackish spots. Eclipse ♂ like ♀ but greater-coverts with white triangular stripe extending very faintly onto tertial-coverts. Also, in nominate race, outer vanes of outer tertials edged black contrasting with grey or white inner vane. Secondaries with narrow white tips. Speculum wholly green on outer vane of 4th inner secondary, s4.

♀  Triangular white stripe on greater-coverts more evenly shaped than in ♂, less angular and extending clearly onto tertial-coverts. Outer vane of outer tertial dark grey-brown and lacking contrast with inner vane. Secondaries with broad white tips. Speculum only partly green on outer vane of 4th inner secondary. Black spots along sides of upper mandible.

## Autumn/Winter

3  Tail notched at tip with bare shafts showing; tail can be moulted out by end of August. Tertials and tertial-coverts narrow and pointed, fringed when fresh, retained until at least late autumn. Greater-coverts narrow and tapered (Fig), median-coverts similar with light edgings forming scaly pattern. Belly can be marked with narrow dusky shaft-streaks and spots; these are lacking in adult breeding, though can be present in adult non-breeding.

1w (3/5)  In some, not all individuals, worn appearance of juvenile wing and shape of tertials is a reasonable indicator of age. Many birds have moulted out into breeding plumage by the end of the 1st calendar year. ♀♀ tend to retain tertials until spring.

Adult (4/6)  Wing-coverts broad and rounded and lacking fringes (Fig). Tertials very long, broad and blunt-tipped. Underparts become mottled in non-breeding plumage - beware of immature birds which also show mottling or spotting.

### Greater-coverts

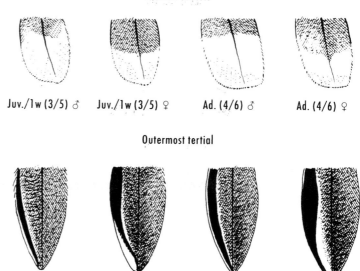

Juv./1w (3/5) ♂      Juv./1w (3/5) ♀      Ad. (4/6) ♂      Ad. (4/6) ♀

### Outermost tertial

Juv./1w (3/5) ♀      Ad. (4/6) ♀      Juv./1w (3/5) ♂      Ad. (4/6) ♂

## Spring/Summer

All ages        As Autumn/Winter.

## Moult

3               Partial post-juvenile moult of head, neck, body, tertials and tail August-September in ♂, slightly later in ♀. First pre-breeding partial moult confined to body, tertials and tail, September-spring; ♂♂ usually completed by November, ♀♀ normally a little later seldom renewing tertials and tail until spring.

Adult           Complete post-breeding moult into non-breeding plumage from June-August; ♂ slightly earlier than ♀. Flight feathers shed simultaneously, July-September, when birds remain flightless for 3-4 weeks. Partial pre-breeding moult again from September includes body, tertials and tail though tertials and tail in some birds not until spring.

**Geographical variation** Clinal: becomes slightly larger from west to east. Extralimital *A.c. carolinensis* (North America) occurs rarely in western Europe; similar in size to nominate *crecca*, but plumage different in breeding ♂, recognized by white vertical line at side of breast, and absence of horizontal white stripe on scapulars. Non-breeding, ♀, and juvenile plumages indistinguishable from nominate race.

**Biometrics**    Nominate *crecca* (Salminen 1983).

| | | | | | | | |
|---|---|---|---|---|---|---|---|
| Wing | ad. ♂ | 186 | (4;36) | 179-200 | ♀ 178 | (3;14) | 172-183 |
| | juv. | 181 | (5;25) | 173-192 | 175 | (3;17) | 170-180 |
| Bill | ad. | 36.2 | (1.3;49) | 34-40 | 34.3 | (1.1;23) | 32-36 |
| | juv. | 36.3 | (1.5;24) | 32-39 | 34.3 | (1.1;17) | 33-36 |

(BWP).

| | | | | | | | |
|---|---|---|---|---|---|---|---|
| Wing | ad. ♂ | 187 | (3.26;34) | 181-196 | ♀ 180 | (2.67;22) | 175-184 |
| | juv. | 184 | (4.20;63) | 176-192 | 177 | (4.48;30) | 166-185 |
| Bill | | 36.4 | (1.37;85) | 34-40 | 34.9 | (1.29;50) | 32-38 |
| Tarsus | | 30.4 | (0.95;38) | 29-32 | 29.8 | (0.98;32) | 28-31 |

# MALLARD *Anas platyrhynchos*

**Identification**    Adult and eclipse ♂ unmistakable. ♀ and juvenile distinguished from Gadwall and Black Duck *A. rubripes* by one or more of: white-bordered purple-blue speculum, dark bill with orange near tip, orange legs, mottled brownish belly and dark eye-stripe.

**Sexing**    All ages by cloacal examination, at any season. Plumage characters in adults as follows:

♂    Bill yellow and unspotted. Head bottle-green, separated from purple-brown breast by narrow white collar. Speculum blue or purple. Legs orange. In eclipse superficially like ♀ and distinguished by yellower bill, blacker crown, paler and greyer face and neck; also, eclipse ♂ lacks the white tips to greater tertial-coverts. Period of eclipse when adult or juvenile lacks all breeding plumage is very short.

♀    Mainly brown and always mottled, spotted and streaked with blackish. Bill usually dull orange to olive, with blackish ridge and tip. White tips to greater tertial-coverts.

117

## Autumn/Winter

3          Tail dark grey-brown, edged pale buff, lacking white edge to outer feathers as in 2nd generation feathers, notched at tips with bare shafts showing; tail can be completely moulted out by end of August. Tertials narrow, fringed and dark when fresh, lacking any pearly colour. Tertial-coverts narrow, tapered and fringed, darker brown with, in ♀, narrow dull or off-white edgings (Fig). Greater-and median-coverts narrow and tapered, brownish-grey, lacking cinnamon. Greater-coverts 4,5, and 6 with small rounded black tips (Fig).

1w (3/5)   Growing tertials after 1st December indicate first-winter. One or more juvenile tertials retained in ♀, and some worn tertial-coverts may be retained in both sexes. Greater- and median-coverts retained.

Adult (4/6)  Tertials broad and long, with unbroken tips, more greyish than on juvenile ♀. Tertial-coverts broad and rounded with unbroken white tips (♀) or evenly dark grey throughout (♂) with cinnamon tips (Fig). Greater-coverts 4, 5, and 6 with large angular black tips (Fig).

Greater tertial-coverts

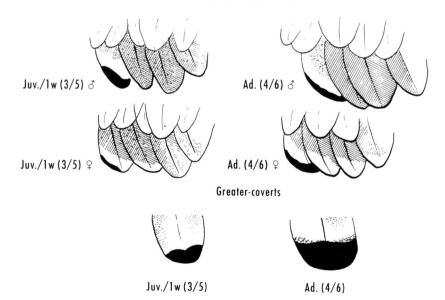

Juv./1w (3/5) ♂          Ad. (4/6) ♂

Juv./1w (3/5) ♀          Ad. (4/6) ♀

Greater-coverts

Juv./1w (3/5)          Ad. (4/6)

## Spring/Summer

All ages    As Autumn/Winter.

118

## Moult

**3/5**

Partial post-juvenile moult confined to head, and/or breast, scapulars and flanks. Tail often completely moulted by late August, though some not complete until October. First pre-breeding moult partial, confined to body, tertials and tail; August-December in ♂, slightly later in ♀. Some birds may not finish until spring.

**Adult**

Complete post-breeding moult into non-breeding plumage from June (♀) to late September, or late June (♂) to late August. Flight feathers moulted simultaneously when birds become flightless for 4-5 weeks. Partial pre-breeding moult confined to body, tertials and tail, starts shortly after end of wing moult, August-October (♂), more protracted in ♀ finishing in November. Further moult of body, tertials and tail may be apparent in spring also.

**Biometrics**

Nominate *platyrhynchos* (BWP).

| | | | | | | | | |
|---|---|---|---|---|---|---|---|---|
| Wing | *ad.* | ♂279 | (4.08;13) | 272-285 | ♀265 | (4.66;13) | 257-273 |
| | *juv.* | 272 | (8.06;27) | 258-287 | 257 | (7.61;23) | 245-272 |
| Bill | | 55.4 | (2.44;58) | 51-61 | 51.8 | (2.21;48) | 47-56 |
| Tarsus | | 45.3 | (1.51;45) | 42-48 | 43.4 | (1.38;37) | 41-46 |

# PINTAIL *Anas acuta*

**Identification**

Largely unmistakable on shape in all plumages. For ♀ and immatures, combination of dark grey bill, longish neck, pointed tail and pale, but not clear white belly distinguish from ♀/immature Wigeon.

**Sexing**

All ages by cloacal examination, at any season. Plumage characters in adult as follows:

**♂**

Adult ♂ unmistakable: Head, throat and hind-neck chocolate-brown. Lower foreneck, stripe up sides of neck, breast, and centre of underparts white. Elongated, pointed scapulars and tertials grey, with black central stripes. Central pair of tail feathers greatly elongated and narrowly pointed. Black undertail-coverts. Eclipse ♂ from ♀ by metallic green speculum. Underwing-coverts finely speckled or vermiculated grey and white. Juveniles show some green on speculum.

♀　　　　　　　Mainly pale brown, mottled, spotted and streaked blackish or brown. Speculum gingery-brown, speckled dusky. Underwing-coverts light brown with broad pale margins and barring.

## Autumn/Winter

3　　　　　　　Tail feathers notched at tip, bare shafts projecting, retained into October. Tertials narrow and pointed, brownish-grey with dark centres. Greater-coverts pointed, usually with pale tips, more obvious in ♀ (Fig).

1w (3/5)　　　Worn juvenile feathers on wing; if very worn, ♀♀ can be difficult to age, though pale anterior border to speculum normally very narrow. Tertials growing during December indicates 1st-winter.

Adult (4/6)　Tertials pearly-grey with black centres, outer vanes edged with fine vermiculations, lanceolated and pointed (♂), or grey-brown with dark centres, prominent smooth white edges extending round tips (♀). Greater-coverts broad with darker tips (♂) or with pale tips (♀).

### Greater-coverts

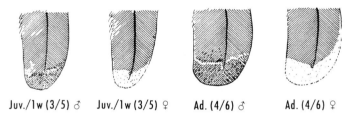

Juv./1w (3/5) ♂　　Juv./1w (3/5) ♀　　Ad. (4/6) ♂　　Ad. (4/6) ♀

## Spring/Summer

All ages　　　As Autumn/Winter.

## Moult

3/5　　　　　Partial post-juvenile moult of body August-November. Partial pre-breeding moult involving body, tertials and tail from October, mostly complete by December, but many juvenile feathers retained, especially on back, rump and belly; sometimes tail and tertials not moulted until spring. ♀ moults more slowly, with juvenile feathers on many parts of body and wings retained until spring.

| Adult | Complete post-breeding moult starting June is usually complete by August (September in ♀♀). Flight feathers from July when birds become flightless for about 4 weeks. Partial pre-breeding moult involving body, tail and tertials begins soon after wings complete. Full breeding plumage attained by November (♂) or December (♀), but some body feathers, tertials and tail in ♀ not until spring. |
|---|---|

**Biometrics**    Nominate *acuta* (Salminen 1983).

| | | | | | | |
|---|---|---|---|---|---|---|
| Wing *ad.* | ♂275 | (4;20) | 268-281 | ♀258 | (6;12) | 247-265 |
| *juv.* | 269 | (6;101) | 252-286 | 254 | (7;126) | 238-273 |

(BWP).

| | | | | | | |
|---|---|---|---|---|---|---|
| Wing *ad.* | ♂275 | (4.00;20) | 267-282 | ♀260 | (3.80;12) | 254-267 |
| *juv.* | 266 | (5.96;35) | 254-279 | 248 | (6.70;20) | 236-260 |
| Bill | 50.9 | (2.07;55) | 47-56 | 46.7 | (1.91;31) | 44-51 |
| Tarsus | 42.6 | (1.26;40) | 40-45 | 41.0 | (0.98;30) | 39-43 |

# GARGANEY *Anas querquedula*

| **Identification** | Adult ♂ unmistakable. Eclipse ♂ retains adult wing characters, especially blue-grey median- and lesser-coverts, and green speculum. ♀ from teals by larger size (see Biometrics), greenish or greyish-brown speculum with broad white border, dark head and prominent dark eye-stripe. |
|---|---|

| **Sexing** | All ages by cloacal examination, at any season. Plumage characters in adult as follows: |
|---|---|

| ♂ | Brownish-black crown with golden-brown cheeks divided by broad white supercilium which extends well down the nape. Elongated and drooping scapulars striped grey, dark green, black and white; forewing pale blue-grey. Speculum has strong light green sheen. Tips of secondaries and greater-coverts broadly tipped white (>10mm). In eclipse, like ♀ but with pale blue-grey forewing and green speculum. |
|---|---|

| ♀ | Forewing (lesser- and median-coverts) dark grey-brown (sometimes adult ♀ may have slightly bluish tips to otherwise dark coverts). Speculum |
|---|---|

dull grey-brown, sometimes with slight green tinge but only to innermost secondaries. White tips to greater-coverts relatively narrow (<10mm), and on secondaries confined to outer vanes.

## Autumn/Winter

3 ♂           Tail feathers notched at tips with bare shafts projecting. Lesser- and median-coverts dirty blue-grey. Greater-coverts narrow and pointed with 10-15mm white tips, often with dark spot at tip of inner vane (Fig). Speculum dull metallic green, secondaries with white tips.

3 ♀           Greater-coverts and secondaries narrow and pointed with narrow white or buff-white tips (Fig). Speculum dull grey-brown and without any green sheen.

1w (3/5)      Worn wings retained throughout until summer moult.

Adult ♂ (4/6)  Lesser- and median-coverts blue-grey. Greater-coverts broad and rounded, half or more of feather length white (Fig). Speculum bright metallic green with broad white tips.

Adult ♀ (4/6)  Lesser-, median- and greater-coverts broad and rounded, latter with white tips usually about one-third or less of feather length (Fig). Speculum dull grey-brown, sometimes with slight green metallic sheen, usually confined to innermost secondaries.

**Greater-coverts**

♂
└─── Juv./1w (3/5) ───┘

♀
└─── Juv./1w (3/5) ───┘

♂            ♀
└─── Ad. (4/6) ───┘

## Spring/Summer

All ages       As for Autumn/Winter.

**Moult**

3/5       Partial post-juvenile moult of head, neck, body, from August or shortly after arrival in winter quarters. Tail, a few tertials and some wing-coverts replaced from September. Partial pre-breeding moult involving body, tertials and tail from March, often though with retained immature feathers on mantle, back, rump or some tertials; moulted out in post-breeding moult in mid-summer.

Adult       Complete post-breeding moult late May or June starting with body (slightly later in ♀), followed shortly after by simultaneous moult of flight feathers, June-August, when birds become flightless for about 3-4 weeks. In autumn some breast, flank and scapular feathers replaced as well, but still largely in eclipse when migrates south. Partial pre-breeding moult of head, body, tail and tertials November to early March.

**Biometrics**       (BWP).

| | | | | | | |
|---|---|---|---|---|---|---|
| Wing ad. | ♂198 | (4.36;34) | 190-211 | ♀189 | (3.14;16) | 184-196 |
| juv. | 194 | (4.22;35) | 187-201 | 186 | (3.26;17) | 182-194 |
| Bill | 39.6 | (1.18;70) | 38-43 | 38.0 | (1.06;34) | 36-40 |
| Tarsus | 31.3 | (1.03;38) | 29-33 | 30.1 | (1.00;20) | 28-32 |

# BLUE-WINGED TEAL *Anas discors*

**Identification**       Sky-blue forewing, clearly brighter than blue-grey of Garganey, distinguishes this species in all plumages from other teal except Cinnamon *A. cyanoptera* which occurs as an escape. ♀♀ of Blue-winged and Cinnamon are very similar; those of latter are typically much warmer, almost rufous-brown in tone, rather than dull greyish-buff. The head is plainer and darker, with less distinct pale loral spot.

**Sexing**       All ages by cloacal examination, at any season. Plumage characters in adults as follows:

♂       Unmistakable in breeding plumage; bold white crescent between eye and base of bill. Lead-blue head. Black undertail-coverts with bold white patch on front of rear flanks. In eclipse like ♀ but with broad white tips to greater-coverts and metallic green speculum.

123

♀　　　　　　Greyish-buff overall, mottled, spotted and streaked dark brown or black-ish. Greater-coverts only narrowly tipped white, and this white often obscured with brown. Dull greenish speculum.

## Autumn/Winter

3　　　　　　Tail feathers notched at tip with bare shafts projecting. Greater-coverts narrow with small dusky dots (♂) or solid bar (♀) to white tips. Tertials short and narrow, edged and broadly tipped pale buff or off-white (♂), or plain, somewhat frayed at tip.

1w (3/5)　　As above.

Adult ♂ (4/6)　Outer web of secondaries metallic green (except some outer feathers), sometimes narrowly tipped white. Outer greater-coverts black with broad white tips. Tertials black with blue-green gloss and off-white shaft-streak; long and broad.

Adult ♀ (4/6)　Speculum duller than ♂, usually black with dark green tinge. Greater-coverts blue with narrow white tips and usually symmetrical sharply angled V-shaped marks. Tertials sepia, edged and streaked buff.

## Spring/Summer

All ages　　As Autumn/Winter.

**Moult**　　Apparently as Garganey, except adult ♂♂ appear to attain breeding plumage earlier in winter.

**Biometrics**　Adult (BWP).

| | | | | | | |
|---|---|---|---|---|---|---|
| Wing | ♂191 | (3.52;8) | 186-195 | ♀183 | (4.45;5) | 176-188 |
| Bill | 40.8 | (1.52;18) | 38-44 | 40.0 | (1.30;5) | 37-41 |
| Tarsus | 31.9 | (1.06;18) | 30-34 | 31.1 | (0.89;5) | 30-32 |


# SHOVELER *Anas clypeata*

**Identification**　The heavy spatulate bill makes this species unmistakable in all plumages. Note that ♂ Shoveler, along with other blue-winged ducks such as

Garganey and Blue-winged Teal adopts an intermediate, supplementary plumage between eclipse and breeding (post-breeding and pre-breeding moults respectively). This is more noticeable in Shoveler than in the other species. ♂ ♂ in late autumn acquire a white facial crescent and pale sides to the head. Full breeding plumage is often not complete until February-March. Juvenile ♂ ♂ moult into an adult-like plumage in the autumn, but also at least partially moult via a supplementary plumage, and can exhibit feathering from three different plumage types simultaneously.

**Sexing**

All ages by cloacal examination, at any season. Plumage characters in adult as follows:

♂

Unmistakable in breeding plumage: head and upper neck glossy green-black. Lower neck and breast white. Flanks and centre of underparts chestnut. Out of breeding plumage, by strong green colour of speculum on all secondaries, while outer vanes of secondaries have 1-2mm white tips or all-black tips. Lesser- and median-coverts light blue lacking pale edges, or with minimal light edgings along leading edge of wing, especially at wrist.

♀

Mainly light brown with dark brown or blackish mottling or speckling. Speculum lacks the strong metallic gloss, sometimes though with slight green tinge on proximal 3 or 4 secondaries (s1-s4), while tips have dirty white tips, 1-4mm, lacking contrast with rest of feather. Lesser- and median-coverts pale blue or blue-grey with varying amounts of creamy-white edgings.

**Autumn/Winter**

3

Tail notched at tip, bare shafts projecting. Some tail feathers moulted out by late August or September, but outers usually retained until November in ♂ and March of the following year in ♀.

3 ♂

Tertials and tertial-coverts brownish, narrow and pointed, with narrow white margin along the outer vane sometimes extending round slightly blunt tip. Lesser- and median-coverts narrow and tapering, dull blue. Greater-coverts narrow and tapering, majority of birds having dark spots on inner vanes at tips (Fig).

3 ♀

Tertials and tertial-coverts brown with brownish-white tips. Median- and lesser-coverts narrow and tapering, usually only showing faint blue. Greater-coverts narrow and pointed; white tips form narrow, even-width stripe, though dark on feather often reaches tip, or with ill-defined spots on inner vane (Fig).

1w (3/5)  Many juvenile feathers retained throughout winter, especially on wing.

Adult (4/6)  Tertials long and pointed; black with dull greenish on outer vanes and white flare along distal third of shaft, mainly on inner vane (♂), or dark brown with contrasting smooth pale buff tips on outer margins (♀). Eclipse ♂ tertials, which may be present in late autumn, shorter than adult ♂ but still retaining white flare along distal half. Greater-coverts broad and square-ended and normally with larger area of white on tips (Fig).

**Greater-coverts**

└───── Juv./1w (3/5) ♂ ─────┘    Ad. (4/6) ♂    └──── Juv./1w (3/5) ♀ ────┘    Ad. (4/6) ♀

## Spring/Summer

All ages  As Autumn/Winter.

## Moult

3/5  Complex and probably more-or-less continuous. Partial post-juvenile moult of body August-September in ♂, September-October in ♀. Partial pre-breeding involving body, tertials and tail September-December in ♂, in ♀ not finishing until February-March (April).

Adult  Complete post-breeding moult early May-early June in ♂, about one month later in ♀. Simultaneous moult of flight feathers from mid-June to mid-August in ♂, late July-early September in ♀, rendering birds flightless for 3-4 weeks. Partial pre-breeding moult involving body, tertials and tail August-December in ♂, September-February (March) in ♀.

**Biometrics** (BWP).

| | | | | | | | | |
|---|---|---|---|---|---|---|---|---|
| Wing | ad. ♂ | 244 | (3.77;27) | 239-249 | ♀ 230 | (4.52;18) | 222-237 |
| | juv. | 235 | (5.04;41) | 227-251 | 222 | (4.45;29) | 213-229 |
| Bill | | 66.1 | (1.91;61) | 62-72 | 60.7 | (2.12;47) | 56-64 |
| Tarsus | | 37.2 | (1.14;48) | 35-40 | 36.0 | (0.86;39) | 35-38 |

# RED-CRESTED POCHARD *Netta rufina*

**Identification**  Breeding ♂ unmistakable: head and nape rust-orange, becoming yellower on crown. Neck, breast, centre of underparts, ventral region, uppertail and undertail-coverts, tail, rump and back black. Bill reddish-pink. ♀ has chocolate-brown crown and hindneck with contrasting whitish cheeks and foreneck.

**Sexing**  All ages by cloacal examination, at any season. Plumage characters in adults as follows:

♂  Adult ♂ in breeding plumage unmistakable (see above). In eclipse distinguished at all times from ♀ by more extensive white along leading edge of wing.

♀  Leading edge of wing brownish and same colour as rest of wing-coverts, sometimes with traces of a pale leading edge, though never as extensive or intense as in ♂.

## Autumn/Winter

3  Tail feathers, notched with bare shafts projecting, retained at least until September, sometimes until December. Greater-coverts narrow with rounded tips (Fig).

1w (3/5)  Like adult, but ♂ mottled on belly and around the vent, not black as adult; ♀ greyer-brown on upperparts and crown.

Adult (4/6)  Greater-coverts broad and square-tipped (Fig).

### Greater-coverts

Juv./1w (3/5)          Ad. (4/6)

## Spring/Summer

All ages          As Autumn/Winter.

## Moult

3/5          Partial post-juvenile moult commencing July, involving head, body, tail, and tertials, completed by October. Partial pre-breeding moult from September, replacing most of remaining juvenile feathers by December. Tail August-December. ♀ generally much slower to moult, not finishing until spring.

Adult          Complete post-breeding moult commencing May (♂) with head and body, followed by wings and tail in June-August when feathers shed simultaneously. Birds flightless for about 4 weeks. Moult in ♀ about 1 month later. Partial pre-breeding moult late August when birds assume breeding plumage. Moult confined to head, and body, completed mostly before November.

## Biometrics          (BWP).

| | | | | | | |
|---|---|---|---|---|---|---|
| Wing ad. | ♂264 | (5.21;16) | 255-273 | ♀260 | (7.28;14) | 251-275 |
| juv. | 257 | (5.16;7) | 250-264 | 248 | (7.11;10) | 237-259 |
| Bill | 48.2 | (2.04;25) | 45-52 | 46.6 | (2.14;26) | 42-50 |
| Tarsus | 44.1 | (1.37;25) | 42-47 | 42.2 | (1.46;26) | 40-45 |

# POCHARD *Aythya ferina*

**Identification**  Adult ♂ unmistakable. ♀♀, immatures and eclipse ♂♂ from other Old World members of the genus by body greyer than brown of head, neck and breast, and by pale, often whitish, facial shading and line behind eye; also from North American pochards by head and bill shapes (Fig).

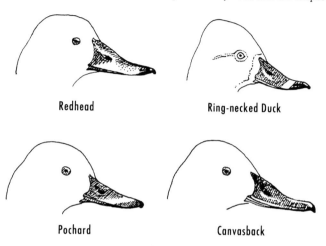

Redhead        Ring-necked Duck

Pochard        Canvasback

**Sexing**  All ages by cloacal examination, at any time. Plumage characters as follows:

♂  Unmistakable in breeding plumage; head chestnut-red. Breast and upper mantle black. Body vermiculated grey except for uppertail- and undertail-coverts which are blackish. In eclipse recalls ♀ but body greyer, head lacks facial pattern, iris reddish. Juveniles can be difficult but usually have distinct white spotting on tips of lesser-, median- and greater-coverts.

♀  Overall medium-brown, with pale greyish-white areas on throat, lores, sides of head and stripe behind eye, variable in extent and intensity. Tertials more-or-less uniform dusky-brown, sometimes with faint and minute white peppering, but never vermiculated. Iris brown or yellowish-brown. Wing-coverts generally uniform grey-brown, some-times faintly spotted near tips of feathers.

**Autumn/Winter**

3  Tail feathers narrow, notched at tip and with bare shafts showing -

retained until about November, though some, especially outer, not moulted until spring. Lesser- and median-coverts even grey-brown, narrow and rounded-tipped. Greater-coverts grey-brown with little or no whitish peppering, narrow and rounded at tips (Fig).

1w (3/5)      Much variation in moult timing. Wing-coverts often moulted, but new ones contrast with old retained juvenile feathers. Tertials often very worn, brown, frayed and faded but some birds moult them out October-November.

Adult (4/6)      Lesser- and median-coverts grey, vermiculated or peppered with white, broad with rounded tips. Greater-coverts grey-brown vermiculated or peppered white, amount increasing with age, broad with square tips (Fig).

### Greater-coverts

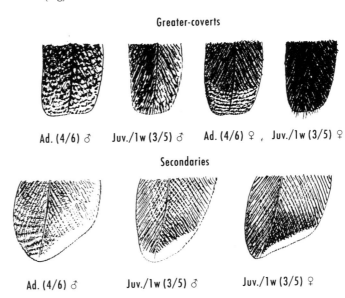

Ad. (4/6) ♂    Juv./1w (3/5) ♂    Ad. (4/6) ♀ , Juv./1w (3/5) ♀

### Secondaries

Ad. (4/6) ♂     Juv./1w (3/5) ♂     Juv./1w (3/5) ♀

## Spring/Summer

All ages      As Autumn/Winter.

## Moult

3/5      Partial post-juvenile moult, variable and protracted, often suspended in December and resumed in the spring. Body from July-October (December); tail by October-November, some feathers retained until spring. Tertials replaced in spring (rarely by October-November), and usually also some inner greater-coverts, or more rarely inner secondaries, contrasting with worn juvenile feathers. ♀ moult less complete, retaining more juvenile feathers through winter.

Adult  Complete post-breeding moult commencing with body in ♀ February-March, and in ♂ June-July. Simultaneous shedding of flight feathers, late June to early September (♂), early July to late October (♀), when birds are flightless for about 3-4 weeks. Partial pre-breeding moult confined to head and body, September-November, after which birds are in full breeding plumage.

**Biometrics**  (Salminen 1983).

| | | | | | | |
|---|---|---|---|---|---|---|
| Wing *ad.* | ♂215 | (3;56) | 204-222 | ♀207 | (4;40) | 202-216 |
| *juv.* | 211 | (4;42) | 203-218 | 207 | (3;31) | 199-212 |
| Bill | 46.9 | (1.8;62) | 43-52 | 44.8 | (1.6;41) | 41-48 |

(BWP).

| | | | | | | |
|---|---|---|---|---|---|---|
| Wing *ad.* | ♂217 | (3.22;19) | 212-223 | ♀206 | (4.61;22) | 200-216 |
| *juv.* | 213 | (4.47;41) | 202-220 | 206 | (7.85;23) | 185-215 |
| Bill | 47.1 | (1.80;62) | 43-52 | 44.9 | (1.48;47) | 42-48 |
| Tarsus | 39.5 | (1.02;52) | 37-42 | 38.8 | (1.19;47) | 36-41 |

# FERRUGINOUS DUCK *Aythya nyroca*

**Identification**  Adult ♂ unmistakable with rich dark chestnut on head, breast and flanks, with darker upperparts and conspicuous pure white undertail-coverts. White eye. Eclipse ♂ and ♀ similar in appearance to Tufted Duck, but with conspicuous white undertail-coverts (some ♀ Tufted have white on undertail-coverts but never so extensive or so sharply defined). Immatures might be confused with Pochard which has paler, greyer back, no rufous tinge, and grey wing stripe.

**Sexing**  All ages by cloacal examination, at any season. Plumage characters in adults as follows:

| ♂ | More extensive white towards tips of outer primaries than ♀. P6 white with faint grey hue, strongly contrasting with black tip and edge (Fig). |

| ♀ | White in primaries less extensive, washed grey, especially on outer edge and towards tips. P6 grey over much of its length, showing little contrast with black-brown tip and outer edge (Fig). |

## Primary 6

♀       ♂

## Autumn/Winter

Ageing essentially similar to Pochard using shape of wing-coverts plus:

1w (3/5)    Iris grey-brown. During winter, iris changes to pale grey in ♂, brown in ♀.

Adult (4/6)    Iris white in ♂, brown in ♀.

**Moult**    Sequence of plumages and timing as in Pochard, and equally highly variable.

**Biometrics**    (BWP).

| | | | | | | | |
|---|---|---|---|---|---|---|---|
| Wing *ad.* | ♂188 | (3.87;31) | 180-196 | ♀182 | (2.39;8) | 178-185 |
| *juv.* | 185 | (3.65;27) | 177-192 | 177 | (2.98;21) | 171-183 |
| Bill | 40.3 | (1.27;58) | 38-43 | 38.2 | (1.11;28) | 36-40 |
| Tarsus | 32.7 | (0.93;58) | 31-35 | 32.2 | (1.07;29) | 30-34 |

132

# TUFTED DUCK *Aythya fuligula*

**Identification**   Breeding ♂ unmistakable: compared with Scaup, ♂♂ have uniform blackish wing-coverts, sometimes minutely speckled near tip, and also distinguished by overall smaller size (see Biometrics). ♀♀ and immatures from other small diving ducks principally by head and bill shape, and smaller size (see Biometrics). Also from Ferruginous Duck by less obvious white undertail-coverts, and yellow not brown iris.

**Sexing**   All ages by cloacal examination, at any season. Plumage characters in adult as follows:

♂   Lesser- and median-coverts black with fine grey-white speckling towards tips. Mantle and scapulars black, speckled white. In breeding dress unmistakable, with black, glossed violet-purple head and breast, tuft on head and white sides of body.

♀   Lesser- and median-coverts black-brown, sometimes almost as black as ♂, and sometimes also with white spots as ♂. Scapulars plain dusky-black edged paler brown. In breeding plumage easily told from ♂ by duller blackish-brown head and neck, no head crest, and flanks brown, not white.

## Autumn/Winter

3   Tail feathers narrow, notched at tip with bare shafts projecting. Moult variable and slow, some feathers sometimes retained until spring. All wing-coverts narrow and tapered, dull sooty-brown (Fig). Tertials short often faded, dull brown to sooty-brown. Inner secondaries with slight bronze-green bloom.

1w (3/5)   Much variation in moult timing with tertials and their coverts often moulted, but then showing good contrast with worn feathering on rest of wing. Iris always duller than adult, more so in ♀.

Adult (4/6)   Wing-coverts dusky-black, often with greenish bloom, broad with gently rounded tips, but greater-coverts almost square-ended.

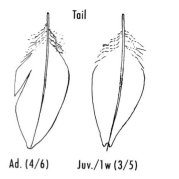

Tail

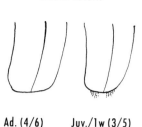

Greater-coverts

Ad. (4/6)    Juv./1w (3/5)        Ad. (4/6)    Juv./1w (3/5)

## Spring/Summer

All ages       As Autumn/Winter.

## Moult

3/5       Partial post-juvenile moult, variable and protracted, often suspended through winter, finishing spring/summer; confined to body, tertials and tail from August, complete or arrested November. ♀ slower than ♂.

Adult       Complete post-breeding moult commencing in March in ♀, involving body and tertials, March-May. Wings not until July or August, tail April-September. Further moults may occur but details and timing sketchy. Pre-breeding moult partial involving body, August-October. In ♂ moult begins later than in ♀, late May to early July. Flight feathers June-September, shed simultaneously, flightless for about 3-4 weeks. Pre-breeding moult partial, involving head and body, October-November.

**Biometrics**       (BWP).

| Wing | | | | | | | |
|---|---|---|---|---|---|---|---|
| *ad.* | ♂206 | (3.78;46) | 198-215 | ♀199 | (3.38;40) | 193-205 |
| *Juv.* | 202 | (4.20;37) | 194-210 | 196 | (3.55;36) | 185-203 |
| Bill | 39.9 | (1.41;66) | 37-44 | 38.6 | (1.27;73) | 36-41 |
| Tarsus | 35.5 | (0.80;40) | 34-37 | 34.7 | (1.16;40) | 32-37 |

134

# SCAUP *Aythya marila*

**Identification**  Bulk, broad bill and large size best indicators at all times (see Biometrics). Compared with Tufted Duck, ♂ ♂ have rough white spotting and reticulations on wing-coverts, scapulars and mantle, while ♀ has marked reticular pattern on scapulars. Juvenile ♀ in autumn and adult ♀ in non-breeding plumage harder to separate. Upperpart feathering on Scaup shows some white spots, ca. 1mm diameter, often joined into reticulations, while in Tufted any white spotting is very fine, 0.1mm, and separated. Tufted shows indication of tuft at back of crown, absent in Scaup.

**Sexing**  All ages by cloacal examination, at any season. Plumage characters as follows:

♂  In breeding plumage unmistakable: head, neck, breast and upper mantle glossy black, with green gloss on head; flanks and belly white; lower mantle and scapulars vermiculated pale grey or white with narrow black bars (Fig). In eclipse appearance closer to breeding ♂ than are eclipse ♂ ♂ of many others of genus. Juveniles can be difficult to sex by plumage; lesser- and median-coverts show fine whitish vermiculations and white spotting at tips, absent in juvenile ♀, except faintly on marginal coverts.

♀  Overall dull brownish, with clear white patches surrounding bill base. Lower mantle and scapulars dark brown with narrow white bars or flecks (Fig). Lesser- and median-coverts more-or-less uniform dull dark grey or grey-brown, sometimes with very fine white flecking along feather margin (Fig).

## Autumn/Winter

3  Tail feathers narrow, notched at tip and with bare shafts showing - moult variable but sometimes retained until spring of 2nd calendar year. Wing-coverts generally worn, narrow and pointed at tip, and dark brown (Fig). Tertials pointed and worn. Iris yellowish-brown. Secondaries of ♂ white with dull grey-brown tips.

1w (3/5)  Some juvenile tail feathers may be retained. Some tertials moulted in early spring, when contrast with rest of wing apparent. Iris yellowish-brown (♀) but in ♂ may already be bright yellow as adult.

Adult (4/6)  Wing-coverts broad and smooth; greater-coverts almost square-ended (Fig). Tertials round-tipped, blackish in ♀, finely vermiculated black-and-white in ♂. Secondaries of ♂ white with broad black tips with white reticulations; secondaries are brownish-black in ♀ and without reticulations.

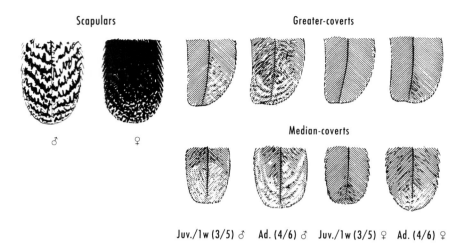

Scapulars  Greater-coverts

Median-coverts

♂  ♀

Juv./1w (3/5) ♂   Ad. (4/6) ♂   Juv./1w (3/5) ♀   Ad. (4/6) ♀

## Spring/Summer

All ages      As Autumn/Winter.

## Moult

3/5           Partial post-juvenile moult involving body, tertials and tail, but much variation; sometimes some or all of these retained partly or fully until spring, occasionally summer.

Adult         Complete post-breeding moult commencing in March in ♀ involves body and tertials. Wings not moulted until July or August, and tail between April and September. Further moults (partial) do occur but extent and timing uncertain. Pre-breeding moult partial involving body, August-November. In ♂ body moult starts later than in ♀, late May or early July followed by flight feathers; wing and tail feathers shed simultaneously, when birds become flightless for about 3-4 weeks, June-September.

**Geographical variation** Pigmentation of lower mantle and scapulars of adult ♂ increases from west to east. Pacific *A.m. mariloides* (extralimital) more boldly vermiculated black than nominate race. Birds from east Asia somewhat smaller.

136

**Biometrics**  Nominate *marila* (Salminen 1983).

| | | | | | | | |
|---|---|---|---|---|---|---|---|
| Wing | *ad.* ♂224 | (4;50) | 218-232 | ♀217 | (4;50) | 210-229 |
| | *juv.* 220 | (5;50) | 206-228 | 212 | (5;50) | 202-221 |
| Bill | 43.3 | (1.5;49) | 41-48 | 42.1 | (1.6;36) | 38-46 |

(BWP).

| | | | | | | | |
|---|---|---|---|---|---|---|---|
| Wing | *ad.* ♂227 | (4.09;45) | 219-237 | ♀217 | (3.78;35) | 211-225 |
| | *juv.* 220 | (5.33;56) | 208-229 | 213 | (4.55;34) | 202-222 |
| Bill | 44.0 | (1.31;46) | 41-47 | 42.9 | (1.31;36) | 40-45 |
| Tarsus | 39.9 | (1.26;56) | 38-42 | 38.6 | (1.08;45) | 37-41 |

# EIDER  *Somateria mollissima*

**Identification**  Adult ♂ unmistakable. ♀♀ and immatures from King Eider by more triangular head shape and by pattern of feathering at bill which extends into a point along sides of bill, just below nostril; also in adult ♀ by feather pattern on sides of breast (Fig).

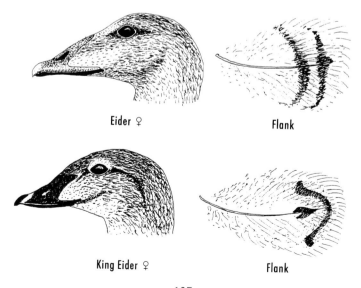

Eider ♀                    Flank

King Eider ♀                    Flank

| **Sexing** | All ages by cloacal examination, at any season. Plumage characters in adults as follows: |
|---|---|
| ♂ | Crown black. Nape and hindneck green. Breast and upperparts white. Underparts and rear upperparts black. |
| ♀ | Overall dark brown, uniformly barred black on body. |

## Autumn/Winter

| 3 | Tail feathers narrow, notched at tip and with bare shafts showing - retained until about September-November. Resembles adult ♀ but lacks distinct bars on upperparts, feathers being plain sepia with only narrow buff edges and a dull black bar subterminally. Lesser- and median-coverts dark sepia, faintly edged pale buff. Lacks white at tips of secondaries and greater-coverts. |
|---|---|
| 1w (3/5) | As above but variable amount of plumage replaced by adult-type feathers. Wing, back, rump, usually underparts, and tail retained until summer. |
| 2w ♂ (5/7) | Limited white on upper surface of wing, mainly confined to median- and some lesser-coverts. Inner secondaries decurved and pointed, basal halves varying between individuals from white to smoky-grey, grading to blackish towards tips. Much blackish suffusion and tips to feathers of upperparts, especially centre of back and rump. |
| 2w ♀ (5/7) | No proven plumage features to distinguish from adult though greater-coverts and secondaries probably with narrower white tips than older birds. Taking the wing as a whole this shows up as an incomplete double wing bar, whereas in adult all greater-coverts and secondaries tipped white forming complete double wing bar. |
| 3w ♂ (7/9) | Some darkish median- and lesser-coverts admixed with white adult-type, usually around leading edge of wing and at wrist. Two longest alula feathers black, as are small primary-coverts lying beneath them. Tertials and innermost secondaries usually white, mottled dull black at tips. |
| Adult ♂ (8/10) | Lesser- and median-coverts all white with no dark or blackish markings. Tertials wholly white. Generally some white tips to black secondaries and to primary- and greater-coverts. |
| Adult ♀ (6/8) | Secondaries and greater-coverts with broad white tips, forming complete double wing bar. |

138

## Spring/Summer

All ages      As Autumn/Winter.

## Moult

3      Partial post-juvenile moult. Amount of plumage and areas involved highly variable but usually involves head and some feathers of upperparts, sides and flanks, September, followed in October by partial pre-breeding moult involving more-or-less same areas. Wing, back, rump, and usually underparts and tail retained until summer. First full post-breeding moult is like that of adults except less complete and more prolonged, retaining some immature breeding plumage. 2nd pre-breeding moult complete; like adult but usually finished later, perhaps retention of some non-breeding feathers too.

Adult      Complete post-breeding moult into eclipse plumage, June-August. Starts with head, neck, and parts of body, mid-June or mid-July, followed by remainder of body and simultaneous shedding of wing and tail mid-July to late August. ♀ about 1 month later. Partial pre-breeding moult confined to head and parts of body; in ♂ mid-August-November, ♀ October-March.

**Geographical variation** Considerable. About 6 subspecies recognized. Variation concerns body size and development of frontal processes of bill, extent of feathering on sides of bill and colour (♂) and colour of breeding plumage of ♀. *S.m. faeroeensis* (Faroes) similar to nominate *mollissima*, but smaller and shorter-billed; narrow short frontal processes dark olive-grey while ♀ is also much darker brown. The arctic subspecies *borealis* (arctic North Atlantic, Iceland, Greenland, Baffin Island region of Canada) is smaller than nominate race (except those in Spitsbergen); feathering on bill rarely extends below level of nostril though Spitsbergen birds more like nominate *mollissima*.

**Biometrics** Nominate *mollissima* (Salminen 1983).

| | | | | | | |
|---|---|---|---|---|---|---|
| Wing *ad.* | ♂300 | (;18) | 294-307 | ♀290 | (;17) | 280-304 |
| *juv.* | 282 | (;50) | 263-293 | 273 | (;16) | 259-288 |
| Bill | 58.4 | (;18) | 55-64 | 55.0 | (;17) | 47-58 |

Adult (BWP).

| | | | | | | |
|---|---|---|---|---|---|---|
| Wing | ♂304 | (7.37;20) | 289-315 | ♀301 | (5.74;21) | 286-312 |
| Bill | 57.2 | (2.07;22) | 53-61 | 54.4 | (2.10;23) | 51-59 |
| Tarsus | 54.2 | (1.47;21) | 52-57 | 52.8 | (1.64;23) | 50-56 |

# KING EIDER *Somateria spectabilis*

**Identification** see Eider.

**Sexing**    All ages by cloacal examination, at any season. In eclipse adult ♀ has generally paler speculum than ♂ as well as broader buff edgings to back and rump feathers.

## Autumn/Winter

3    Tail feathers narrow, notched at tip and with bare shafts showing - probably retained September-November. Resembles adult ♀ but secondaries and greater-coverts edged cinnamon-buff instead of white.

1w (3/5)    As above but variable amount of contour feathers replaced with adult-type non-breeding plumage. Wing, back, rump, most of underparts, and tail retained until summer.

2w ♂ (5/7)    Limited white on upper surface of wing, usually confined to lesser- and median-coverts.

2w ♀ (5/7)    Greater-coverts and secondaries with narrow white tips. Taking the wing as a whole this shows up as an incomplete double wing bar.

3w ♂ (7/9)    White on upper surface of wing usually with darkish tips to lesser- or median-coverts.

Adult ♂ (8/10)    Median- and longer lesser-coverts white, without dark tips.

Adult ♀ (6/8)    Secondaries and greater-coverts with broad white tips, forming complete, broad double wing bar.

## Spring/Summer

All ages    As Autumn/Winter.

## Moult

3    Partial post-juvenile moult. Amount and areas involved highly variable but usually head and some feathers of upperparts, sides and flanks, September; followed in October by partial pre-breeding moult involving more-or-less same areas. Wing, back, rump, usually underparts and tail retained until summer. First complete moult is like that of adult except

less complete and more prolonged. 2nd pre-breeding moult complete; like adult but usually finished later.

Adult    Complete post-breeding moult, July-September, involving head, neck, and parts of body, followed by simultaneous moult of wing and tail between late July and late September. ♀ ♀ moult usually 1, sometimes 2 months later. Partial pre-breeding involving head and some body; in ♂ September-November, ♀ late November-January.

**Biometrics**    (Salminen 1983).

| | | | | | | | |
|---|---|---|---|---|---|---|---|
| Wing *ad.* | ♂278 | (;75) | 261-293 | ♀265 | (;50) | | 248-281 |
| *juv.* | 257 | (;50) | 242-270 | 249 | (;30) | | 230-275 |
| Bill | 31.6 | (;75) | 26-34 | 32.0 | (;50) | | 27-39 |

(BWP).

| | | | | | | |
|---|---|---|---|---|---|---|
| Wing *ad.* | ♂277 | (7.75;15) | 266-293 | 270 | (7.32;7) | 256-276 |
| Bill | 30.9 | (1.37;17) | 27-34 | 32.6 | (1.34;10) | 31-35 |
| Tarsus | 46.5 | (1.92;17) | 44-50 | 45.5 | (1.41;10) | 44-48 |

# LONG-TAILED DUCK *Clangula hyemalis*

**Identification**    Juvenile and ♀ may be confused with ♀ Harlequin Duck *Histrionicus histrionicus*, but latter has dark flanks (always whitish in Long-tailed) and has circular spot on ear-coverts, whereas Long-tailed has whitish streak behind eye.

**Sexing**    All ages by cloacal examination, at any season. Juveniles and immatures through autumn difficult if not impossible to sex on plumage, but variably timed acquisition by ♂ of broad pale band on bill best guide but see details below.

Note: plumages in this species are particularly complex and controversial and difficult to fit into conventional terminology as used in this guide. 3 or 4 plumages recognized: (1) transitional autumn plumage (September-November), (2) winter plumage (November-early April), (3) transitional summer (May-June), (4) full non-breeding (July-early September). Plumages 1 and 2 are very similar and can be thought of as full breeding plumages, but is replaced just before breeding period by special 'semi-eclipse' plumage.

## Autumn/Winter

3      Tail sepia with narrow off-white margin; outers paler, grey; bare shafts projecting beyond abraded square tips. Tertials short, narrow, blunt with greyish-brown fringe. Median- and lesser-coverts evenly dark olive-brown, narrow and with tapering fringed tips. From October or November ♂ recognized by presence of pink band on bill and by the first totally white scapulars.

1w (3/5)      Plumage strongly variable and in transitional period resembles adult autumn plumage. Wing-coverts and tertials as above; sometimes central tail feathers replaced, but outers retained.

2w ♂ (5/7)      Like adult ♂ but some may have retained median- or lesser-coverts, or tertials.

2w ♀ (5/7)      Like adult ♀ but some with scapulars broadly edged white instead of cinnamon; may also have retained wing-coverts or tertials.

Adult ♂ (6)      Outer tail feathers white, central pair black. Tertials long, broad and pointed with warm brown or dark chestnut outer web, inner web black. Median- and lesser-coverts black, broad and rounded.

Adult ♀ (6)      Tail feathers sepia, with white sides; outer feathers mainly white. Lesser- and median-coverts sepia, broadly edged cinnamon, broad and rounded. Tertials long, broad and pointed.

## Spring/Summer

1s (5)      Similar to 1st-winter but plumage highly variable. Ageing characteristics the same but some may have replaced central tail feathers.

Adult (6)      As Autumn/Winter.

**Moult**      Highly peculiar and complex. Involves 3 incomplete moults a year (up to 5 in juveniles before flight feathers dropped) involving 4 ornamental scapulars, some smaller scapulars, sides of head and neck. Plumage anterior to breast line (head, neck, upper mantle, chest and some smaller scapulars) and flanks moulted twice a year; posterior to breast line (remainder of back, rump, vent, belly, tail-coverts, wing and tail) once a year.

Partial post-juvenile moult September-December. Highly variable but usually involves some or most of body. Retarded birds retain almost all juvenile plumage until spring; advanced attain winter plumage, except for breast, belly, vent, and outer tail feathers. Partial spring moult into non-breeding plumage involving head, neck and body though usually less complete; mid-April to late May in ♂, April to early May in ♀. Partial summer moult from mid-July onwards involving further body feathers and flight feathers; last juvenile feathers, including tail and wing, lost in August. Subsequent moults as adult.

**Adult ♂**  Partial spring moult, April-May, involving head, neck and body. Summer partial moult, late June-September. Includes wing, tail, and feathers not replaced during spring moult; flight feathers shed simultaneously late July, completed late August; central tail feathers not before October. Partial autumn moult begins 2-4 weeks after end of summer moult involving head and body, mid-September to October. Partial winter moult involving only sides of head and neck, October to mid-November.

**Adult ♀**  Spring moult slightly later than ♂, April to early June, and involves more-or-less same plumages as ♂. Other moults as ♂ but most average slightly later.

**Biometrics**  (Salminen 1983).

| | | | | | | | |
|---|---|---|---|---|---|---|---|
| Wing | ad. | ♂224 | (5;95) | 210-236 | ♀211 | (4;42) | 202-220 |
| | juv. | 212 | (7;36) | 198-224 | 201 | (6;43) | 183-210 |
| Bill | | 27.2 | (1.1;97) | 24-30 | 25.9 | (1.0;44) | 24-29 |

(BWP).

| | | | | | | | |
|---|---|---|---|---|---|---|---|
| Wing | ad. | ♂228 | (4.60;45) | 218-241 | ♀212 | (4.35;20) | 204-220 |
| | juv. | 214 | (6.71;14) | 205-227 | 202 | (5.07;16) | 192-211 |
| Tail | ad. | 215 | (17.7;43) | 188-254 | 70.4 | (3.74;17) | 64-78 |
| | juv. | 66.1 | (3.57;14) | 61-74 | 56.8 | (3.83;17) | 51-64 |
| Bill | | 27.2 | (1.10;97) | 24-30 | 25.9 | (1.00;44) | 24-29 |
| Tarsus | | 35.8 | (1.23;70) | 34-38 | 34.1 | (1.18;36) | 32-37 |

# COMMON SCOTER *Melanitta nigra*

**Identification**  Distinguished in all plumages from Velvet Scoter by absence of white in wing, and from Surf Scoter by less massive bill with little or no feather extension down centre.

**Sexing**  All ages by cloacal examination, at any season. Plumage characters as follows:

♂  Contour feathers entirely glossy-black. Juveniles difficult to distinguish on plumage before any adult-type feathers appear - usually by November on head, neck, upperparts, upper breast, flanks and undertail.

♀  Black-brown above. Underparts glossy dark brown. Juveniles resemble adult ♀ plumage but are whiter on belly with grey-brown subterminal spot on feathers. Sexing only on plumage is not recommended until adult-type feathers apparent - late November.

## Autumn/Winter

3  Tail feathers narrow and notched at tip, bare shafts projecting. Browner overall than adult ♀, which otherwise resembles, with whitish underparts, and with small brown spots on belly and vent. Upper wing-coverts brown with paler margins.

1w (3/5)  Similar to adult but some juvenile feathers usually retained on belly. Tail unmoulted and very worn, though some birds may have replaced some or all of tail by January, normally April-May. Immature ♂ recognized by emergence of first adult-type black feathers (not dark brown).

2w (5/7)  Like adult but in ♂ black on head and belly less glossy than adult. In ♀ some immature feathers present on belly and sometimes upperparts until about midwinter.

Adult ♂ (6/8)  Head, neck and upperparts black, glossed violet-blue; glossed green on underparts.

Adult ♀ (6/8)  Belly evenly dark glossy brown.

## Spring/Summer

All ages  As Autumn/Winter. However, adult plumage less glossy (before moult) due to wear.

144

**Moult**

3/5 Partial post-juvenile moult is slow and protracted, starting September, involving head, lower flanks and sometimes a few tertials and scapulars. Partial pre-breeding moult of head, flanks and scapulars from November; partial replacement of some feathers on other parts of the body, completed by April-May. Tail usually replaced April-May, sometimes as early as January.

Adult Complete post-breeding moult starting with tail in late March to early May; some feathers on mantle, scapulars, chest April-May; remainder of body later, overlapping with flight feathers which are moulted simultaneously; birds become flightless for about 3-4 weeks, in ♂ mid-July to mid-September, ♀ September-October. Partial pre-breeding moult involving body, scapulars, tail and some mantle feathers; in ♂ September-December; ♀ about 1 month later. Belly in some ♀♀ not until February. There are two head and neck moults in ♀, October and April-May, but 3 in ♂, September-October, December-January, and April-May.

**Geographical variation** None within Europe. East Asiatic and North American populations (*M.n. americana*) similar to nominate race, but bill smaller and with more extensive yellow on upper mandible, including wholly yellow knob, which itself is wider and longer (♂).

**Biometrics** Nominate *nigra* (Salminen 1983).

| | | | | | | |
|---|---|---|---|---|---|---|
| Wing *ad.* | ♂234 | (4;40) | 227-243 | ♀227 | (5;40) | 215-234 |
| *juv.* | 224 | (4;34) | 216-234 | 218 | (6;28) | 207-227 |
| Bill | 47.2 | (1.6;40) | 44-51 | 43.5 | (1.7;40) | 40-47 |

(BWP).

| | | | | | | |
|---|---|---|---|---|---|---|
| Wing *ad.* | ♂234 | (4.73;91) | 224-247 | ♀226 | (4.78;31) | 216-239 |
| *juv.* | 226 | (5.68;30) | 217-241 | 218 | (4.25;30) | 206-226 |
| Bill | 47.5 | (1.68;47) | 43-51 | 43.4 | (1.19;32) | 41-46 |
| Tarsus | 45.4 | (1.28;69) | 43-48 | 43.5 | (1.35;55) | 41-46 |

# SURF SCOTER *Melanitta perspicillata*

**Identification**    Massive bill with feathering extending down centre towards nostrils distinguishes all ages from other scoters.

**Sexing**    All ages by cloacal examination, at any season. Plumage characters in adult as follows:

♂    Contour feathers black, slightly glossed. Forehead with white patch. Bill white, black and orange. Juveniles not sexable until about November when black feathers start to emerge, usually on head, neck, upperparts, upper breast, flanks, and undertail.

♀    Black-brown above. Sometimes a pale patch on nape.

## Autumn/Winter

3    Tail feathers notched at tip, bare shafts projecting. Resembles adult ♀ but feathers of underparts short and narrow, white with grey-brown centres giving spotted appearance. Lacks white on nape.

1w (3/5)    Similar to juvenile but in some birds tail may have been replaced by January (normally April-May). Body feathers with admixture of old juvenile feathers and new immature pre-breeding.

2w (5/7)    In ♂ black on head and belly with little gloss, while ♀ retain some juvenile feathers on belly and possibly upperparts until about midwinter.

Adult ♂ (6/8)    Black, slightly glossed, contour feathers. White patch on forecrown and large white patch of elongated hair-like feathers projecting in point downwards on nape.

Adult ♀ (6/8)    Rear crown and nape feathers elongated, with white shaft-streaks of varying width, forming fairly distinct pale patch on nape. Underparts more-or-less uniform dark brown.

## Spring/Summer

All ages    As Autumn/Winter.

## Moult

3/5    Partial post-juvenile moult from September, involving mostly head and body, sometimes also a few tertials and scapulars. Partial pre-breeding moult from November, head, body, tertials and scapulars; slow or arrested during midwinter. Upper mantle, chest, sides of breast, tail-coverts and tail from January, more usually April-May, though tail in some advanced birds replaced by January. Wing late June-October. Subsequent moults virtually as adult.

Adult        Complete post-breeding moult starting with tail in late March to early May; mantle, scapulars, chest and flanks April-May; rest of body later and interrupted by simultaneous shedding of flight feathers, mid-July to mid-September in ♂, September-October in ♀; birds flightless for about 3-4 weeks. Partial pre-breeding moult involving parts of body and tail feathers, September-December in ♂, one month later in ♀; overlaps to some degree with post-breeding body moult. Up to 3 active moults of head and neck in ♂ - September-October, December-January, and April-May.

**Biometrics**    (Salminen 1983).

| | | | | | | | | |
|---|---|---|---|---|---|---|---|---|
| Wing | *ad.* | ♂243 | (6;30) | 227-256 | ♀229 | (6;8) | 218-236 |
| | *juv.* | 236 | (9;7) | 225-248 | 218 | (4;5) | 214-223 |
| Bill | | 35.6 | (1.8;32) | 30-40 | 37.0 | (1.7;9) | 35-41 |

# VELVET SCOTER *Melanitta fusca*

**Identification**  White secondaries distinguish all plumages from other scoters.

**Sexing**        All ages by cloacal examination, at any season. Plumage characters as follows:

♂            In adults plumage entirely black except for small white crescent behind and below eye, white secondaries and tips to greater-coverts. Note that in non-breeding plumage black is less glossy and some scapular and flank feathers may be dark brown tipped olive-brown. Juveniles similar to adult ♀ plumage but belly feathers mostly grey-brown with white edges.

♀            Head and neck dark brown. Rest of upperparts, chest and flanks, dark brown with dark olive-brown edges. Feathers of lores and ear-coverts basally white, showing as 2 pale patches at side of head (in fresh plumage these may be obscured since newly moulted feathers have dark tips). Juvenile belly feathers white with grey-brown subterminal spot.

147

**Autumn/Winter**

3           Tail feathers narrow and notched at tip, bare shaft projecting. Browner overall than adult ♀, with whitish underparts and small brown spots on belly and vent. Upper wing-coverts brown with paler margins. Tips to greater-coverts with narrow pale spot, although this may often be absent altogether.

1w (3/5)    Similar to adult but some juvenile feathers usually retained on belly. Tail unmoulted and now very worn. Wing-coverts narrow and brown (Fig); some pale spots on outer, retained, greater-coverts, and white tips to new inners broken by black centre (Fig). Immature ♂ recognized by emergence of first adult-type black feathers (not dark brown) and also by reddish hue on sides of bill.

2w (5/7)    Like adult but black of ♂ less glossy on head and belly. Perhaps some juvenile feathers of belly and, sometimes, upperparts retained. White tips to greater-coverts with small black terminal spot (Fig). In ♀ some immature feathers present on belly and upperparts until about midwinter.

Adult ♂ (6/8)    Multicoloured bill. Glossy-black contour feathers and white eye-crescent. Greater-coverts tipped white. Remainder of wing-coverts uniformly black.

Adult ♀ (6/8)    Wing-coverts and tertials broad and rounded, blackish-brown or dark grey-brown (Fig). Belly feathers evenly dark brown or sometimes with whitish patches giving blotchy appearance.

### Greater-coverts

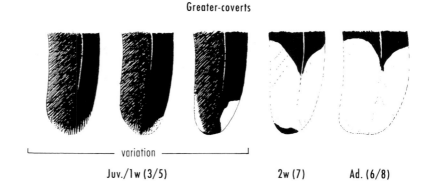

L———— variation ————⌐

Juv./1w (3/5)        2w (7)        Ad. (6/8)

**Spring/Summer**

All ages    As Autumn/Winter.

148

## Moult

3/5 Partial post-juvenile moult starting with head in November. By spring some have replaced some feathers of scapulars, flanks, tail-coverts, breast, or, occasionally, all of body. A few moult out all tail feathers. Remainder of juvenile feathers and flight feathers moulted in late summer, like adult; some belly feathers often not replaced before 2nd autumn.

Adult Post-breeding moult commencing with body feathers in April-May involves parts of flanks, scapulars and mantle; also tail but this does not always complete. In ♀, moult less extensive, perhaps just a few body feathers. Simultaneous shedding of flight feathers, July-August in ♂, August-October in ♀, when birds become flightless for about 3-4 weeks. Partial pre-breeding moult of head, body and sometimes tail October-November in ♂, somewhat later in ♀.

**Geographical variation** None within Europe. *M.f. stejnegeri* (East Asia) and *deglandi* (North America) have base of upper mandible higher and with purple-red shading to orange, rather than yellow-orange as in nominate race; knob extending over nostrils.

**Biometrics** Nominate *fusca* (Salminen 1983).

| | | | | | | | |
|---|---|---|---|---|---|---|---|
| Wing *ad.* | ♂279 | (6;66) | 267-293 | ♀263 | (4;40) | 239-263 |
| *juv.* | 266 | (6;26) | 252-278 | 251 | (6;24) | 233-263 |
| Bill | 44.9 | (1.8;66) | 40-48 | 41.1 | (1.5;48) | 39-45 |

(BWP).

| | | | | | | | |
|---|---|---|---|---|---|---|---|
| Wing *ad.* | ♂280 | (4.81;31) | 269-286 | ♀263 | (4.80;7) | 255-271 |
| *juv.* | 268 | (5.68;17) | 260-282 | 251 | (7.00;22) | 232-262 |
| Bill | 44.9 | (1.71;47) | 41-51 | 40.8 | (1.87;27) | 37-44 |
| Tarsus | 48.8 | (1.56;43) | 46-53 | 45.8 | (1.71;27) | 43-49 |

# GOLDENEYE *Bucephala clangula*

**Identification** From Barrow's Goldeneye *B. islandica* by small rounded white spot behind bill of ♂ (large white facial crescent in ♂ Barrow's). In ♀ ♀ and juveniles, greyish-brown body contrasts with darker brown head and white on median-coverts (lacking in Barrow's). Typically only a yellowish tip to mainly dark bill.

**Sexing**

All ages by cloacal examination, at any time. Biometrics and plumage characters as follows:

♂ Known age: Juvenile wing 202-224mm; Adult 209-231mm. In adults marginal upper wing-coverts black with white tips, rest of wing-coverts white. In juvenile mainly white greater-coverts (Fig).

♀ Known age: Juvenile wing 186-200mm; Adult 197-207mm. In adults white patch on wing smaller and confined to median-coverts; greater-coverts tipped black. Juvenile wing-coverts mainly dark grey to grey-brown with only tips pale or whitish (Fig).

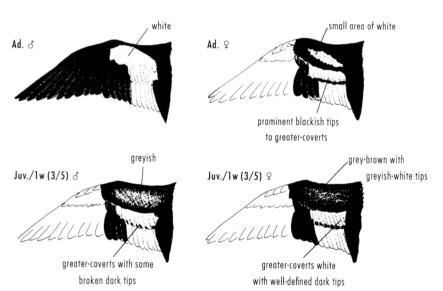

Ad. ♂ — white

Ad. ♀ — small area of white / prominent blackish tips to greater-coverts

Juv./1w (3/5) ♂ — greyish / greater-coverts with some broken dark tips

Juv./1w (3/5) ♀ — grey-brown with greyish-white tips / greater-coverts white with well-defined dark tips

**Autumn/Winter**

3 ♂ Tail feathers notched at tip, bare shafts showing. Greater-coverts white with some well-defined dark tips. Posterior median-coverts blackish-brown with pale tips, remainder grey.

| 3 ♀ | Tail feathers notched at tip, bare shafts showing. Greater-coverts white, with some brownish tips, forming incomplete bar. Posterior median-coverts dark brown with minute pale tips, remainder grey to grey-brown with greyish-white tips. |
| --- | --- |
| 1w (3/5) | Essentially as above; some adult feathers starting to appear on body, i.e. in ♂ black on head and white on sides of chest. Wing-coverts remain best guide. |
| 2w ♂ (5/7) | Greater-coverts white, some usually with faint dusky tips. Some black median-coverts. Feathers of crown short, brown bases showing through. |
| Adult ♂ (6/8) | Greater-coverts pure white, no dusky tips. |
| Adult ♀ (4/6) | Greater-coverts white, all with prominent dusky-black tips forming complete bar. Posterior median-coverts black with white tips, remainder white. |

### Greater-coverts

Juv./1w (3/5)          Ad. (4/6) ♀

## Spring/Summer

| All ages | As Autumn/Winter. |
| --- | --- |

## Moult

| 3/5 | Partial post-juvenile moult early autumn, September-October, involving head and body, but back and sides of breast not until midwinter; scapulars and tail prolonged and often retained into summer. Partial pre-breeding moult involving head and body from October, usually December. Sub- |
| --- | --- |

sequent moults similar to adult, but more prolonged and more variable in timing.

Adult    Complete post-breeding moult starting with head and body June or early July (♀ sometimes May). Simultaneous shedding of flight feathers renders bird flightless for 3-4 weeks mid-July to mid-September in ♂, about 3 weeks later in ♀; tail about the same time but more prolonged. Partial pre-breeding moult confined to head and body starts when flight feathers are full-grown, completes by late October in ♂, ♀ by early December.

**Biometrics**    Nominate *clangula* (Salminen 1983).

| | | | | | | | |
|---|---|---|---|---|---|---|---|
| Wing ad. | ♂222 | (4;35) | 214-231 | ♀202 | (3;22) | 195-209 |
| juv. | 212 | (3;21) | 207-217 | 196 | (5;17) | 188-203 |
| Bill | | 34.3 | (1.4;39) | 32-37 | 30.3 | (1.0;25) | 28-32 |

(BWP).

| | | | | | | | |
|---|---|---|---|---|---|---|---|
| Wing ad. | ♂220 | (5.33;31) | 209-231 | ♀203 | (2.57;24) | 197-207 |
| juv. | 214 | (6.06;21) | 202-224 | 195 | (3.62;16) | 186-200 |
| Bill | | 33.3 | (1.27;57) | 30-36 | 29.4 | (0.98;48) | 28-31 |
| Tarsus | | 38.8 | (0.95;40) | 37-41 | 35.1 | (1.06;46) | 33-37 |

# SMEW *Mergus albellus*

**Sexing**    All ages by cloacal examination, at any season. If age known then can be sexed on wing length with juvenile ♂ >186mm, ♀ <185mm. Otherwise juveniles very similar until adult-type feathers appear. Adults also separable on wing length, but plumage characters distinctive:

♂    Head white with black facial disc. In eclipse plumage very like ♀, but white tips to greater-coverts, especially inners, and secondaries broad.

♀    Head chestnut with white throat. White tips to greater-coverts, and secondaries narrow.

## Autumn/Winter

3 Tail feathers narrow, notched at tip and with bare shafts showing - retained until October, usually until November; sometimes retained until spring. Median and greater tertial-coverts white with grey-brown or dusky-brown margins and tips.

1w (3/5) As above but variable number of adult-type feathers showing. Wing-coverts retained.

2w ♂ (5/7) Scapulars white but with tips suffused grey.

Adult (4/6) Median and greater tertial-coverts white. ♂ showing pure white scapulars can be aged 3+ calendar years (6/8).

## Spring/Summer

All ages As Autumn/Winter.

## Moult

3 Partial post-juvenile moult involving head and body September-January, tail usually by late November. Partial pre-breeding moult overlaps with post-juvenile moult, usually finishing March-April.

Adult Complete post-breeding moult mid-June to September. Flight feathers simultaneously from mid-July to late September, flightless for about 1 month, ♀ somewhat later. Partial pre-breeding moult starts when wing fully grown September-November, later in ♀.

**Biometrics** (Salminen 1983).

| | | | | | | | |
|---|---|---|---|---|---|---|---|
| Wing *ad.* | ♂202 | (4;54) | 194-211 | ♀184 | (3;11) | 179-191 |
| *juv.* | 194 | (5;33) | 185-203 | 176 | (3;28) | 172-181 |
| Bill | 29.7 | (1.1;54) | 27-32 | 25.8 | (1.2;11) | 25-28 |

(BWP).

| | | | | | | | |
|---|---|---|---|---|---|---|---|
| Wing *ad.* | ♂202 | (2.68;25) | 197-208 | ♀184 | (2.63;10) | 181-189 |
| *juv.* | 196 | (3.50;20) | 188-202 | 177 | (3.78;24) | 171-184 |
| Bill | 29.6 | (1.11;46) | 27-32 | 26.8 | (1.01;33) | 25-29 |
| Tarsus | 34.0 | (1.02;46) | 31-36 | 30.6 | (0.72;33) | 29-32 |

# RED-BREASTED MERGANSER *Mergus serrator*

**Identification** Provided sex is known, no overlap in wing length with Goosander. Also, nostrils closer to eye than tip of bill, cf. Goosander in which nostrils lie about halfway between eye and bill tip. Feathering at sides of upper mandible has rounded outline and projects further forward than on sides or underneath of lower mandible, where in Goosander feathering on lower mandible projects as far or farther than that on upper mandible, coming to a point (Fig).

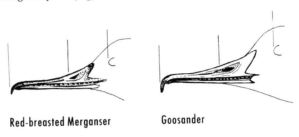

Red-breasted Merganser          Goosander

**Sexing**          All ages by cloacal examination, at any time. If age is known can be sexed on wing length; juvenile ♂ >225mm, ♀ <222mm. Adults also separable on wing length, but plumage characters distinctive:

♂          Head glossy-green with white collar. White upper wing-patch on median- and lesser-coverts. In eclipse plumage like ♀ but retains white upper wing-patch.

♀          Brown head and neck. Grey underparts. Lesser- and median-coverts grey-brown.

**Autumn/Winter**

3          Tail feathers narrow, notched at tip and with bare shafts showing - retained until December, often until spring. Greater tertial-coverts narrow dark grey to grey-black with worn tips. Inner greater-coverts narrow with rounded white tips, often with small darkish tip, outers dark grey. Tertials dark grey with black margins, worn and pointed (Fig). Grey- brown streak through face.

1w (3/5)          As above but variable amounts of plumage replaced by adult-type feathers. Some or all of tail, greater tertial-coverts and greater-coverts retained. ♀ usually without grey-brown streak through face. Tertials pale grey, outermost with clearly defined black margin (♂), less clearly defined in ♀ (Fig).

Adult (4/6)    Greater tertial-coverts round-ended; innermost white, outers black in ♂; all black in ♀. Greater-coverts broad and square-ended, outers black. Outermost tertials white, broad and rounded with clearly defined black outer margins (♂) or pale grey with darker margins (Fig).

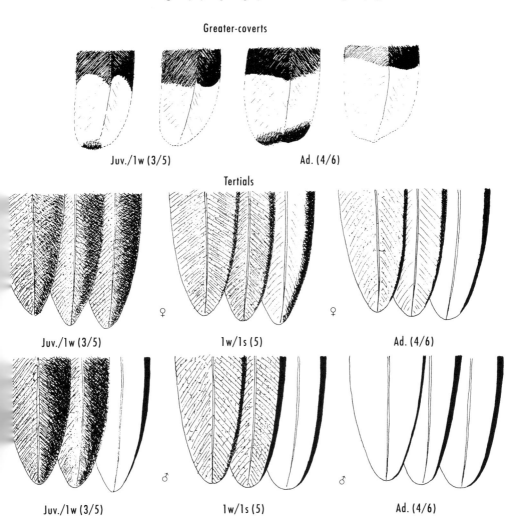

**Greater-coverts**

Juv./1w (3/5)                    Ad. (4/6)

**Tertials**

Juv./1w (3/5)          1w/1s (5)          Ad. (4/6)

Juv./1w (3/5)          1w/1s (5)          Ad. (4/6)

### Spring/Summer

All ages      As Autumn/Winter.

### Moult

3           Partial post-juvenile moult involving mostly head, neck, flanks and scapulars, some body feathers, October-January. Partial pre-breeding moult of head, body, tail and tertials, but highly variable, December onwards.

Adult      Complete post-breeding moult May-August with simultaneous moult of flight feathers mid-July to late August, about 1 month later in ♀; moult of tail often prolonged. Partial pre-breeding moult starts before completion of main moult, usually completed by December, January in ♀.

### Biometrics

(Salminen 1983).

| | | | | | | |
|---|---|---|---|---|---|---|
| Wing *ad.* | ♂248 | (5;39) | 238-259 | ♀229 | (6;14) | 221-240 |
| *juv.* | 236 | (4;10) | 230-240 | 218 | (3;16) | 214-223 |
| Bill | 59.6 | (1.9;40) | 54-63 | 54.1 | (1.7;20) | 50-57 |

(BWP).

| | | | | | | |
|---|---|---|---|---|---|---|
| Wing *ad.* | ♂247 | (5.18;32) | 235-255 | ♀228 | (6.54;14) | 216-239 |
| *juv.* | 236 | (6.13;12) | 226-245 | 217 | (4.18;14) | 208-221 |
| Bill | 59.2 | (2.16;46) | 56-64 | 52.1 | (2.21;28) | 48-55 |
| Tarsus | 47.0 | (1.47;45) | 44-50 | 42.7 | (1.51;28) | 40-45 |

# GOOSANDER *Mergus merganser*

**Identification**  See Red-breasted Merganser.

**Sexing**      All ages by cloacal examination, at any season. If age known, then can be sexed on wing length with juvenile ♂ >262mm, ♀ <261mm. Otherwise, juveniles very similar until adult-type feathers appear, though outer median-coverts of ♂ paler than inner ones, forming palish patch, not present in ♀. Also tertials longer and outer ones more obviously pale greyish. Adults separable on wing length, but plumage characters distinctive:

♂           Head and neck glossy-green. Underparts creamy-white with salmon hue. Large white upper wing-patch on lesser- and median-coverts. In eclipse plumage like ♀ but retains white wing-patch on lesser- and median-coverts.

♀     Brown head and neck. Grey underparts. Lesser- and median-coverts greyish.

## Autumn/Winter

3     Tail feathers narrow, notched at tip and with bare shafts showing - retained until about October-November, less commonly thereafter. Greater-coverts narrow, white tips with indistinct and inconsistent grey-brown spots or patches at tips, though these never form a complete bar along the row of greater-coverts (Fig). Tertials narrow and pointed.

1w (3/5)     As above but variable amounts of plumage replaced by adult-type body feathers. Greater-coverts and tertials retained.

Adult (4/6)     Forewing of ♂ white or white-pink, as are median- and lesser-coverts. Greater-coverts of ♀ broad, square-ended, with well-defined dark spot at tips of most, forming complete dark bar along bottom edge of coverts (Fig).

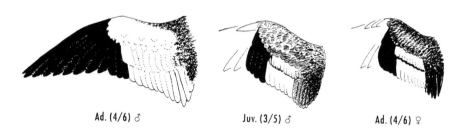

Ad. (4/6) ♂     Juv. (3/5) ♂     Ad. (4/6) ♀

Greater-coverts

Juv./1w (3/5)     Ad. (4/6) ♀

157

**Spring/Summer**

All ages          As Autumn/Winter.

**Moult**

3                 Partial post-juvenile moult involving head, body and tail, September-
                  November. Partial pre-breeding moult from November involving some
                  feathers of body and tertials, latter usually replaced in spring or even
                  summer; may suspend/arrest moult December-March.

Adult             Complete post-breeding moult mid-June to September. Flight feathers
                  simultaneously from mid-July to late September, flightless for about 1
                  month, ♀ somewhat later. Back, rump and underparts suspended during
                  wing moult, therefore only moulted once a year. Partial pre-breeding
                  moult starts when wing is fully grown September-November, later in ♀.

**Biometrics**    Nominate *merganser* (Salminen 1983).

| | | | | | | |
|---|---|---|---|---|---|---|
| Wing *ad.* | ♂286 | (5;44) | 279-299 | ♀261 | (5;18) | 251-273 |
| *juv.* | 272 | (5;10) | 262-280 | 251 | (5;7) | 244-258 |
| Bill | 56.4 | (2.2;47) | 52-60 | 48.8 | (1.6;21) | 46-53 |

(BWP).

| | | | | | | |
|---|---|---|---|---|---|---|
| Wing *ad.* | ♂285 | (5.23;30) | 275-295 | ♀262 | (4.04;23) | 255-270 |
| *juv.* | 275 | (5.76;27) | 263-291 | 252 | (4.96;20) | 242-260 |
| Bill | 55.8 | (1.92;58) | 52-60 | 48.7 | (1.83;43) | 44-52 |
| Tarsus | 51.7 | (1.40;58) | 49-55 | 47.4 | (1.76;43) | 44-51 |

# RUDDY DUCK *Oxyura jamaicensis*

**Identification**  From White-headed Duck *Oxyura leucocephala* by shorter bill: 37-
                  41mm, compared to 43-48mm.

**Sexing**        All ages by cloacal examination, at any season. Plumage characters in
                  adults as follows:

♂                 All-white or whitish cheeks.

158

♀           No white in cheeks. Well-defined dark cheek stripe.

## Autumn/Winter

3           Tail feathers narrow, notched at tip and with bare shafts showing -
            moulted mainly November-February, some retained until spring. Feathers
            of underparts and flanks narrow, rounded, grey-brown with paler tips
            giving distinctly scaly appearance to breast and belly. Flanks barred.

1w (3/5)    Much of the body replaced by adult-type feathers, but tail and belly
            feathers retained. Axillaries taper to a point.

Adult (4/6) Breast and belly grey-brown, broadly tipped silver-white. Undertail-
            coverts white. Axillaries broad and rounded at tip.

## Spring/Summer

All ages    As Autumn/Winter.

## Moult

3           Partial post-juvenile moult involving head and body August-October, and
            tail mainly between November and February. Subsequent moults thought
            to be much as adult.

Adult       Complete post-breeding moult starting with simultaneous moult of flight
            feathers, late July and August in ♂, late August in ♀, followed by head,
            body and tail. A further complete moult takes place in March-April.

**Biometrics**   Full-grown. Nominate *jamaicensis* (B. Hughes, unpubl.data).

| | | | | | | |
|---|---|---|---|---|---|---|
| Wing | ♂151 | (5.53;55) | 144-186 | ♀147 | (4.73;59) | 125-158 |
| Tarsus | 34.1 | (1.14;55) | 31-38 | 33.3 | (1.27;59) | 30-37 |

Full-grown (BWP).

| | | | | | | |
|---|---|---|---|---|---|---|
| Wing | ♂149 | (1.97;7) | 142-154 | ♀143 | (3.61;7) | 135-149 |
| Bill | 40.4 | (0.64;8) | 38-41 | 38.4 | (1.00;7) | 37-40 |
| Tarsus | 33.5 | (1.29;8) | 32-38 | 31.5 | (1.38;7) | 30-33 |

# Eagles and Hawks *Accipitridae*

Small to large hawk or hawk-like birds of prey. Bodies variable, slender in small hawks (e.g. *Accipiter*) to bulky in large eagles. Wings short, broad and rounded (*Accipiter*), long and rounded in others. Plumages variable, often brown, dark grey, or black above, lighter and often barred or streaked below.

## Feather structure
Primaries = 11 (p7 p7/8 or p8 longest, p11 vestigial)
Secondaries = 13-17 (mostly 13-14 in *Circus, Milvus, Accipiter* and *Buteo*).
Tail = 12

## Sexes
Mostly similar in plumage but *Circus* and *Accipiter* especially sexually dimorphic.
♀♀ larger than ♂♂.

## Moult
Strategy: in large species (e.g. *Aquila*) wing is often in continuous moult, full cycle not being completed in one year: primaries replaced serially descendantly, irregularly in adults, in sequential order in juveniles. Secondaries ascendant and descendant. In small species primaries replaced descendantly; secondaries ascendant and descendant. Often suspends. Tail centrifugal.
Sequence: primaries irregular in large species. Descendant in smaller species. Secondaries serially descendantly from 2 centres starting at s1 and s5, and both descendantly and ascendantly from 3rd centre on longer inner secondaries.
Frequency: in large birds almost continuous; suspended in wing and tail. In smaller species once annually; SC.
Timing: Throughout year in large species. Spring-summer finishing late autumn.

## HONEY BUZZARD *Pernis apivorus*

**Identification**  Lores and base of bill densely covered with small scale-like feathers, diagnostic among diurnal birds of prey; also adults have 3 diagnostic dark underwing bands across wing and 3-4 on tail.

**Sexing**  Adults only.

♂  Head mainly light grey. Upperparts normally grey-brown or brown-grey. Secondaries and rectrices with broad light brown area between subterminal band and next proximal band (Fig).

♀ Head sometimes grey but only around the eye and on the lores; normally head same colour as rest of the body. Ground colour of upperparts brown, not grey. Secondaries and rectrices with narrower light brown area between subterminal band and next proximal band (Fig).

## Autumn

1w (3/5)  All plumage fresh and all flight feathers uniform, showing no age differences. No moult. Secondaries dark with even but sparse darker barring. Tail dark with many bars and barring unevenly distributed (Fig). Outer primaries dark across the entire notched and emarginated portion. Iris dark brown. Cere yellow.

2w (5)  Old juvenile outer primaries retained, contrasting in pattern and wear with new adult-type inners; replaced primaries also 10-20mm longer than corresponding juvenile ones. Some tail feathers also retained.

Adult (6)  Wing shows 2 age-groups of primaries (see Moult); new inners have same pattern as old retained outer primaries. Secondaries relatively pale with wide black subterminal bar. Tail paler with bars fewer and more clearly defined (Fig). Outer primaries with just the tip black. Iris yellow. Cere black or dark blue-grey.

**Tail**

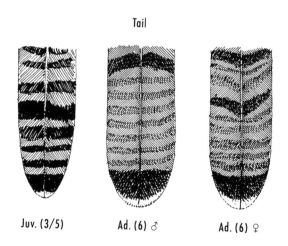

Juv. (3/5)          Ad. (6) ♂          Ad. (6) ♀

## Spring/Summer

1s (5)  Similar to 1st-winter but the plumage is more worn, perhaps with single new body feathers sporadically distributed. Iris lighter, grey- yellow and with darkening cere.

Adult (6)      As Autumn adult but the plumage is newly moulted and fresh.

Note: It is doubtful whether 1st-summer birds return to northern breeding grounds, most, seemingly, staying in the wintering quarters.

## Moult

5              Complete post-juvenile moult from about April or May of 2nd calendar year, confined to body, some wing-coverts; inner 2 or 3 primaries, and perhaps some tail feathers moulted later, June onwards. Advanced birds may almost complete body moult before migration, though wings rarely progress beyond 3 new inner primaries before suspending. Moult resumed and completed in winter quarters, December-January.

Adult          Complete post-breeding moult starting in ♀ ♀ with body in June, later in ♂ ♂ by a few weeks. Flight feathers from end of July but only 2 or 3 inner primaries replaced and some tail feathers before suspending moult, just prior to migration; some (males) do not start wing or tail moult until in winter quarters. Moult resumed/started on wintering grounds and completed by January or February.

**Geographical variation** None is known. However, plumage variation is great; typical adults being distinctly barred below on both wings and body. Others may be almost uniformly dark brown on body and underwing-coverts but with typical barring on flight feathers. Very pale cream-coloured birds are frequent, showing no barring at all on body but, again, with typical bars on tail and wing feathers.

**Biometrics**   (BWP).

| | | | | | | | |
|---|---|---|---|---|---|---|---|
| Wing | ad. ♂ | 404 | (12.4;22) | 386-434 | ♀ 415 | (11.5;21) | 398-439 |
| | juv. | 383 | (13.3;14) | 360-401 | 390 | (9.94;8) | 376-404 |
| Tail | ad. | 251 | (10.2;23) | 232-270 | 259 | (7.94;22) | 245-273 |
| | juv. | 235 | (9.22;12) | 214-246 | 238 | (14.7;9) | 218-265 |
| Bill | | 20.5 | (1.12;22) | 19-23 | 21.3 | (0.86;22) | 19-23 |
| Tarsus | | 51.9 | (1.45;16) | 49-55 | 53.6 | (2.33;18) | 48-57 |

# BLACK KITE *Milvus migrans*

**Identification**  From Red Kite by olive-brown, warm brown or red-brown tail. Fork of tail <45mm; total tail length <290mm. In Red Kite fork >55mm, tail > 300mm.

**Sexing**  Plumage similar. Wing length may separate extremes but much overlap (see Biometrics).

♂  Wing <445mm.

♀  Wing >470mm.

## Autumn/Winter

1w (3/5)  Overall plumage condition fresh and without signs of moult. Neck, mantle and back feathers with well-defined whitish tips. Upper wing-coverts and underwing-coverts brown with conspicuous pale rufous or pale buff tips. Greater-coverts brown with conspicuous pale tips forming bar across wings. Belly feathers with wide pale shaft-streaks. Crown feathers brown tipped pale (Fig).

2w (5)  Ageing possible up to completion of moult: admixed new adult-type feathers and old and worn juvenile ones, most prominent on upper wing-coverts and primary-coverts -latter corresponding to unmoulted primaries. Once moult is completed birds can only be aged as 4.

Adult (6)  Can only be recognized during moulting period by both new and old feathers having the same markings; most evident on primary-coverts (renewed as corresponding primaries) where the old unmoulted feathers have the same appearance as the new ones (they lack the juvenile pale and worn tips). After moult (late autumn) birds can only be aged as 4.

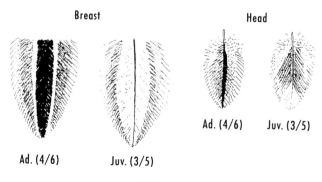

Breast

Ad. (4/6)          Juv. (3/5)

Head

Ad. (4/6)          Juv. (3/5)

163

## Spring/Summer

1s (5)     In early spring (before moult commences) flight feathers uniformly worn and same age. Body feathers and wing-coverts mostly juvenile-type, though tips worn and faded to off-white. Late spring and summer; wing in active moult (as in adult) but ageable up to point just before last primary is moulted by old and pale-tipped (juvenile) corresponding primary-coverts.

Adult (6)     As Autumn/Winter.

## Moult

5     Partial moult of small body and head feathers in winter quarters, probably January onwards. Complete post-juvenile (or post-breeding) moult of wings and tail starting in April or May, completed by September or October. Primary moult is rarely completed before start of migration; normally suspends with outer 4-5 primaries unmoulted and completed in winter quarters.

Adult     Complete post-breeding moult starting in ♀♀ with inner primaries during incubation, April-May, somewhat later in ♂; completed by September or October. Body and secondaries moulted later. Most (all?) suspend wing moult before onset of migration with up to 4-5 primaries, the middle secondaries, and some body feathers unmoulted. Moult resumed and completed in winter quarters.

**Geographical variation** Involves mostly size and colour: *M. m. lineatus* (east Palearctic to China) larger than nominate *migrans;* browner on head and on underparts with pale buff lower belly and undertail-coverts, not rufous; white at base of primaries more extensive. Wing of *aegyptius* shorter than nominate form with more deeply forked tail; plumage overall paler and more rufous; bill in adult yellow, juvenile black. 3 other subspecies recognized.

**Biometrics** Adult. Nominate *migrans* (BWP).

| | | | | | | |
|---|---|---|---|---|---|---|
| Wing | ♂447 | (10.5;15) | 426-463 | ♀464 | (12.4;8) | 448-482 |
| Tail | 256 | (10.1;15) | 239-279 | 268 | (10.7;8) | 254-282 |
| Bill | 25.1 | (1.42;14) | 23.4-28.5 | 27.0 | (1.01;7) | 25.8-28.6 |
| Tarsus | 55.2 | (2.90;12) | 51-60 | 55.9 | (2.12;7) | 53-60 |
| Claw | 20.5 | (1.27;8) | 19.4-23.0 | 22.2 | (0.98;6) | 21.0-23.7 |

# RED KITE *Milvus milvus*

**Identification**   From Black Kite by tail which is rust coloured (light rust-yellow-brown in worn plumage), longer, >300mm, and with deeper fork, >55mm. In Black Kite tail length <290mm, fork <45mm.

**Sexing**   Plumage similar. Weight may be a useful indicator of sex but for reliable determination use in conjunction with biometrics. Many birds cannot be confidently sexed on external characters due to size overlap.

♂         <950g.

♀         >1230g.

## Autumn/Winter

1w (3/5)   Overall plumage condition fresh and without signs of moult. Upper wing-coverts tipped pale rufous in fresh plumage becoming white later. Primary-coverts with narrow pale tips. Breast feathers with narrow blackish-brown shaft-streak, pale margin and off-white tip (Fig).

2w (5)    Identifiable until moult is completed by admixed adult-type and worn juvenile feathers on upper wing-coverts, latter still showing white but ragged tips. Primary-coverts corresponding to unmoulted primaries with worn off-white tips. New adult-type breast feathers with much broader dark central streak, bordered darker rufous-buff. Once moult is completed birds can only be aged as 4.

Adult (6)   Can only be identified during moulting period by the similarity of new and old feathers; most evident on primary-coverts (renewed in the same order as corresponding primaries) where the old unmoulted feathers lack the juvenile white and worn tips. After moult (late autumn) birds can only be aged as 4.

**Breast**

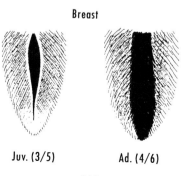

Juv. (3/5)         Ad. (4/6)

## Spring/Summer

**1s (5)**  Some are still in almost full juvenile plumage in spring (April), while others have renewed majority of body feathers and some wing-coverts. However, latter show admixture of new adult-type and old juvenile pale-tipped and worn feathers. Flight feathers uniformly worn and of one age. In later part of spring and summer wing is in active moult (as in adult) but ageable up to point just before last primary is dropped, by old and pale-tipped (juvenile) corresponding primary-covert.

**Adult (6)**  As Autumn/Winter.

## Moult

**3**  Some birds undergo partial post-juvenile moult of body feathers in October; others may still be in juvenile plumage in April of 2nd calendar year!

**5**  Complete post-juvenile (or post-breeding) moult of wings and tail starting late March or May and completed usually by September-October. Some evidence of suspended moult exists but information scanty.

**Adult**  Complete post-breeding moult starting with inner primaries in ♀ (April) May, slightly later in ♂, and usually completed by September-October. Body, tail and secondaries moult later. Suspended moult is commonly recorded, both in migratory and resident populations.

**Geographical variation** *M.m. fasciicauda* (Cape Verde Islands) is smaller than nominate *milvus*, with shorter and more rounded wing (p1 200mm shorter than longest, in *milvus* 218-251mm; wing 434-482mm, av. 453, sexes combined); fork less deep (30-50mm from t1 to t6). Upperparts with less pronounced feather margins and underparts duller rufous with narrower shaft-streaks. Plumage variation great, some resembling nominate form while others very like Black Kite.

**Biometrics**  Nominate *milvus* (BWP).

| | | | | | | |
|---|---|---|---|---|---|---|
| Wing *ad.* ♂490 | (25.8;7) | 448-532 | ♀503 | (16.2;20) | 478-535 |
| Tail | 327 | (22.6;5) | 301-351 | 343 | (16.2;15) | 314-376 |
| Bill | 27.4 | (1.07;7) | 25.9-29.2 | 27.7 | (1.03;19) | 25.6-29.5 |
| Tarsus | 53.2 | (1.50;4 | 52-55 | 52.8 | (0.83;9) | 51-54 |
| Claw | 22.2 | (0.75;3) | 21.3-22.6 | 21.9 | (1.03;9) | 20.6-23.8 |
| Wing *juv.* | 477 | (22.1;10) | 436-505 (sexes combined). | | | |

# MARSH HARRIER *Circus aeruginosus*

**Identification** Underside of tail unbarred (sometimes outer tail in subadult ♂ ♂ can show bars). Upper body and wing-coverts uniformly dark brown. Emargination on 2nd outermost primary (p9) shallow and falls around tips of longest primary-coverts (Fig).

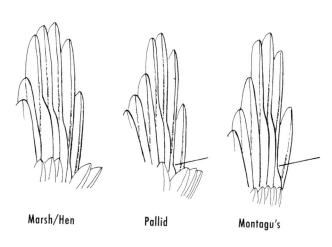

Marsh/Hen        Pallid        Montagu's

**Sexing**       Most immatures cannot reliably be sexed on plumage features until their first complete moult, but most can be using combination of wing and weight:

♂       Wing <390mm; Weight <670g.

♀       Wing >410mm; Weight >700g.

## Autumn/Winter

1w (3/5)       Plumage fresh and no traces of moult. Tail black-brown with rufous markings on inner web of outermost pair of feathers. Scapulars, upper wing- and tail-coverts usually chocolate-brown with narrow rufous tips.

2w (5/7) ♂       Birds in moult may retain old outer brown juvenile tail feathers or primaries, which differ markedly from the new light secondaries and the new white-and-black outer primaries. Completely moulted birds like adult except upperparts darker and lacking obvious contrast, though with grey tinge on wing and tail. Outer underwing-coverts rufous-brown. Black on long outermost primaries reaches up as far as under primary-coverts. Tail with broad dark subterminal band, rufous on inner web (sometimes barred). Streaked rust-coloured head with bold dark ear-coverts. Belly dark reddish-brown with lighter breast patch and throat. Uppertail-coverts rufous.

3w (7/9) ♂     Like 2nd-winter but showing clearer contrast between pale and dark areas on upperparts; secondaries and inner primaries and tail above are clearly grey, latter most often with a clear darker subterminal spot on inner webs and with rufous tinge. Head rufous-yellow and variably streaked, but lacking dark ear-coverts. Throat and breast variable, from chestnut with rufous-buff feather edges to pale cream or white with broad brown shaft-streaks, becoming strongly rufous on belly.

Adult (8/10)     Tail feathers uniform light grey with white edges to inner ♂ web. Uppertail-coverts rufous anteriorly, becoming grey-white towards rear. Distal portion of outer primaries black extending only over the 'fingered' portion of the wing. Outer underwing-coverts white.

Adult (4/6) ♀     Tail dark brown (sometimes with greyish tinge) with rufous mottling on inner webs of all but central pair of feathers. Under primary-coverts uniform, without pale tips.

## Spring/Summer

1s (5)     Similar to 1st-winter but plumage faded and worn but with some light feathers coming through on underparts. Birds with some replaced tail feathers can be sexed: ♂ feathers being greyish with dark subterminal markings and rufous inner webs, and ♀♀ having dark brown feathers with rufous mottling on inner webs.

2s (7) ♂     As 2nd-winter though plumage tone and condition somewhat faded and worn.

3s (9) ♂     As 3rd-winter though plumage tone and condition somewhat faded and worn.

Adult (10) ♂     As adult winter though plumage tone and condition somewhat faded and worn.

Adult (6) ♀     Like adult winter but plumage tone and condition comparatively faded and worn.

## Moult

5

Partial post-juvenile moult confined to head, some body and occasionally some tail feathers during the winter. Flight feathers later, at much the same time as adult, May-July, usually completed by September or October.

Adult

Complete post-breeding moult; ♀♀ starting before ♂♂ by about 1 month, and usually dropping first primary at start of egg-laying, May-June. Tail moult begins shortly after start of primaries, then followed by secondaries. Secondaries moult from at least 3 centres; some remain unmoulted by the end of the moulting period, October (November).

**Geographical variation** Within Europe very slight. *C.a. harterti* (Northwestern Africa and possibly southern Spain): ♂ is darker on the back and scapulars and paler below than nominate *aeruginosus* (western & central Eurasia), while ♀♀ have paler, whiter head, nape and breast. About 6 other races recognized.

**Biometrics**      Nominate *aeruginosus* (Nieboer 1973).

| | | | | | ♀ | | |
|---|---|---|---|---|---|---|---|
| Wing | ad. ♂ | 393 | (12.7;16) | 372-418 | 413 | (6.9;17) | 404-426 |
| | juv. | 389 | (9.2;31) | 370-407 | 410 | (8.8;28) | 391-427 |
| Tail | ad. | 224 | (6.58;21) | 213-237 | 239 | (7.17;17) | 225-252 |
| | juv. | 225 | (6.51;32) | 207-238 | 236 | (6.52;27) | 222-251 |
| Bill | | 21.6 | (0.71;19) | 20.2-23.0 | 25.2 | (1.02;13) | 23.8-27.0 |
| Tarsus | | 84.7 | (3.12;21) | 79-92 | 88.4 | (2.06;17) | 86-93 |

**References**      Nieboer (1973).


# HEN HARRIER *Circus cyaneus*

**Identification** Primaries 6-9 emarginated (see fig. under Marsh Harrier). Uppertail-coverts white, though sometimes with dark shaft-streaks or spots.

**Sexing**

♂

Wing <340mm; Iris grey or grey-brown.*

169

♀                Wing >360mm; Iris dark brown.*

                  * Large nestlings can be sexed by iris colour.


## Autumn/Winter

1w (3/5) ♂    Undersides of primaries and underwing-coverts dark brown with rufous tips; former with inner webs slightly barred, outers plain. Greater-coverts brown with rufous tips. Central tail feathers dark brown and lightly barred. Iris yellowish-grey or greyish-yellow.

1w (3/5) ♀    Like 1st-winter ♂ but iris dark brown.

2w (5/7) ♂    Upperparts blue-grey tinged brown but some brown juvenile feathers may be retained, often on crown, neck, or breast. Possibly some old greater-coverts with worn rufous tips retained. Other birds moult all the brown juvenile feathers and cannot be distinguished from older ♂ ♂, although the colour of the upperparts tends to be a duller grey than on some adult ♂ ♂, which usually have a light silver- or blue-grey back and mantle. Such birds, if not showing characteristics of adult (6) ♂, cannot be aged beyond 2+ calendar years (4).

2w (5/7) ♀    Like adult ♀ but old juvenile underwing primary-coverts with complete or partially worn pale tips and uniform outer web. Iris honey-brown with some golden flecks.

Adult (6) ♂    Birds in wing moult, or in suspended moult, with old feathers showing the same markings and pattern as the new ones: especially evident on greater-coverts, but also on crown, neck or breast. Birds which have completed moult cannot reliably be aged beyond 2+ calendar years (4). Wing <340mm.

Adult (6) ♀    Birds in wing moult with old underwing primary-coverts lacking juvenile-type rufous tips and showing grey-brown and barred outer web, as in the new feathers, can be aged accordingly. After completion of moult birds cannot reliably be aged beyond 2+ calendar years (4). However, as the eye colour becomes progressively more yellow until completely so at 6+ years, age can be assessed appropriately (at least 8). Wing >350mm.


## Spring/Summer

All ages    The plumage is not altered very much in the winter period. Generally the plumage condition becomes slightly more worn by the spring/summer and the colours somewhat faded. Ageing and sexing criteria can be defined by the same principles as during Autumn/Winter.

**Moult**

5
Only very partial moult of body feathers during winter, sometimes an odd tail feather too. Generally moult is less extensive in this species at this time than other harrier spp. First complete moult as in adult.

Adult
Complete post-breeding moult starting in ♀♀ with wing at start of egg-laying, usually April or May, ♂♂ a few weeks later, late May or June; continuous until completion, usually September or October (November). Secondaries moult from 3 centres, and odd old ones, as well as corresponding greater-coverts, sometimes remain unmoulted.

**Geographical variation** In Palearctic, clinally larger from west to east. Within Europe differences small. Two further races in the Americas.

**Biometrics**  Nominate *cyaneus* (Nieboer 1973).

| | | | | | | | |
|---|---|---|---|---|---|---|---|
| Wing | *ad.* ♂ | 338 | (7.8;18) | 323-351 | ♀ 376 | (8.2;25) | 358-392 |
| | *juv.* | 331 | (5.2;19) | 323-338 | 370 | (10.5;28) | 355-385 |
| Tail | *ad.* | 213 | (6.42;17) | 202-224 | 243 | (8.71;24) | 222-255 |
| | *juv.* | 219 | (6.00;11) | 209-228 | 243 | (7.95;21) | 221-254 |
| Bill | | 15.5 | (0.52;18) | 14.6-16.6 | 18.0 | (7.24;25) | 16.8-19.8 |
| Tarsus | | 69.3 | (2.14;13) | 65-72 | 74.5 | (2.09;20) | 70-79 |

**References**   Nieboer (1973), Picozzi (1981*a*).


# GOSHAWK *Accipiter gentilis*

**Identification** Large *Accipiter* resembling Sparrowhawk: from that species by longer wing, >285mm and tail >195mm: in Sparrowhawk wing <260mm, tail <190mm.

**Sexing**
Birds decrease in size from north to south and from east to west. Sexing birds by wing is reliable and within regional populations there is no overlap in biometrics: however, between countries there may be significant size variation and overlap. The following table indicates the

division in wing length between sexes of birds across Europe. Measurements for adults only (data from BWP).

| Holland | ♂<325mm. | ♀>335mm. |
|---|---|---|
| Sweden | <342 | >344 |
| Denmark | <335 | >342 |
| Germany (East) | <327 | >340 |
| Switzerland | <330 | >345 |
| Czechoslovakia | <329 | >342 |
| Hungary | <322 | >335 |
| Yugoslavia | <323 | >340 |

Juveniles can be significantly smaller and this should be borne in mind when attempting to determine sex using biometrics. For example for Dutch birds of all ages: ♂ wing <330mm, tail <245mm; ♀ wing > 285mm, tail >244mm.

On upperparts ♂ ♂ older than 2 years are generally cleaner blue-grey, while ♀ ♀ are browner.

Nestlings over 14 days old can be sexed reliably. The tarsus and feet of ♀ are considerably thicker and larger respectively. The difference is easy to see when both sexes are together in the same nest to give direct comparison. Single chicks or single-sexed broods require more experience.

## Autumn/Winter

1w (3/5)    Upperparts brown with rufous edges and tips. Underparts white or pale cinnamon with broad black-brown longitudinal streaks or drops (Fig). Iris pale green-grey or green-yellow.

2w (5/7)    Upperparts grey-brown admixed with some old brown and worn juvenile feathers, mainly on the lesser-coverts, rump and back. Underparts cross-barred - the breast feathers each with 3-4 broad grey-brown horizontal bars, often tinged rufous. Iris yellow or orange-yellow.

Adult (6/8)    Upperparts uniform slate-brown or brown, sometimes feathers narrowly tipped white. Breast feathers finely cross-barred brown-grey, each feather with 4 or 5 horizontal bars, the distal bar being narrower than the others and bow-shaped (Fig). Iris orange-yellow, orange-red or red.

172

**Breast**

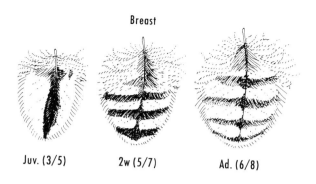

Juv. (3/5)    2w (5/7)    Ad. (6/8)

## Spring/Summer

1s (5)　　　Similar to 1st-winter but rufous edges to upperparts often worn away leaving faded and abraded feathers, particularly evident on rump and upper wing-coverts. Usually in wing and tail moult by late April or May onwards.

2s (7)　　　Like 2nd-winter but from April onwards in active wing moult (later in ♂♂ by about 2 weeks). By end of summer most of the body feathers replaced with adult-type, though worn juvenile feathers should still be in evidence, especially on rump or upper wing-coverts.

Adult (8)　　As Autumn/Winter but in active wing moult from April onwards.

## Moult

5　　　Complete post-juvenile moult from April or May onwards of 2nd calendar year: the moult starts slightly later than in adults but progress is similar and usually finishes September; mostly complete but some juvenile feathers retained on the rump and upper wing-coverts. Subsequent moult and timing as in adult.

Adult　　　Complete post-breeding moult from April. ♀♀ start wing moult during incubation in April or May, followed by body moult in June. Primaries lost rapidly in first month, thereafter at a much slower rate; primaries replaced in irregular and asymmetrical fashion. Secondaries usually moult from 3 centres, from s1 and s5 in ascendant mode, but descendant and ascendant from s13. Sometimes moult of tail and secondaries suspended and completed early the following year.

**Geographical variation** Marked: involves mostly size and colour. Populations in the north and east are paler, and in the south and west smaller and darker.

*A.g. buteoides* (northern Sweden, Finland and northern Russia) is largest and palest race (♂ av. wing 323mm, ♀ 369mm), less heavily barred on underparts and more conspicuous white supercilium. Nominate *gentilis* (most of west Palearctic) large and pale in Scandinavia (♂ av. wing 327mm, ♀ 367mm); running southwards in Europe head becomes darker, supercilium less conspicuous and barring on underparts denser; running eastwards upperparts become greyer, and barring on underparts paler and narrower. *A.g. arrigonii* (Corsica and Sardinia) smaller and darker than nominate form (♂ av. wing 300mm, ♀ 345mm). About 4–6 more subspecies recognized from Asia and North America .

**Biometrics**     Nominate *gentilis* - Holland (BWP).

| | | | | | | | |
|---|---|---|---|---|---|---|---|
| Wing | *ad.* ♂ | 312 | (5.85;13) | 306-323 | ♀ 353 | (9.20;13) | 336-366 |
| | *juv.* | 308 | (7.60;19) | 292-322 | 338 | (20.9;16) | 289-367 |
| Bill | *ad.* | 22.0 | (0.90;11) | 20.5-23.7 | 25.0 | (1.18;12) | 22.0-26.1 |
| | *juv.* | 21.5 | (0.74;18) | 20.1-22.7 | 24.9 | (1.44;15) | 22.0-27.3 |
| Tarsus | | 74.4 | (1.05;11) | 72-76 | 84.0 | (2.14;8) | 81-87 |
| Claw | | 27.5 | (0.94;14) | 25.5-28.9 | 32.5 | (1.47;11) | 30.1-35.3 |

# SPARROWHAWK *Accipiter nisus*

**Sexing**     Nestlings can be sexed according to tarsus measurements once leg is fully grown (>day 17).

♂     Wing 188-212mm; Bill 10-12mm; Tarsus 51-55mm. Nestling tarsus is full-grown by day 18. Note however that same-brood nestlings can be sexed from day 9 on thickness of tarsus and size of foot even though these are still growing.

♀     Wing 222-256mm; Bill 13-15mm; Tarsus 59-64mm. Nestling tarsus is full-grown by day 18.

Above measurements are for nominate *nisus.*

### Autumn/Winter

3     Upperparts dark brown fringed chestnut especially around nape: not uniform blue-grey or slate-brown as in adult. Breast with bold heart-

shaped brown markings at tips of feathers. Iris grey-olive.

1w (3/5)      Similar to juvenile but some new feathers on nape and back lack the chestnut fringes.

2w (5/7)      Retained juvenile feathers (dark brown fringed chestnut) present, usually on lesser-coverts and on the rump. Sometimes an old tail feather or secondary retained. Some birds may have moulted these feathers out and thus resemble adult. However, retained feathers with contrasting chestnut-buff tips visible with careful inspection. Iris lemon to bright yellow, sometimes with slight orange tinge in ♂♂.

Adult (6/8)   Upperparts uniform blue-grey or slate-brown, according to sex. Barring on breast usually narrow. Iris usually bright yellow, but in some ♂♂ may be bright orange to orange-red; in some birds 5+ years old, iris has black rim and black flecks!

## Spring/Summer

3             As for Autumn/Winter.

1s (5)        As 1st-winter but many have some blue-grey or slate-brown adult-type feathers on the upperparts, increasing as moult progresses.

2s (7)        In early spring some, but not all individuals may still show some fawn or chestnut fringes to brownish feathering on upper rump, or lesser-coverts; some may also show a retained juvenile feather in the tail or inner secondaries. Old feather with buff tip usually retained between tertials and scapulars. Iris bright yellow sometimes with slight orange tinge.

Adult (8)     As Autumn/Winter.

## Moult

5             No evidence of moult before late April of 2nd calendar year. Moult starts at much the same time as adult, and is a little faster.

Adult         Complete post-breeding moult starting in May (♀) or June (♂). Usually completed by September, sometimes early October. Primaries moulted in conventional manner but secondaries have up to three centres of simultaneous moult.

**Geographical variation** Clinal: involving increased size and decreasing colour saturation from west to east. Within Europe only slight; *wolterstorffi*

(Corsica, Sardinia) is the smallest of all the races (wing ♂ av. 186mm, ♀ 219mm), somewhat darker than nominate *nisus*, more heavily and broadly barred below. 4 other subspecies recognized.

**Biometrics**   Nominate *nisus* (Newton 1986).

Wing   ad. ♂200.8 (4.60;18)   193-211   ♀236.9 (5.23;43)   226-251
     juv.  198.9 (3.71;41)   192-209     234.1 (4.59;98)   223-246


(BWP).

| | | | | | | |
|---|---|---|---|---|---|---|
| Wing | ad. ♂203 | (4.25;35) | 196-212 | ♀240 | (3.96;28) | 231-256 |
| | juv. 201 | (4.10;50) | 192-209 | 239 | (4.41;65) | 228-256 |
| Tail | ad. 149 | (3.66;25) | 143-156 | 180 | (3.26;27) | 169-184 |
| | juv. 152 | (3.17;52) | 142-157 | 180 | (3.99;46) | 171-187 |
| Bill | 11.4 | (0.38;23) | 10.5-12.1 | 14.4 | (0.51;25) | 13.3-15.5 |
| Tarsus | 53.4 | (1.07;24) | 51-55 | 61.0 | (1.07;19) | 59-64 |

**References**   Baker (1979), Marquiss (1980), Newton & Marquiss (1982), Newton (1986).


# BUZZARD *Buteo buteo*

**Identification**   Plumage variation in this species is considerable. From Honey Buzzard by brown, yellow-brown, grey or white eye, not orange or yellow; tarsus longer, >65mm; tail shorter, <235mm. From Long-legged Buzzard *B. rufinus* by shorter wing, <420mm, and tarsus, <85mm. From Rough-legged Buzzard *B. lagopus* by shorter wing (some overlap) <420mm and by greater barred area of tail - in Rough-legged the basal half of the upper tail is greyish or white with 2-4 clear-cut and rather broad black bars on distal half; Buzzard tail is more uniform with a greater number of narrow dark bars, rarely showing bold black subterminal bands. From pale-phase Booted Eagle *Hieraaetus pennatus* by dark patch on underwing at carpal joint.

**Sexing**   No plumage difference. ♂ ♂ average smaller than ♀ ♀, but considerable overlap in measurements. Advisable only to sex those birds falling well outside known overlap zone (see Biometrics for details).

1w (3/5)   Plumage fresh or evenly worn. Upper wing-coverts brown with pale tips or edges. Streaks on belly and/or breast longitudinal. Dark trailing edge on underwing diffuse. Subterminal tail band narrow and similar in width to other tail bars (Fig). Iris light grey-brown.

2w (5/7)   General plumage pattern similar to adult, except breast and/or belly markings with admixture of longitudinal streaks and adult-type cross-barring. Juvenile outer primaries retained, number variable - usually two or three outermost (p8-p10), but can be up to five; some secondaries also retained, s4 and s7-s8 or s8-s9. Old juvenile secondaries can be identified by narrower and more pointed appearance; they are also marginally shorter (10-15mm) than newly moulted secondaries. Sometimes juvenile outer tail feathers (t6) retained and comparatively worn and faded, and also with narrower subterminal band (Fig). Iris greyish-brown. Some may complete wing moult in 2nd calendar year; such birds are similar to adults and can only be reliably aged on eye colour.

3w (7/9)   A small percentage of birds retain the outermost primary (p10) which appears very faded and abraded. In such birds (as distinct from juveniles) primaries will show 3 generations of feather - new inner primary wave (3rd generation), middle to outer primary wave (2nd generation) and the old retained juvenile outer primary (1st generation).

Adult (8/10)   Wing-coverts uniform dark brown usually with some old and pale feathers admixed. Dark markings on breast and/or belly horizontally cross-barred. Body feathers with admixture of new and old. Flight feathers with regular, consistent markings. Iris dark brown.

**Tail**

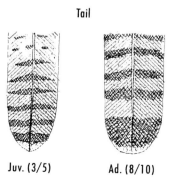

Juv. (3/5)          Ad. (8/10)

**Spring/Summer**

1s (5)        Like 1st-winter but light feather edges to upper wing-coverts very worn and often absent.

2s (7)        Similar to 2nd-winter and usually in active wing moult - showing 3 generations of primaries. Degree of primary replacement variable but normally outermost 1 or 2 primaries still juvenile and comparatively worn - usually last primary replaced September-October.

Adult (8)        As for Autumn/Winter except birds in active moult.

**Moult**

3/5        In nominate *buteo*, complete post-juvenile moult starting with body November-December. Wing and tail slightly earlier than adult, (March) April-May, and usually suspends or arrests September leaving up to 5, more normally 2-4, old outer primaries; several secondaries also retained, distributed throughout tract; rarely, wing completely renewed by September. Tail normally complete but sometimes outermost (t6) retained. In 'Steppe Buzzard' *B.b. vulpinus*, partial body moult in winter quarters, January-February. Wing and tail moult from April-May of 2nd calendar year in summer quarters, suspending or arresting moult before migration. Moult resumed and completed in winter quarters, usually by February-March, though a small percentage of immatures retain outer primary.

7        Timing of moult apparently as in adult. Wing moult resumes at the point where moult was arrested so that old juvenile outer primaries are replaced during this moult; a second cycle of moult begins at same time at p1 so that there are 3 generations of primaries present in the early part of the moulting period. Occasionally outermost primary (p10) retained and not moulted out until 4th calendar year.

Adult        In nominate *buteo* complete post-breeding moult starting with body feathers in March-April. Wings follow (serially descendant) in April or May, but timing highly variable. ♀ starts earlier than ♂ by a few weeks; primaries moulted in irregular and asymmetrical fashion - starts in descendant manner but quickly jumps to older feathers in the moulting cycle; secondaries may have up to 4 or even 5 active moult centres. Completed September-October. In Steppe Buzzard wing and tail moult begins late May or June (July); only a few inner primaries and secondaries are replaced before migration at which point moult is suspended and resumed in winter quarters.

**Geographical variation** In size slight; individual variation considerable and complex, especially in nominate *buteo* group. 3 distinct groups generally recognized - nominate *buteo* group, comprising several subspecies (Europe); *vulpinus* group - 2 subspecies (Eurasia, north and east of nominate *buteo*), and *japonicus* group - 2 to 4 races (eastern Palearctic, east of *vulpinus*). In all groups 2 or more colour phases represented, but the predominant colouration is brown above in *buteo* and *japonicus* groups, and rufous throughout in *vulpinus*. In *japonicus* group the underparts are paler and more uniform than in *buteo* group.

**Biometrics**   Nominate *buteo* (BWP).

| | | | | | | | |
|---|---|---|---|---|---|---|---|
| Wing | *ad.* ♂387 | (10.1;42) | 368-404 | ♀398 | (11.9;39) | 374-419 |
| | *juv.* 381 | (11.6;33) | 359-405 | 396 | (10.5;38) | 375-422 |
| Bill | *ad.* 21.6 | (0.75;41) | 20.0-23.6 | 23.0 | (1.37;37) | 19.3-24.9 |
| | *juv.* 21.1 | (1.27;32) | 18.0-23.5 | 22.8 | (0.88;37) | 20.7-25.3 |
| Tarsus | 75 | (2.6;26) | 69-80 | 76.5 | (2.8;27) | 72-83 |
| Claw | 22.3 | (1.01;24) | 20.6-24.9 | 23.4 | (1.14;25) | 21.5-25.4 |

*B.b. vulpinus* and *menetriesi.*

| | | | | | | |
|---|---|---|---|---|---|---|
| Wing | ♂360 | (11.6;27) | 341-387 | ♀375 | (13.3;21) | 352-400 |
| Tarsus | 72 | (1.8;14) | 70-75 | 74 | (3.0;13) | 71-79 |
| Claw | 20.8 | (0.96;22) | 18.7-22.2 | 22.8 | (1.67;16) | 20.0-25.1 |

# GOLDEN EAGLE *Aquila chrysaetos*

**Identification**   Tarsus feathered down to the toes. Hind claw long and powerful (> 43mm, longer than any other *Aquila*).

## Sexing

♂   Wing <632mm (adult), <623mm (juveniles & immatures).

♀   Wing >635mm (adult), >624mm (juveniles & immatures).

## Autumn/Winter

1w (3/5)   Lesser-coverts dark brown, evenly worn or fresh. Wing and tail feathers fresh and all of same age with no noticeable difference in wear. Outer primary and secondaries relatively narrow and pointed (Fig). On underwing bases of primaries and secondaries white, contrasting sharply with blackish distal portions and brown underwing-coverts.

2w (5/7)  Greater- and median-coverts mainly worn and faded (juvenile retained); lesser-coverts show old, faded juvenile feathers admixed with new and darker ones. Inner 3-4 (5) primaries new and contrasting with old juvenile outers. Secondaries mostly old but perhaps inner 1 or 2 replaced (s15,s16), sometimes also s1 - these new secondaries are broader and blunter and have wide dark broken markings (or bands) on the tips (Fig). Tail 1st generation (juvenile) - white or mottled pale brown base with sharply defined dark brown terminal bar - but often with replaced, new and contrasting central pair which have broader dark brown terminal band, contrasting less sharply with white base.

3w (7/9)  Juvenile median- and lesser-coverts mostly replaced by darker 2nd generation feathers. Greater-coverts, however, show admixture of old juvenile and new feathers (corresponding to old and replaced secondaries). Primaries 4/5 - 6/7 replaced leaving retained juvenile outers; some birds may show new moulting wave at p1 (3rd generation). Secondaries also replaced but most show at least two centres with old retained juvenile feathers (s3-s4, s7- s11). Up to half of the tail replaced by 2nd generation feathers - white with wide dark terminal band.

4w (9/11)  Wings retain 1-3, brown, very worn and abraded juvenile outer primaries (p8-p10); also 1 or more old, 1st generation secondaries in the region of s8-s10. Primaries 1-4 replaced (3rd generation) as are p7-(p8/9). New secondaries include s4 and some others either side of the few retained faded pale brown juvenile feathers. Tail with 2nd/3rd generation feathers which appear rather juvenile-like , but 3rd generation feathers have signs of cross-ribbing.

5w (11/13)  Many can be identified by moult pattern: all primaries and secondaries now at least 2nd generation with (p9)-p10 recently replaced; also new wave (3rd generation) in (p4)p5-p6. In some another new wave at p1/p2 (4th generation) started, along with s1-s2, s5 and s8-s10. The bases to primaries and perhaps some secondaries may still show significant traces of white on the underside, usually cross-barred.

Adult (14/16)  No white at base of primaries, secondaries or on tail.

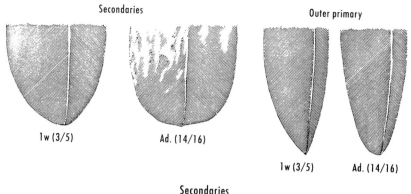

Secondaries

Outer primary

1w (3/5)        Ad. (14/16)

1w (3/5)        Ad. (14/16)

Secondaries

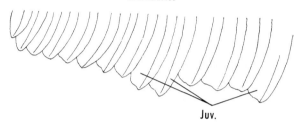

Juv.

Longer tips of retained juvenile secondaries in
right wing of immature bird.

## Spring/Summer

All ages        Moult is suspended during the winter period; only changes are feathers
becoming slightly paler due to fading or wear. Age descriptions, therefore,
are as for Autumn/Winter.

## Moult

3/5        Complete post-juvenile moult commencing March- April of 2nd calendar
year with body; wing and tail moult from June and suspend (some arrest)
October-November (December) at which point only the inner 3-4 (5)
primaries are renewed and 2 or 3 inner secondaries, together with 2 or
3 tail feathers.

7        In March of 3rd calendar year moult is resumed from the point at which
it was interrupted; primaries continue from p4-p5 (p6), descendantly to
p6-p7 (p8) and again suspend; a few birds show new moulting centre

from p1 (3rd generation); secondary moult now from 2 centres. Up to half of the tail replaced by end of the moulting period, September-October.

9    During 3rd moult (4th calendar year) all remaining juvenile wing feathers may be moulted though it is more usual for 1 or 2 outer primaries, and a similar number of secondaries (s8-s10), to be retained. 2nd serially descendant primary wave begins at p1, so there are usually 2 active centres of primary moult at this stage. Tail fully renewed showing 2nd generation feathers.

Adult    Complete post-breeding moult commencing March-April; flight feathers suspended or arrested September-October. Primaries apparently replaced in irregular sequence; secondaries with up to 3 centres of moult; tail also irregular. Old eagles have several different moulting waves in their wings at the same time allowing them to renew all their feathers over 2 years; young eagles, because of their protracted moult and the fact that most only have one moulting wave at any one time, can take up to four years to lose the juvenile remiges.

**Geographical variation** Slight, involving mostly size and colour: wing length decreases from north to south in Eurasia, and populations in southern parts of range in Eurasia are darker. Nominate *chrysaetos* palest race with pale, elongated nape feathers longer and broader than other races. Birds from central Europe darker brown than northern birds; Scottish birds somewhat intermediate. There is also considerable individual variation in plumage and, to a lesser extent, size.

**Biometrics**    Nominate *chrysaetos* (BWP).

| | | | | | | | |
|---|---|---|---|---|---|---|---|
| Wing | ad. ♂ | 591 | (17.7;13) | 565-630 | ♀ 661 | (13.8;13) | 637-685 |
| | juv. | 601 | (12.4;28) | 572-621 | 648 | (14.0;22) | 625-686 |
| Bill | ad. | 41.4 | (1.83;9) | 39.5-45.3 | 45.3 | (2.84;14) | 40.1-50.3 |
| | juv. | 40.2 | (1.17;29) | 37.0-42.4 | 44.3 | (2.03;22) | 41.0-47.9 |
| Tarsus | | 103 | (5.6;34) | 94-114 | 109 | (6.0;30) | 97-122 |
| Claw | | 47.4 | (0.92;9) | 46.4-49.2 | 52.5 | (2.57;14) | 47.8-57.0 |

**References**    Edelstam (1984).

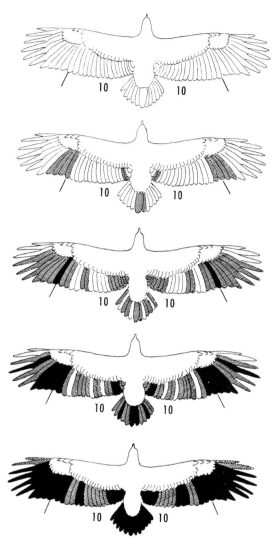

Juvenile: 1st generation feathers

Immature 2w (5/7). 2nd generation feathers at 2 moult centres in wing.

Immature 3w (7/9). 3rd generation feathers (p1) may start. Up to 3 or 4 moult centres present in wing.

Immature 4w (9/11). 3rd generation feathers present in at least 3 moult centres. Some juvenile secondaries and outer primaries still present.

Immature 5w (11/13). 3rd generation feathers in 3 centres. 2nd generation now replaced all juvenile feathers. Sometimes new wave (4th generation) starts from p1.

# Falcons *Falconidae*

Small to medium-sized diurnal birds of prey. Body slender. Wings long and pointed. Plumage variable but often grey or chestnut above and rufous or buff below, often with small black streaks or spots above and below. Colour morphs found in some.

### Feather structure
Primaries = 11 (p9 longest, p11 vestigial)
Secondaries = 11-14
Tail = 12

### Sexes
Mostly similar in plumage. ♀ ♀ larger than ♂ ♂.

### Moult
Strategy: primaries and secondaries descendant and ascendant. Often suspends. Tail centrifugal.
Sequence: primaries starting from p4. Secondaries from s4.
Frequency: once annually; SC.
Timing: spring-early summer finishing autumn-winter; later in migratory species.

# KESTREL *Falco tinnunculus*

**Identification** Immatures and ♀♀ might be confused with Red-footed Falcon *F. vespertinus* but that species has a more pointed wing, p8 9-16mm shorter than p9, p7 26-38, and pale claws; in Kestrel p8 1-5mm, p7 16-24, and dark claws. Lesser Kestrel *F. naumanni* also has a more pointed wing, p8 5-10mm, p7 17-22mm, and pale claws.

## Sexing

Juvenile & 1w

Some juveniles cannot be sexed with certainty early on but all should be sexable by December having acquired some adult feathers. However, at any age, those with grey heads or grey rumps, uppertail-coverts and tail are ♂♂.

Adult

♂      Crown and tail bluish-grey.

♀      Crown and tail pale chestnut.

## Autumn/Winter

3

Plumage evenly fresh. Breast and belly with broad central streak (Fig). Dark centres to flank feathers indented only on one side (Fig). Broad buff-coloured tips to primaries, broadest on innermost primaries (3-5mm), narrowest on outermost. Primary-coverts narrow with pale tips (Fig).

1w (3/5)

As 3 though some body feathers replaced by adult-type feathers.

2w ♀ (5)

After moult much the same as adult. Some advanced individuals are impossible to separate from adult; such birds cannot be aged beyond 2+ calendar years (4). However, some may still have some old feathers on flanks. Beware of confusion with advanced 1st-winter birds which can also show adult-type flank feathers - check inner primary tips. 2nd-winter birds will have newly grown primaries and thus small pale tips (<2mm wide).

2w ♂ (5)

Some old worn feathers should be present on back and mantle. One or two old barred tertials may be found, contrasting sharply with fresh and

185

uniform adult feathers. Advanced individuals or birds having completed moult cannot be aged beyond 2+ calendar years (4).

Adult ♀ (4/6)   Breast and belly feathers with thin central streaks or spots (Fig). Dark markings to flanks indented on both sides of the feather (Fig). Buff primary tips (innermost group) <2mm wide.

Adult ♂ (4/6)   Upperparts chestnut-red with black subterminal dots or arrowheads. Tail dove-grey with black subterminal band.

Adult ♂ ♀ (6)   Birds in active wing moult with both old and new feathers of the same adult-type pattern; perhaps best seen in primary-coverts (Fig). After moult cannot be aged beyond 2+ calendar years (see above).

**Spring/Summer**

1s (5)   Dark centres to flank feathers indented on one side only (Fig). Some advanced birds will have some adult-type feathers too. Buff tips to inner primaries 3-5mm wide. Primary-coverts with pale indents (Fig).

Adult (6)   As for Autumn/Winter.

**Moult**

3/5   Partial post-juvenile moult, mostly confined to body, begins after fledging, and is almost continuous, but highly variable between individuals, until adult-type plumage is attained. Wing and tail moulted in June-July of 2nd calendar year, normally completed by October-November.

Adult   Complete post-breeding moult starting with wing and tail about mid-May in ♀ or late May in ♂. Primaries moulted ascendantly and descendantly from the moult centre at p4 or p5 and usually follows sequence 4/5-6-3-7-8/2-9-1-10. Secondaries start with s4 or s5 and moult ascendantly and descendantly. Body moult at same time or just after start of flight feathers. Wing, tail and body moult usually completed by early September or October (November).

**Geographical variation** Slight: involves size and colour. All 5 other west Palearctic races (Africa and Atlantic islands) smaller than nominate *tinnunculus*. Within Europe differences negligible. About 5 other subspecies recognized in Africa and Asia.

186

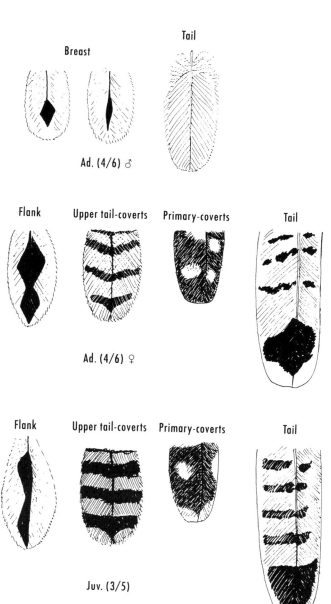

Breast

Tail

Ad. (4/6) ♂

Breast

Flank

Upper tail-coverts

Primary-coverts

Tail

Ad. (4/6) ♀

Breast

Flank

Upper tail-coverts

Primary-coverts

Tail

Juv. (3/5)

**Biometrics**  Nominate *tinnunculus* (BWP).

| | | | | | | | |
|---|---|---|---|---|---|---|---|
| Wing | *ad.* ♂ | 246 | (6.30;37) | 233-258 | ♀256 | (8.48;45) | 229-272 |
| | *juv.* | 240 | (12.42;32) | 204-258 | 249 | (13.93;61) | 210-270 |
| Tail | *ad.* | 163 | (5.60;37) | 150-175 | 171 | (6.88;44) | 154-183 |
| | *juv.* | 157 | (12.18;32) | 123-173 | 165 | (12.53;62) | 129-189 |
| Bill | | 13.9 | (0.61;36) | 12.9-15.5 | 15.0 | (0.85;43) | 13.1-17.0 |
| Tarsus | | 39.6 | (0.93;36) | 37-41 | 39.6 | (1.20;37) | 36-42 |

**References** Baker (1979), Village, Marquiss & Cook (1980).

# MERLIN *Falco columbarius*

## Sexing

Nestlings          Length of outermost (10th) primary or wing length versus weight (Fig).

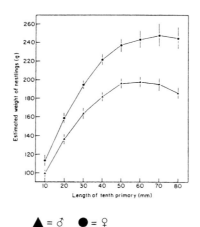

▲ = ♂   ● = ♀

(after Picozzi 1981)

Full-grown

♂          Wing <206mm; Weight <200g. Bright yellow legs.

♀                Wing >209mm; Weight >200g. Greenish-yellow legs.

(Icelandic race *F. c. subaesalon* slightly longer-winged: ♂ <211mm; ♀ >223mm).

## Autumn/Winter

3 ♂          Plumage similar to ♀. Dark brown upperparts heavily fringed rufous. Median-, greater- and primary-coverts and tertials with broad rufous barring. Broad light bands on tail grey (often proximal half only).

3 ♀          Plumage similar to adult ♀ but more heavily fringed rufous on upperparts. Rufous barring on median-, greater- and primary-coverts and tertials much more pronounced - very often absent or only faintly barred on inner webs in adult. Broad light bands on tail fringed rufous.

1w (5)      Similar to juvenile though fringes not as rufous due to wear.

2w (5/7) ♂   Appearance very like adult ♂ but leading edge of largest outermost alula feathers white, sometimes tinged rufous and with white blotches on inner web; pattern not unlike 3/5 but differently coloured (Fig).

3w (7) ♂      Like adult ♂ but ageable until old large alula feather is moulted (Fig). Thereafter birds cannot be aged beyond 3+ calendar years (see below).

Adult (6/8) ♂  Uniform slate-grey upperparts, with conspicuous black shaft-streaks. Large alula feather uniform or with dark grey leading edge (Fig).

Adult (6) ♀    Only ageable during active moult: both new and old tail feathers are adult-type (Fig). After moult cannot be aged beyond 2+ calendar years (see below).

Adult (4/6) ♀  Greyish-brown to dark brown mantle and back with faint rufous fringes. Wing-coverts and tertials more-or-less uniform grey-brown, sometimes with rufous spots or barring, more especially on inner webs. Pale tail-barring rufous and smaller than young birds.

189

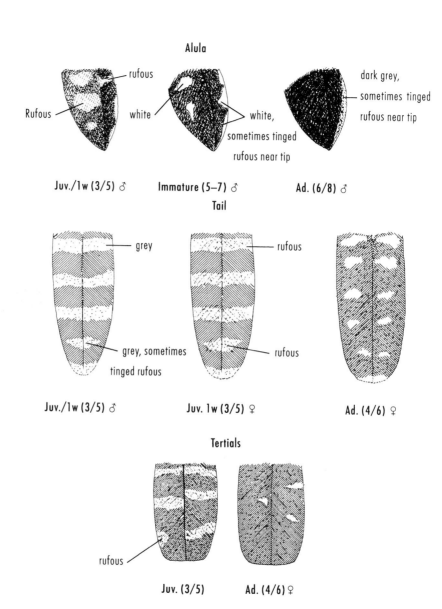

**Alula**

rufous

Rufous

white

white, sometimes tinged rufous near tip

dark grey, sometimes tinged rufous near tip

Juv./1w (3/5) ♂          Immature (5–7) ♂          Ad. (6/8) ♂

**Tail**

grey

grey, sometimes tinged rufous

rufous

rufous

Juv./1w (3/5) ♂          Juv. 1w (3/5) ♀          Ad. (4/6) ♀

**Tertials**

rufous

Juv. (3/5)          Ad. (4/6) ♀

## Spring/Summer

1s (5) ♂          Upperparts admixed with old juvenile feathers and new slate-grey adult-type ones. Some wing-coverts likely to show similar contrast.

| 1s (5) ♀ | As juvenile ♀ but greyer feathers replacing gingery immature ones on back, rump and mantle. Similar contrast in wing-coverts and tertials. After moult similar in appearance to adult. |
|---|---|
| 2s (7) ♂ | Before second complete moult large outermost alula feather with white- or rufous-fringed leading edge (Fig). |
| Adult (8) ♂ | As Autumn/Winter. |
| Adult (6) ♀ | As Autumn/Winter. |

**Moult**

| 5 | Partial post-juvenile moult confined to parts of body and perhaps central tail feathers (t1), February-May. Subsequent moults complete and as adult, though first complete moult in non-breeding birds probably earlier. |
|---|---|
| Adult | Complete post-breeding moult starting April in ♀, May in ♂. Primary sequence variable, usually 5-4-6-3-7-8-2-9-1-10, but can start with 4-5-6-, or 6-5-4-. Completed by September or October (November). |

**Geographical variation** Slight: involves mostly colour but clinally larger from west to east. *F.c. subaesalon* (Iceland) darker and larger than N. European *aesalon*. Eight other races recognized.

**Biometrics**   *F.c. aesalon* (BWP).

| Wing | ad. ♂199 | (3.55;24) | 191-206 | ♀217 | (3.62;20) | 209-222 |
|---|---|---|---|---|---|---|
|  | juv. 198 | (2.99;25) | 193-205 | 218 | (3.53;14) | 213-223 |
| Tail | ad. 119 | (2.53;26) | 114-124 | 129 | (3.21;32) | 122-135 |
|  | juv. 117 | (2.94;26) | 111-123 | 130 | (4.00;13) | 123-136 |
| Bill | 12.4 | (0.36;24) | 11.7-13.0 | 13.8 | (0.56;27) | 12.9-14.8 |
| Tarsus | 36.0 | (0.89;20) | 34-37 | 37.9 | (0.68;17) | 36-39 |

*F. c. subaesalon* (BWP).

| Wing | ♂208 | (4.69;4) | 201-211 | ♀227 | (2.61;11) | 223-230 |
|---|---|---|---|---|---|---|

**References**   Temple (1972), Picozzi (1981*b*), Baker (1983*a*).

## HOBBY *Falco subbuteo*

**Identification** Most likely to be confused with juvenile or 1st-summer Red-footed Falcon *Falco vespertinus* but that species has dark trailing edge to underwing; heavily barred uppertail and uppertail-coverts; shorter toe and claw, <27mm and <9.5mm respectively (in Hobby toe >29mm and claw >9.7mm).

### Autumn

3            Upperparts sooty-black with distinctive rufous margins. Undertail-coverts and thighs buffish-yellow, not rufous. Central pair of tail feathers slate, tipped rufous; remainder of tail barred and tipped rufous (Fig).

2w (5)      Similar to adult but tail with both adult-type and juvenile feathers, latter heavily abraded with sharply contrasting barring, while adult-type feathers are fresh with less distinct barring (Fig).

Adult (6)    Upperparts uniform slate-grey, or slate tinged brown. Tail uniformly worn with feathers similarly patterned (except for central pair which are uniform slate-grey). The pale barring on the tail feathers greyish becoming sharper and clearer towards the base (Fig). Undertail-coverts and thighs rusty-red.

Tail

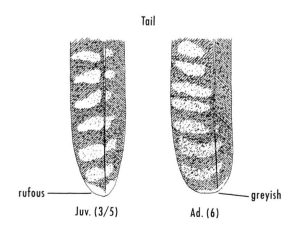

rufous ——————————— greyish

Juv. (3/5)              Ad. (6)

## Spring/Summer

1s (5)
Like juvenile, but the rufous tips on the upperparts usually worn away; some adult-type slate-grey feathers admixed with juvenile feathers, especially on wing-coverts, mantle, scapulars and uppertail-coverts. Some individuals may have replaced central pair of tail feathers (t1).

Adult (6)
Like adult Autumn, but plumage is fresh.

## Moult

5
Partial post-juvenile moult in the winter quarters confined to some parts of the body, sometimes wing-coverts and perhaps central pair of tail feathers, March-April. Partial post-breeding moult, starting earlier than adult: June or July, some August. Wing moult includes replacement of 2 primaries only (p4, p5) before suspending, shortly before migration; resumed and completed in winter quarters. Some, however, may not start wing moult at all before migration. Subsequent moults apparently as adult.

Adult
Complete post-breeding moult starting with replacement of body feathers August-September. Only a small proportion of birds start wing moult September (October), usually only 1 or 2 primaries replaced before suspending (p4, p5). Completed in winter quarters. Sequence of primary moult 4-5-3-6-7-2-8-9-10-1. Most do not start wing or tail moult until in winter quarters. Moult always completed by February-March.

**Geographical variation** Slight; involves colour and size. West European birds slightly darker than birds from central Asia. *F.s. streichi* (China) same colour as nominate *subbuteo* but smaller.

**Biometrics** Nominate *subbuteo* (BWP).

| | | | | | | | |
|---|---|---|---|---|---|---|---|
| Wing | *ad.* ♂ | 256 | (9.13;53) | 237-279 | ♀ 268 | (7.87;37) | 248-282 |
| | *juv.* | 252 | (4.00;10) | 247-258 | 256 | (10.6;19) | 235-271 |
| Tail | *ad.* | 130 | (4.87;27) | 124-143 | 135 | (4.69;28) | 128-145 |
| | *juv.* | 127 | (2.37;10) | 123-131 | 128 | (5.02;19) | 119-136 |
| Bill | | 12.6 | (0.48;29) | 11.7-13.4 | 14.0 | (0.77;24) | 12.2-15.1 |
| Tarsus | | 33.2 | (0.91;26) | 32-35 | 34.8 | (0.75;21) | 33-37 |
| Toe | | 31.5 | (1.16;28) | 29.9-34.5 | 32.9 | (1.17;24) | 31.5-35.2 |
| Claw | | 10.3 | (0.39;26) | 9.8-11.4 | 11.3 | (0.42;23) | 10.3-12.3 |

# PEREGRINE *Falco peregrinus*

**Identification** From other large falcons by notch on inner web of longest primary (p9). Also outer toe considerably longer than the inner; these toes on other large falcons are roughly the same length.

## Sexing

Nestlings         Large nestlings (ca. 3-4 weeks old) can be sexed on weight: 6-700g = ♂, >900g = ♀.

Full-grown        (nominate *peregrinus*).

♂                 Wing <330mm; Weight <800g.

♀                 Wing >340mm; Weight >900g.

## Autumn/Winter

1w (3/5)          Upperparts dark brown with narrow rufous feather-margins. Tail feathers with pale tips and well-defined incomplete rufous-buff bars (except for central pair which are more uniform). Belly beige with dark brown longitudinal streaks.

2w (5)            Before completion of moult some brown juvenile feathers remain, usually on back or in greater-coverts. After moult birds cannot be aged beyond 2+ calendar years (4), unless there are retained juvenile feathers.

Adult (6)         Identifiable only in active moult when both the new and old wing or tail feathers can be compared, being evenly worn (wing) or similar in pattern (tail). After moult birds cannot be aged beyond 2+ calendar years (4); upperparts become uniformly blue-grey (lightest on the rump and upper-tail-coverts). Tail feathers grey with darker cross-barring. Belly with fine lateral streaking.

## Spring/Summer

The plumage is not altered significantly during the winter months. It becomes generally worn, and in the case of juveniles the rufous margins to the upperparts may wear off altogether. Ageing methods are therefore as Autumn/Winter.

## Moult

5          Complete post-juvenile moult starting in spring (March) of 2nd calendar year, but onset of moult highly variable (individually and geographically), some not until late summer or even autumn; starts with wing at p4 and follows similar sequence to adult. Normally completed October-December, though in northern populations January-February. Subsequent moults and timing as adult.

Adult      Complete moult starting in ♀ at time of egg-laying, March-May (May-June in northern populations) with p4 and then replaces primaries in following sequence 5-3-6-7-2-8-1-9-10. Tail starts 10-47 days after start of wing moult. Moult in ♂ usually starts 3-4 weeks after ♀. In southern and central European populations, moult completed by October-November; in northern birds moult often suspended just prior to migration, August-September, when about 4 primaries replaced, resumed in winter quarters and completed February-April.

**Geographical variation** Within Europe slight; northern populations slightly paler above, less heavily marked on underparts, and with narrower moustachial stripe than central and southern European populations. Wing length averages slightly larger in northern birds. *F.p. brookei* (Iberia, northern Morocco, southern France and Italy, Mediterranean Islands, Greece, and Asia Minor) is smaller than nominate *peregrinus*, more densely barred and more rufous below with darker upperparts. About 15 subspecies recognized.

**Biometrics**  Nominate *peregrinus* (BWP).

| | | | | | | | |
|---|---|---|---|---|---|---|---|
| Wing | *ad.* ♂ | 309 | (7.55;20) | 291-320 | ♀ 356 | (6.76;21) | 348-367 |
| | *juv.* | 315 | (5.85;11) | 305-325 | 360 | (6.60;15) | 350-375 |
| Tail | *ad.* | 144 | (5.31;21) | 134-156 | 173 | (4.29;23) | 163-180 |
| | *juv.* | 153 | (4.32;11) | 147-159 | 182 | (4.55;15) | 173-190 |
| Bill | | 20.0 | (1.03;18) | 18.3-22.8 | 24.0 | (0.91;21) | 22.7-26.4 |
| Tarsus | | 46.9 | (1.06;16) | 45-49 | 53.5 | (1.51;16) | 51-56 |

# Rails *Rallidae*

Small to medium-sized terrestrial, marsh and aquatic birds. Body short and rather compressed. Wings short and broad. Plumage predominantly brown or black often with barred flanks, vent and undertail-coverts sometimes contrastingly coloured. Upperparts frequently streaked or speckled.

## Feather structure
Primaries = 10 (p8 or p9 longest)
Secondaries = 10-20
Tail = 12 (12-16)

## Sexes
Similar or nearly so in plumage. ♂ ♂ average larger.

## Moult
Strategy: simultaneous.
Sequence: simultaneously.
Frequency: twice annually;SC, Wp.
Timing: mid-late summer finishing late summer-early autumn; late winter finishing spring.

# WATER RAIL *Rallus aquaticus*

### Sexing

♂        Wing >122mm; Bill (to feathering) >41mm; Tarsus >42mm.

♀        Wing <120mm; Bill <40mm; Tarsus <40mm.

### Autumn/Winter

3        Easily distinguished from older birds by white/buff breast, and upper-parts admixed with brown-mottled feathers. Perhaps some sub-adult slate-grey feathers in these areas especially on the neck. Lacks black and white barring on thighs. Iris light brown.

1w (3/5)        After post-juvenile moult, appearance similar to adult but can be distinguished by prominent buff or off-white streak running from base of upper mandible to upper part of eye. Chin and throat white, light beige or light grey; sometimes white with black tips. Breast slate-grey fringed olive-brown or buff, becoming whiter towards belly. Iris fawn to bright orange-brown. Tarsus brown or grey.

Adult (4/6)        Breast and underparts slate-grey, sometimes with dark brown fringes. Iris rich dark orange or red. Tarsus flesh or yellow-brown, often with orange-red or green tinge. Chin slate-grey, sometimes white, merging into uniform slate-grey throat.

### Spring

1s (5)        Some birds still have buff, light brown or olive-brown streak from bill to eye, but some may be indistinguishable from adults especially late on.

Adult (4)        As adult Autumn/Winter.

### Moult

3        Body moult begins soon after fledging. Normally finished by mid-July to early October, very occasionally December.

Adult        Complete post-nuptial moult begins June or July, completed by August or early September (November). Wings and tail moulted simultaneously, leaving birds flightless for short period in July or August.

**Geographical variation** Slight colour and size difference only in the four races, *R.a.*

*indicus* (east Asia) being the most distinct from nominate form (Europe, North Africa and west Asia): more contrasting head pattern, with whiter chin; wing-coverts more boldly and extensively barred. *R.a. hibernans* (Iceland) is warmer brown above and paler, less slaty; *korejewi* (southwest and central Asia) is paler than nominate form and less streaked with black.

**Biometrics**    Full-grown. Nominate *aquaticus* (BWP).

| | | | | | | |
|---|---|---|---|---|---|---|
| Wing | ♂125 | (2.84;126) | 119-132 | ♀116 | (2.45;124) | 110-121 |
| Bill | 41.4 | (1.73;55) | 39-45 | 37.0 | (1.28;58) | 34-40 |
| Tarsus | 42.6 | (1.47;63) | 39-46 | 38.5 | (1.40;58) | 36-41 |

**References**    Flegg & Glue (1973), de Kroon (1979), Baker (1980*a*).

# SPOTTED CRAKE *Porzana porzana*

**Identification**  Similar in size and appearance to Sora Rail *P. carolina* (Nearctic vagrant), but that species has diagnostic black lores and chin, giving masked appearance, though young birds rather similar; juvenile Sora has tawny brown or chestnut crown with central black stripe; also Sora lacks white speckling on hind neck, head or breast, while bill lacks yellow-orange base of Spotted's. From Baillon's and Little Crakes by much larger size, wing >111mm, and by white speckling on head, breast and nape, which the smaller species lack.

**Sexing**    Adults, or immatures in breeding plumage only:

♂    Supercilium, cheeks, chin and throat are pure slate-grey with small area of white speckling bordering brown ear-coverts. In non-breeding plumage cheeks, chin and sides of head more heavily speckled with white; supercilium grey with some white speckling mainly to the rear of head.

♀    Supercilium, and chin slate-grey; cheeks and throat more heavily speckled white than breeding ♂; breast usually with more white barring than ♂ but plumage variable. In non-breeding plumage similar to non-breeding ♂ but throat and cheeks heavily speckled white, with pure grey restricted to front part of supercilium.

198

## Autumn/Winter

**3**
Supercilium brown with white speckling. Breast brown with white specks. No grey on head or breast. Iris olive or deep green, grading to brown from pupil outwards. Bill black or dark brown with yellow base.

**1w (3/5)**
Like adult except chin and throat whitish (not grey or grey with white speckling). Bill dark olive-green with orange-yellow base, but becomes like adult's towards end of winter.

**Adult (4/6)**
Chin and throat either slate-grey, or grey speckled with white, depending on sex. Iris yellow-brown to bright red-brown. Bill yellow or yellow-green, shading to olive-green at tip; base orange-yellow to orange-red.

## Spring/Summer

**1s (5)**
Advanced birds indistinguishable from adults but, in many, some old immature feathers retained, best seen as whitish areas on chin and throat.

**Adult (4)**
All other plumages.

## Moult

**3**
Partial post-juvenile moult confined to head and body, August-September, completed by October.

**5**
First moult of flight feathers at roughly same time as adults, possibly slightly earlier.

**Adult**
Complete post-breeding moult between July and October. Flight feathers are moulted simultaneously and replaced within 3 weeks. Partial pre-breeding moult confined to head and some body feathers, late winter/early spring.

**Biometrics** Full-grown (BWP).

| | ♂ | | | ♀ | | |
|---|---|---|---|---|---|---|
| Wing | 122 | (2.68;46) | 117-128 | 118 | (3.07;27) | 111-123 |
| Bill | 19.7 | (1.15;45) | 18-22 | 18.4 | (0.85;27) | 17-20 |
| Tarsus | 34.1 | (1.23;45) | 32-37 | 33.0 | (1.26;27) | 30-35 |

# LITTLE CRAKE *Porzana parva*

**Identification**  From Spotted Crake by smaller size: wing <111mm. Adults lack white speckling on upperparts and neck. Rump dark blackish-brown, compared to brown back and white barring of Spotted. From Baillon's Crake by larger size, wing >98mm, and by much reduced barring on flanks and thighs; wing-coverts with no white streaks or speckling, unlike Baillon's which has quite distinctive markings on median- and greater-coverts. Bill grass-green with red or orange area around gape. From juvenile Spotted by absence of white speckling on breast or neck area; from Baillon's by uniform or near uniform dark brown head and paler hind neck lacking distinctive black dots - a feature of Baillon's; upperparts usually less spotted and more streaky-looking, unlike Baillon's which show well-defined white dots usually surrounded by a black border. From Sora Rail *P. carolina* see identification under Spotted Crake.

**Sexing**  Adults or immatures in breeding plumage only:

♂  Underparts dusky slate-grey, except vent area and thighs which are darker and barred white. Many birds in winter have brown fringes to slate-grey feathers but underlying tone is a dark grey appearance.

♀  Breast and belly light buff-brown to salmon-pink, blending into greyish vent with white barring. Throat and upper neck off-white.

## Autumn/Winter

3  Underparts off-white with varying amounts of brown flecking giving the bird a mottled appearance. Supercilium off-white with brown flecking. Wing-coverts and tertials with varying amounts of white dotting. Iris grey-brown.

1w (3/5) ♂  Much the same as juvenile though flecking on underparts less obvious. Thus, breast, throat and belly much whiter-looking, merging into pale buff vent and brown-and-white barring on undertail-coverts. White dotting on wing-coverts may be restricted (depending on amount of moult) to greater-coverts or just tertials, but even here advanced birds may have only 1 or 2 old tertials with these markings (Fig). Iris reddish-brown.

1w (3/5) ♀  As 1st-winter ♂ but plumage can be very variable depending on progress of moult; some appear to moult quickly into sub-adult plumage showing grey underparts with brown fringes. These birds usually have whitish throats, and some white dotting on old wing-coverts or tertials (Fig).

Adult (4/6)     Iris and narrow ring of bare skin around eye scarlet. Wing-coverts and tertials near-uniform with no white spots. Caution: inner web of tertials is pale buff with whitish fringe giving the appearance of elongated whitish region but this should not be mistaken for white spotting (Fig).

## Tertials

Ad. (4/6)          Juv./1w (3/5)

## Spring/Summer

1s (5)          Some individuals may show unmoulted wing-coverts, usually greaters; rarely a tertial also retained. Much of the white spotting however will have become greatly reduced through wear, often absent altogether, leaving feather with large castellations.

Adult (4)       All other plumages.

## Moult

3               Partial post-juvenile moult confined to body, wing-coverts and tertials beginning August-September and mostly completed by November; others retain juvenile plumage and do not start moult until in winter quarters. Some birds appear to undergo complete moult, including simultaneous replacement of wing and tail feathers, though exact details require further investigation.

Adult           Complete post-breeding moult, involving simultaneous shedding of flight feathers, July-August. In some, moult complete before start of migration - around October; others suspend moult, completing in winter quarters by January. Details of pre-breeding moult sketchy and not fully known. Some body feathers probably renewed.

| | | | | | | |
|---|---|---|---|---|---|---|
| Wing | ♂106 | (2.41;24) | 99-111 | ♀103 | (3.34;22) | 99-109 |
| Bill | 18.5 | (0.60;25) | 17-20 | 17.4 | (0.62;22) | 16-19 |
| Tarsus | 31.9 | (0.89;25) | 30-34 | 30.8 | (1.08;20) | 29-32 |

# BAILLON'S CRAKE *Porzana pusilla*

**Identification** From Little Crake by smaller size and by heavy barring on flanks and thighs. Distinctive white streaks or speckling on median- and greater-coverts. Diagnostic uniform deep-green bill. Juvenile has black dots on crown.

**Sexing**    Adult breeding plumage only:

♂    Chin same colour as underparts (or marginally paler grey).

♀    Chin noticeably paler than rest of underparts.

### Autumn/Winter

3    Upperparts similar to adult though white streaking is shorter and more rounded than elongated white striping of adult (Fig). Underparts have whitish-buff wash with light brown speckling or faded barring on breast and belly. Dark brown-and-white barring on flanks and undertail-coverts. Throat off-white with mottled brown-and-white cheeks, lores and sides of neck. Iris olive-green or olive-brown.

1w (3/5)    Underparts much more like adult but still showing some old brown juvenile feathers. The ear-covert region may also have some brown feathers contrasting sharply with slate-grey adult-type plumage. Some advanced birds may be impossible to separate from adults on plumage but eye colour may still be a useful guide. The transformation from juvenile to adult iris colour takes several months. 1st-winter birds should show an intermediate eye colour.

Adult (4/6)    White elongated streaking on mantle, scapulars and back, broken by black spots or speckling (Fig). Cheeks, neck, breast and upper belly slate-grey. Iris scarlet or bright red-brown.

### Mantle

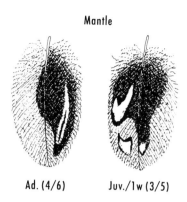

Ad. (4/6)     Juv./1w (3/5)

## Spring/Summer

1s (5)      Some birds may still have a small amount of brown in the ear-covert region.

Adult (4)    All other plumages.

## Moult

3           Partial post-juvenile moult confined to head and body starting July or August. Some have almost completed before autumn migration in October while others appear to wait until winter quarters are reached before undergoing moult.

Adult        Complete post-breeding moult involving simultaneous shedding of flight feathers, August-September; others migrate in worn breeding plumage and moult in winter quarters.

**Geographical variation** Involves mostly depth of grey on underparts, and size: Nominate *pusilla* (Russia, China, Japan) differs from *intermedia* (N. Africa & Europe) in being paler below - more ashy, less deep slate - and having smaller but more numerous white speckles on upperparts. Rufous-brown streaks running from lores through eye to ear-coverts are distinct; these are only faintly indicated, often lacking, in *intermedia*. Juveniles often less heavily barred below. 4 other subspecies recognized.

Adult. *P.p. intermedia* (BWP).

| | | | | | | |
|---|---|---|---|---|---|---|
| Wing | ♂92.9 | (2.62;19) | 89-97 | ♀91.0 | (3.19;11) | 87-96 |
| Bill | 17.2 | (0.82;21) | 16-18 | 16.2 | (0.74;12) | 15-17 |
| Tarsus | 28.3 | (1.01;24) | 26-30 | 27.0 | (1.47;15) | 25-29 |

# CORNCRAKE *Crex crex*

**Sexing**

Adults in breeding plumage only:

♂     Chest, upper breast, sides of breast and cheeks blue-grey with whitish chin and throat. Broad and extensive blue-grey streak over eye which is well-defined against dark brownish-black crown and buff-brown ear-coverts.

♀     Grey on breast, neck and cheeks is browner, less intense than on ♂. Compared with ♂♂ the facial colours tend to merge more, making the markings less distinct.

Note: plumage variation in breeding period is common. Only well-marked birds should be sexed. Many ♂♂ show less clear-cut blue-grey markings on breast and neck, sometimes with a brown wash, perhaps causing confusion with ♀♀.

**Autumn/Winter**

3     Upperparts buff-brown with dark brown centres to feathers and without any greyish fringes. Division between dark feather-centre and buff-brown fringes less clear-cut than adult (Fig). Underparts with pale buffish-brown breast and neck - no grey. Cheeks, ear-coverts and supercilium pale buff, without traces of grey.

1w (3/5)     Much the same as juvenile though upperparts have some or many adult-type feathers (Fig). Some birds moult some wing-coverts, tertials and scapulars: new scapulars have a greyish tone, strongest on the outer and distal portion of the feather. Unmoulted scapulars are buff-brown with pale fringes and rather pointed and narrow by comparison.

Adult (4/6)     Mantle, scapulars and tertials show broad blackish feather-centres with brownish-grey or grey fringes (Fig); these pale fringes are often very worn and much reduced in size (before moult). Breast and neck greyish or brownish-grey. Cheeks and supercilium grey.

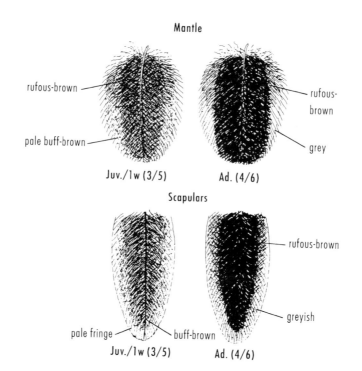

Mantle

rufous-brown

pale buff-brown

rufous-brown

grey

Juv./1w (3/5)      Ad. (4/6)

Scapulars

rufous-brown

greyish

pale fringe      buff-brown

Juv./1w (3/5)      Ad. (4/6)

## Spring/Summer

1s (5)     As adult and usually inseparable unless a few old juvenile feathers have been retained on upperparts. Sometimes a worn old tertial may be retained, contrasting with greyer newer ones. The black centre to old tertials is slightly browner, less black, than on new ones and tends to merge more into the rest of the feather.

Adult (4)     As Autumn/Winter.

## Moult

3     Partial moult starting shortly after fully grown, mid-July to mid-September, and confined to head and body.

5     Partial pre-breeding moult of head, body and some wing-coverts, February-April. Subsequent moults apparently as in adult.

Adult     Complete post-breeding moult starting mid-July to late August. Flight feathers shed simultaneously rendering bird flightless for short period; most birds have completed by late August to mid-September, but a few show active wing growth as late as October. Some populations appear to delay moult until post-nesting dispersal or until in winter quarters. Partial pre-breeding moult confined to head, body, tail and some wing-coverts, December-March (April).

**Geographical variation** Slight, mostly clinal involving colour; eastern populations are paler more greyish, less brownish above and less buff below.

**Biometrics**     Adult (BWP).

| | | | | | | |
|---|---|---|---|---|---|---|
| Wing | ♂144 | (4.21;15) | 139-150 | ♀136 | (6.08;6) | 130-145 |
| Bill | 21.4 | (1.21;37) | 20-25 | 20.5 | (1.44;25) | 19-23 |
| Tarsus | 40.0 | (1.75;36) | 37-43 | 38.1 | (1.46;23) | 35-40 |

# MOORHEN *Gallinula chloropus*

**Sexing**     Adult

♂     Wing >181mm; Tarsus + toe >124mm.

♀     Wing <174mm; Tarsus + toe <123mm.

Sub-adult

♂     Tarsus + toe >123mm.

♀     Tarsus + toe <120mm.

Note: above measurements from D.W. Gibbons *(in litt.)*, based on population from southern Britain. Discriminant function of measurements may vary between populations.

**Autumn/Winter**

3     Belly and breast with mixture of white and brown/grey feathers. Chin off-white. Upperparts olivaceous-brown, with little sheen to plumage. Iris greyish-brown.

1w (3/5)     Less white on underparts though still marked. Chin off-white, especially immediately under bill. Upperparts show mixture of juvenile brown and adult-type ash-grey, especially on head and nape. Iris is greyish-hazel in early autumn, gradually becoming redder and by January is crimson as in adult. 9th primary narrow and pointed (Fig).

Adult (4/6)     Underparts ash-grey fringed white, especially on belly. Head, chin and nape ash-grey. Mantle and back olivaceous-brown with sheen to plumage. Bill red at base, yellow at tip. Iris reddish-brown to crimson. Broad 9th primary (Fig).

**Primary 9**

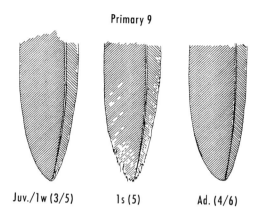

| Juv./1w (3/5) | 1s (5) | Ad. (4/6) |

## Spring/Summer

1s (5)    Similar to adult though tail and wings are browner and much abraded (Fig). Nape or head may have old brown feathers admixed with adult ash-grey plumage. Some birds may also show some white juvenile feathers under chin, even as late as August.

Adult (6)    As for Autumn/Winter.

## Moult

3/5    Partial post-juvenile moult. Body begins in (August) September-October, gradually replacing feathers into non-breeding plumage followed by partial pre-breeding moult, March-June.

Adult    Complete post-breeding moult takes place May-October (November). Moult begins just a few days after bird finishes breeding, at which point wing and tail feathers are moulted simultaneously, rendering bird flightless for a period of approximately 3 weeks. Partial pre-breeding moult (not in all birds) March-June, confined to body.

**Geographical variation** Marked, though in Europe only slight. Mostly clinal involving

207

size, colour of upperparts and shape of frontal shield. New World birds have broad square tops to the shield unlike Old World birds which have more rounded tops. In Old World, northern and western populations are larger. About 12 subspecies recognized.

**Biometrics**  Nominate *chloropus* (BWP).

| | | | | | | |
|---|---|---|---|---|---|---|
| Wing *ad.* ♂185 | (3.56;13) | 178-194 | ♀176 | (3.98;13) | 169-184 |
| *juv.* 184 | (3.35;28) | 175-192 | 172 | (4.12;37) | 160-182 |
| Bill 26.3 | (1.02;70) | 25-28 | 24.5 | (0.98;70) | 23-26 |
| Tarsus 51.3 | (1.86;60) | 49-55 | 47.6 | (1.58;78) | 44-51 |
| Tarsus+toe 125 | (4.80;18) | 118-136 | 115 | (4.52;23) | 107-123 |

(Anderson 1975).

| | | | | | | |
|---|---|---|---|---|---|---|
| Wing *ad.* ♂178 | (5.90;16) | 167-190 | ♀170 | (5.96;18) | 161-183 |
| *juv.* 175 | (6.47;12) | 159-183 | 167 | (4.07;8) | 162-175 |
| Tarsus+toe 126 | (5.60;14) | 115-136 | 115 | (5.18;9) | 108-122 |

**References**  Grant (1911), Anderson (1975), Baker (1979).

# COOT *Fulica atra*

**Sexing**  Adult

♂  Wing >220mm; Tarsus >62mm.

♀  Wing <211mm; Tarsus <57mm.

Sub-adult

♂  Wing >218mm.

♀  Wing <205mm.

## Autumn/Winter

3  Belly, breast and part of face off-white. Upperparts dark brownish-grey.

Bill and minute frontal shield dusky, gradually becoming white. Iris brown.

| | |
|---|---|
| 1w (3/5) | Plumage essentially as adult, though some pale juvenile feathers may be retained on belly, breast or throat. Iris brown at first, becoming reddish. Sides of tarsus grey or bluish, gradually becoming yellow to orange-yellow and usually via a greenish intermediate stage; colour first appears during August-November (depending partly on fledging date) and increases in extent and intensity until adult colouring is reached. Frontal shield of some birds stays very small (ca. 8mm wide) throughout the winter, though most develop further. |
| 2w (5) | Some birds are recognizable in autumn by dull yellow or orange-yellow on sides of tarsus. |
| Adult (4/6) | Adult plumage near-uniform slate-grey and black; some faint narrow white tips to underpart feathers when fresh. Iris brownish-red to crimson. Sides of tarsus with extensive bright yellow, orange or even reddish (most will have some shade of orange-yellow to orange). |
| FG (2/4) | From November onwards an increasing number of "full-grown" birds will not be ageable on leg colour (tarsus sides yellow to orange-yellow). In general, shield size is also of little use as an ageing character. |

**Spring/Summer**

| | |
|---|---|
| 1s (5) | A few birds are still recognizable, with yellowish-grey or yellowish-green sides to tarsus. |
| Adult (6) | Some (older?) adults should also be recognizable as such, from their extensive bright orange or reddish sides of tarsus. |
| FG (4) | Many birds will fall into the 'full-grown' category. Tarsus sides yellow to yellow-orange. |

**Moult**

| | |
|---|---|
| 3 | Partial post-juvenile moult only of head and body. Begins early, and is well advanced by the time that full wing development is achieved; mostly finished by October but can continue as late as December. |
| Adult | Complete post-breeding moult starting in May with body moult, followed by simultaneous shedding of flight feathers and all wing-coverts in June, rendering bird flightless for a short period. Completed mid-September, |

early October. Partial pre-breeding moult December-May, confined to head and neck.

**Geographical variation** Negligible in Europe; elsewhere considerable in size but only slight in colour. Three smaller races found in Australasia.

**Biometrics**   Nominate *atra* (BWP).

| | | | | | | | |
|---|---|---|---|---|---|---|---|
| Wing *ad.* | ♂219 | (4.49;21) | 211-229 | ♀205 | (4.09;23) | 197-213 |
| *juv.* | 216 | (4.73;17) | 208-226 | 202 | (4.50;17) | 193-211 |
| Bill | 29.0 | (1.11;30) | 28-32 | 27.6 | (0.76;30) | 26-29 |
| Tarsus | 61.7 | (1.73;37) | 59-65 | 56.8 | (1.63;38) | 54-60 |

**References**   Parr (1984).

# Skuas *Stercorariidae*

Medium to large, gull-like seabirds. Body robust and stocky. Wings long, narrow and pointed in long-tailed species, broader and blunter in *Stercorarius skua*. Predominantly dark plumaged with prominent white flashes in outer wing. Dark and pale morphs exist in *S. parasiticus*.

## Feather structure
Primaries = 11 (p10 longest, p11 minute)
Secondaries = 19-23
Tail = 12

## Sexes
Similar in plumage. ♀ ♀ average slightly larger.

## Moult
Strategy: primaries descendant. Secondaries presumably ascendant but little published information. Tail irregular.
Sequence: sequentially in primaries. Secondaries uncertain but presumed sequential.
Frequency: twice annually; SC, Wp.
Timing: Body in mid-late summer. Wings early winter finishing spring; body again late winter finishing early spring.

# ARCTIC SKUA *Stercorarius parasiticus*

**Identification** From Pomarine Skua *S. pomarinus* by shorter bill and toe (all ages): <35mm and <44mm respectively, compared to >35mm and >47mm for Pomarine Skua. From Long-tailed Skua *S. longicaudus* by white shafts to 3 outermost primaries (p8-p10); in Long-tailed shaft to p8 is pale horn-brown. Bill length to bill nail ratio useful guide but only for birds of known age. Bill to nail ratio in juvenile 2.23mm (0.14;33) 2.03-2.50mm (rarely below 2.1); in 2nd and 3rd calendar year, 2.19mm (0.06;6) 2.12-2.28mm; in 4th-5th calendar year, 2.13mm (0.08;14) 1.95- 2.21mm; in adult, 2.06mm (0.07;34) 1.98-2.15mm: in Long-tailed Skua juvenile 2.04mm (0.12;36) 1.83-2.20mm (rarely over 2.1); in 2nd to 4th calendar year, 1.98mm (0.09;28) 1.80-2.10mm; in adult, 1.89mm (0.08;93) 1.70-2.02mm (rarely over 2.0).

Colour variation in adults falls into 2 distinct morphs: pale and dark, with just a few intermediates occurring. Juveniles, however, are highly variable, from pale-headed to all-dark and barred forms: the true colour morph is found only in adults since dark juveniles may become pale-morph adults; immatures do not follow any clear-cut pattern and, therefore, should not be classified into a colour morph unless they are nearing adulthood.

## Autumn/Winter

1w (3/5)     For ageing purposes it is necessary to divide colour variations into 3 groupings. Whilst it may be difficult to classify intermediates to one or other of these artificial morphs, a broad understanding of plumage features is all that is necessary in order to determine age.

Light Morph:     Upperparts and upper wing-coverts blackish with broad pale buff tips. Head and neck creamy-yellow faintly streaked black. Underparts black-brown with reddish-brown tinge on vent and undertail-coverts, or heavily mottled and barred dark brown and rufous; some admixed with white on breast or belly. Tips to outer webs of outermost primaries with reddish-brown or pale buff margins, and pointed (Fig). Axillaries barred buff and black. Legs blue-grey, often with some black on upper tibia or toes and webs.

Dark Morph:     The darkest forms are completely sooty-brown to black and differ from dark adults only by shorter central tail feathers (see Biometrics), blue-grey legs, usually by presence of reddish-brown mottling on carpal-coverts and lesser-coverts, sometimes also on vent, tail-coverts and underwing-coverts, and often pale fringes to scapulars. Outer primaries as in Light Morph but less pointed.

Barred Morph:  Upperparts and upper wing-coverts blackish with broad off-white tips. Underparts, including underwing-coverts barred dull black or brown on white, often with faint buff tinge. Legs blue-grey. Outer primary shape as in Dark Morph.

2w (5/7)

Light/Barred Morph: Some barred juvenile-type feathers retained and admixed with adult non-breeding-type plain feathers giving overall less barred appearance. Outer primaries uniform. Axillaries dark grey with off-white edges or a few bars. Outer primaries rounded and uniform (Fig). Legs variably blue-grey and black. Central tail feathers slightly longer or same length as juvenile.

Dark Morph:  Upperparts and upper wing-coverts with mixture of old worn feathers and new ones; sometimes old feathers with mottled rufous edges or tips as on juvenile. Legs variably blue-grey and black (rarely all black). Central tail feathers slightly longer or same length as on juvenile.

3w (7/9)  Plumage very similar to adult non-breeding except that underwing-coverts are more-or-less uniform but with pale edges. Legs mostly black but sometimes with some blue-grey spots.

Adult (8/10)

Light Morph:  Non-breeding plumage like breeding but sides of head and neck pinkish-buff or buff-brown. Mantle barred and fringed pale buff. Chest, flanks, vent and undertail-coverts pale buff with variable black barring. Under-wing-coverts and axillaries uniform dark grey. Legs black. Central tail feathers as adult summer, but sometimes broken off.

213

Dark Morph:    Sooty-grey or sooty-brown underparts and upperparts, latter often narrowly edged or dotted dark rufous.

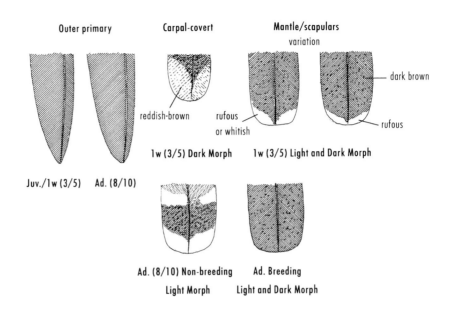

**Spring/Summer**

1s (5)    Plumage still mostly like juvenile, except in light morph crown much darker showing distinct darkish cap. Flight feathers in moult or very new with rounded tips.

2s (7)

Light Morph:    Similar to adult non-breeding. Plumage mostly retained during summer though some may show partial breeding plumage on head, neck and mantle. Axillaries dark grey with off-white edges or a few dark bars. Legs mostly black with some blue-grey speckling or patches. Central tail feathers (t1) marginally longer or same length as juvenile (see Biometrics).

Dark Morph:    Very similar to 2nd-winter. In late summer some old worn feathers replaced but some are retained until birds reach winter quarters (see Moult). Other features as for 2nd-winter.

3s (9)

Light Morph:       Like adult breeding but yellow hackles on hindneck and sides of head with dark shaft-streaks. Mantle perhaps with some white-edged or white-barred non-breeding feathers. Axillaries and some underwing-coverts pale edged. Legs black, perhaps with some blue-grey spots.

Dark Morph:        Indistinguishable from adult but legs may show some blue-grey spotting.

Adult (10)

Light Morph:       Upperparts dark slate-grey to dark umber-brown except for dull black or sooty-brown crown and yellow or golden-brown hackles on hindneck and sides of head. Underparts white with grey patches on sides of breast (sometimes extending across breast to form chest-band); greyish flanks and undertail-coverts. Underwing-coverts and axillaries uniform dark grey. Legs all-black. Central feathers (t1) elongated (see Biometrics).

Dark Morph:        Underparts and upperparts sooty-brown with slightly darker cap and yellowish hackles to hindneck and sides of head. Some birds are entirely blackish except for white shafts on outer primaries. Legs and tail as in Light Morph.

Note: few 1st-summer birds (and probably 2nd-summer) return to breeding colonies. Most remain in pelagic waters.

## Moult

3/5        Complete post-juvenile moult, starting with body sometimes by August but more usually not until in winter quarters, November-April. Wing moult from February, usually completed by June-July; this is followed by post-breeding moult (into 2nd non-breeding plumage) from (July) August-September, completed by March-April. Subsequent moults similar to adult but pre-breeding moult often not completed before return to summer quarters.

Adult      Complete post-breeding moult starting with body in late August-September, completing by November or December. Failed breeders may start body moult as early as July, completing late October or November. Wing moult starts (October) November, completed by March-April. Pre-breeding moult partial, confined to head and much of body, from late February to April (when outer primaries are just finishing).

**Geographical variation** Slight; involving mostly wing length, increasing from south to north (average wing for Scotland 318mm, Spitsbergen 326mm).

Variation in ratio of morphs marked: Dark Morphs predominate in southern parts of range with Light Morphs predominating in high Arctic.

**Biometrics**     Scotland and Faroes (BWP).

| | | | | | | |
|---|---|---|---|---|---|---|
| Wing ad. ♂315 | (5.68;14) | 309-328 | ♀321 | (5.64;13) | 311-33 |
| juv. | 308 | (8.79;19) | 293-320 | 314 | (7.21;14) | 302-323 |
| Bill | 31.1 | (1.18;34) | 29-34 | 31.8 | (1.42;46) | 30-34 |
| Tarsus | 44.3 | (1.66;34) | 41.47 | 44.4 | (2.01;46) | 42-47 |
| Toe | 39.4 | (1.61;33) | 38-41 | 40.3 | (1.69;46) | 38-43 |

Tail-tip=tip of outermost tail feather(t6) to tip of elongated central tail feather (t1) (sexes combined):

| | | | |
|---|---|---|---|
| Juv (3/5) | 17 | (3.64;34) | 12-22 |
| 1s/2w (5/7) | 40 | (8.50;3) | 30-46 |
| 2s/3w (7/9) | 51 | (12.4;8) | 35-63 |
| 3s/4w (9/11) | 61 | (15.1;24) | 40-80 |
| Adult | 82 | (9.91;62) | 60-105 |

**References**     Olsen (1989).


# GREAT SKUA *Stercorarius skua*

### Autumn/Winter

1w (3/5)     Head and throat sooty-brown and unstreaked. Mantle dark sooty-grey or brown, each feather mottled or freckled, with rufous subterminal U-mark, often broken or ill-defined - sometimes just with small dot, sometimes with rufous crescent on terminal fringe forming inverted V-shape pattern (Fig). White on outer web of outer primaries 0-25mm from point of longest primary-covert (folded wing). Outer primary tips pointed (Fig).

2w (5)     Similar to adult non-breeding but moult sequence differs from adult; moult of inner primaries starts in May-June, much earlier than in adult, so that by autumn outer primaries either in moult or very fresh.

Adult (6/8)     Head and neck uniform dark brown with slightly paler streaks at centre of feathers. Mantle with narrow pale shaft-streak ending in buffish elongated dot (Fig). In autumn/early winter new non-breeding feathers admixed with pale and worn breeding plumage. White outer webs to outer primaries 25-60mm from point of longest primary-coverts (folded wing).

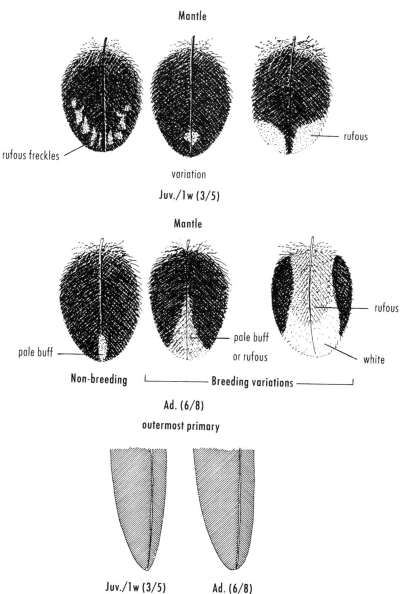

Mantle

rufous freckles

variation

rufous

Juv./1w (3/5)

Mantle

pale buff

pale buff
or rufous

rufous

white

Non-breeding

Breeding variations

Ad. (6/8)

outermost primary

Juv./1w (3/5)

Ad. (6/8)

## Spring/Summer

1s (5)  Assumes partial non-breeding adult-type plumage, especially around head and neck. Mantle usually with some unmoulted/retained juvenile feathers. Wing in active moult; outer old juvenile primaries pointed and somewhat faded, contrasting with new inner ones - possibly all new by late summer (see Moult).

Adult (6)  Crown and neck sepia-brown with faintly paler brown shaft-streaks. Hindneck and sides of head dark brown, with elongated yellow-brown or golden-brown shaft-streaks producing hackled mane. Mantle feathers blackish-brown with broad central cinnamon-rufous streak forming inverted V-shape pattern. White outer web on outer primaries 25-60mm from point of longest primary-covert (folded wing).

## Moult

3/5  Post-juvenile moult complete, starting with head and body from December to February, followed by wing and tail early March-April, usually completed July or mid-August. Subsequent immature moults somewhat earlier than adult; replacement of inner primaries recorded in May of 2nd calendar year, probably completing August-October (November).

Adult  Complete post-breeding moult June-September; flight feathers slow and usually in winter quarters from August to early October, finishing by February to mid-March. Pre-breeding moult partial, confined to parts of body and more-or-less followed on from post-breeding moult. Failed or non-breeders moult earlier than other adults, July onwards and may finish by January.

**Geographical variation** In northern hemisphere (*S.s. skua*) differences are slight; Icelandic population averages very slightly smaller than those from Shetland. In southern hemisphere 3 groups recognized consisting of several subspecies (some of which are considered by some to be specifically distinct) varying most in size and in timing of moult.

**Biometrics** Nominate *skua* (BWP).

| | | | | | | |
|---|---|---|---|---|---|---|
| Wing *ad.* | ♂399 | (7.87;31) | 382-414 | ♀413 | (7.86;17) | 398-428 |
| *juv.* | 383 | (10.2;9) | 367-400 | 399 | (12.3;11) | 381-423 |
| Bill | 50.1 | (1.63;26) | 47-52 | 51.2 | (1.46;20) | 49-53 |
| Tarsus | 67.1 | (2.16;27) | 64-70 | 68.7 | (2.20;22) | 66-72 |

# Gulls *Laridae*

Small to very large seabirds. Body slender to robust. Wings long and narrow. Plumage predominantly grey above, variously patterned with black and white on wingtips, and white below. Non-breeding plumage of adults usually differs on head and neck only.

## Feather structure
Primaries = 11 (p10 longest, p11 minute)
Secondaries = 20-23 (18-25)
Tail = 12

## Sexes
Similar in plumage. ♂♂ average larger.

## Moult
Strategy: primaries descendant. Secondaries ascendant and descendant. Sometimes suspend. Tail centrifugal.
Sequence: primaries sequentially. Secondaries from 2 centres, ascendantly and sequentially from s1, descendantly and sequentially from innermost secondaries.
Frequency: twice annually;SC, Wp. Some migratory species may be prolonged.
Timing: early-late summer finishing autumn;late winter finishing early spring.

# MEDITERRANEAN GULL *Larus melanocephalus*

**Identification** A medium-sized gull distinctly bulkier and larger-headed than Black-headed Gull. Summer adults bear superficial resemblance to Black-headed but lack black tips to outer primaries. Immature plumage more likely to be confused with that of Common Gull rather than Black-headed but smaller-winged (290-320mm) compared to Common Gull; also legs are darker, blackish or brown compared to flesh or bluish-flesh in Common Gull.

## Autumn/Winter

3 — Mantle and scapulars brown-black with clear broad light edges giving scalloped pattern. Head and neck grey-brown. Blackish subterminal tail band.

1w (3/5) — Similar to juvenile but crown and neck whitish. Mantle most often grey, perhaps with some blackish juvenile feathers retained. Blackish subterminal tail band.

2w (5/7) — Basic appearance as adult but 2-5 outer primaries with some black subterminal flecking. Outer primary-coverts sometimes tinged brown along shaft.

Adult (6/8) — Mantle and entire upper wing surface uniform pale pearly-grey shading to white on primary tips. Rump and tail white. Black crescent in front of eye continued on to ear-coverts.

## Spring/Summer

1s (5) — Similar to 1st-winter though generally with fewer brown feathers on wing-coverts, being paler grey-white. Many individuals show partial black hood (occasionally complete).

2s (7) — Outer 2-5 primary tips with black subterminal marks. After moult inseparable from adult.

Adult (8) — Head jet-black with crescent-shaped broken white eye-ring above and below eye. Otherwise as for Autumn/Winter.

## Moult

Timing not well known.

| 3 | Partial moult confined to head and body August-October (November). |
|---|---|

| 5 | Partial moult of head, body and some wing-coverts from February, completed by April. |
|---|---|

| Adult | Complete post-breeding moult starting June (summer hood often lost by August) and usually completed by October. Partial pre-breeding moult, confined to head and body and sometimes inner wing-coverts and 1-2 secondaries, December-March (April). |
|---|---|

**Biometrics**   Adult (BWP).

| | | | | | | |
|---|---|---|---|---|---|---|
| Wing | ♂309 | (7.99;6) | 300-320 | ♀303 | (9.66;5) | 295-316 |
| Bill | 33.8 | (1.85;9) | 30.6-36.2 | 34.0 | (1.99;5) | 31.6-36.2 |
| Tarsus | 50.8 | (2.66;9) | 46.6-53.9 | 50.0 | (1.99;5) | 47.5-52.8 |

# LITTLE GULL *Larus minutus*

**Identification**  Smallest of the gulls, with wing length <246mm (range 204-245mm). All other West Palearctic gulls >250mm except Ross's Gull *Rhodostethia rosea* and some ♀♀ of Sabine's Gull *Larus sabini.*

## Autumn/Winter

| 3 | Crown, mantle, scapulars, ear-coverts and sides of belly blackish-brown; distinctive diagonal bar running from base of wing to carpal joint, continuing along leading edge of outer wing (forms bold blackish W-pattern across wings when open). Black subterminal tail band. |
|---|---|

| 1w (3/5) | Similar to juvenile but mantle, scapulars and lower back grey, sometimes with retained brown juvenile feathers. Crown usually with brown feathering but towards winter changes completely to grey. Some tail feathers replaced by white ones, rarely the whole tail new and wholly white. |
|---|---|

| 2w (5/7) | Similar to adult but outer primary (p10) with outer web black or grey-black (Fig), and p9-p6 with black subterminal marks. Sometimes outer greater-coverts, alula, inner secondaries and tertials with small blackish-brown marks. Axillaries white. |
|---|---|

| Adult (6/8) | Like adult breeding, but head mainly white with dark grey or black |
|---|---|

221

crescent in front of eye, dark grey rear crown, nape and ear-coverts. All primaries and secondaries tipped white, forming prominent white border on trailing edge and tip of wing. Axillaries pale grey.

**Outer primary**

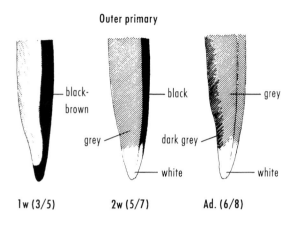

black-brown — 1w (3/5)

grey, black — 2w (5/7)

dark grey, white — grey, white — Ad. (6/8)

## Spring/Summer

1s (5)     Head with varying amounts of velvety black, sometimes completely black. Mantle, scapulars and lower back grey; upperwing pattern like 1st-winter but much faded to pale brown. Subterminal tail band faded to pale brown, sometimes central feathers replaced by new, wholly white ones, rarely all of tail replaced.

2s (7)     Outer webs of p10 blackish. Other outermost primaries with subterminal or terminal blackish marks. Black hood fully developed though usually with white flecking; a few may show winter head pattern. After moult like adult (some birds show dark outer web on p10 and paler underwing - these may be 3rd-year birds but more information required to confirm).

Adult (8)  Mantle, back, scapulars and upperwing uniform pale grey with white tips to all primaries and secondaries, forming prominent white border on trailing edge and tip of wing. Underwing black or lead-grey. Head black. Underparts and hindneck often flushed pink.

## Moult

3          Partial moult confined to head, underparts, mantle and most scapulars, sometimes central tail feathers (rarely all), August-October.

5             Complete post-breeding, starting with head and body March or April and
              followed by wing in June, sometimes finished August, usually September
              (October). Thereafter timing as adult.

Adult         Complete post-breeding moult, starting with head and body July followed
              by wing in late July (more commonly August), completed by September
              or October (November). Partial pre-breeding moult confined to head and
              body March-April (May).


**Biometrics**    Adult (BWP).

Wing*    ♂225    (5.28;37)    209-236    ♀218    (7.99;25)    204-237
Bill     22.0    (0.99;39)    19.6-24.5  21.8    (0.71;24)    19.4-23.2
Tarsus   26.6    (0.99;34)    24.3-28.8  26.1    (0.73;25)    24.1-28.2

\* P. Fearon (*in litt.*) has measured 27 adults with wing lengths >237mm
and 4 >245mm.


# BLACK-HEADED GULL *Larus ridibundus*

**Identification** A medium-small gull with white leading edge to the outer wing
              (primaries) best defined in adults but apparent in all ages to greater or
              lesser degree. Most likely to be confused with Slender-billed *L. genei*,
              Bonaparte's *L. philadelphia* and Grey-headed Gulls *L. cirrocephalus*.
              Measurements separate most: Slender-billed has longer bill (adult 36-
              47mm, av. 41mm) and tarsus (adult 46-56mm, av. 51mm); in summer
              lacks black head. Juvenile mantle feathers grey-brown, not ginger-brown.
              1st-winter (5) paler brown and black wing markings; pale iris. Bonaparte's
              appreciably smaller - wing (adult 252-274mm, av. 264mm), tarsus (adult
              32-37mm, av. 35mm). Grey-headed larger overall but measurements
              overlap to some degree: wing (adult 290-343mm, av. 315mm), bill (adult
              31-42mm, av. 36mm), tarsus (adult 45-56mm, av. 49mm). Grey-headed
              has more rounded wing p10 longest, p9 <0-1mm, p8 9-11mm, p7 26-
              32mm, p6 48-51mm: in Black-headed p9 <0-5mm, p8 7-23mm, p7 33-
              47mm, p6 54-62mm.

## Sexing

♂           Head and bill length >83mm.*

♀           Head and bill length <81mm.*

* Measurements made in UK only.

Accuracy of sex determination in adults is increased using head and bill length and bill depth (at gonys) simultaneously in a discriminant equation: (Head and Bill Length x 0.141) + (Bill Depth x 0.866) − 18.712. If value is greater than zero = ♂, less than zero = ♀.

## Autumn/Winter

3           Head variably smudged light rusty-brown, strongest usually on crown and over brow. Sides of neck and mantle brown. Scapulars, tertials and median-coverts brown with pale buff tips. Black subterminal tail band.

1w (3/5)    Similar to juvenile but sides of neck and mantle grey. Head whiter. Some individuals retain juvenile brown feathers in mantle and neck.

2w (5/7)    Not all can be aged as many now take on appearance of adult. However, those showing dark markings on primary-coverts and alula and/or orange-yellow bill with dark tip, and orange-flesh legs are 2nd-winter.

Adult (6/8)    Wing-coverts uniform grey. Tail feathers white. Bill carmine-red with dark tip. Legs, feet and orbital ring carmine-red.

## Spring/Summer

1s (5)    Wing and tail similar to juvenile except dark areas are somewhat faded and the tips of the coverts are worn. Some tail feathers may be replaced by adult white ones but majority retained and show blackish subterminal band.

Adult (6)    As adult Autumn/Winter.

## Moult

3           Moult of body feathers and sometimes some wing- coverts begins shortly after fledging and is usually complete by September or October (December).

5           Partial moult of head, body, some wing-coverts, and occasionally one or two tail feathers from February or March, completed by April or May.

| Adult | Usually commence primary moult on nesting grounds (May) June-October (November). Hood normally lost when primaries around mid-way through replacement August-September (October). Partial pre-nuptial moult confined to head and body (December) January-March (April). |

**Biometrics**    Adult (BWP).

| Wing | ♂306 | (10.33;26) | 282-323 | ♀295 | (7.00;22) | 284-313 |
|------|------|-----------|---------|------|-----------|---------|
| Bill | 33.4 | (1.42;26) | 30.1-36.9 | 31.6 | (1.57;23) | 28.2-35.2 |
| Tarsus | 44.6 | (1.99;27) | 40.0-47.9 | 43.4 | (1.66;23) | 38.9-46.5 |

**References**    Coulson *et al.* (1983), Allaine & Lebreton (1990).


# COMMON GULL *Larus canus*

**Identification**  From Black-headed Gull by absence of white on leading edge of primaries (all ages). Immatures more likely to be confused with Mediterranean Gull than other gulls due to bulky frame and large bill, but longer winged (320-395mm) compared to Mediterranean Gull (290-320mm); flesh or bluish-flesh legs, not blackish or brown. Ring-billed Gull *L. delawarensis* adults have yellow, not dark, iris. Immatures show prominent pattern of dark round spotting on hindneck and especially breast; pale grey, not brown, greater-coverts. Averages longer in wing and bill: wing - adult ♂ 369-401mm, av. 382, adult ♀ 360-377mm, av. 368; bill - ♂ 37-44mm, av. 41, ♀ 36-39mm, av. 37.

## Sexing

♂    Head and bill length >88mm.*

♀    Head and bill length <87mm.*

     * Measurements made in UK only.

## Autumn/Winter

3    Mantle and scapulars slate grey-brown with neat pale fringes giving

225

scaly pattern. Rump and uppertail-coverts white with dark arrowhead markings or bars. Tail white with broad blackish-brown subterminal band. Bill blackish with diffuse pale flesh or greyish base. Iris dark brown. Legs fleshy or greyish-flesh.

1w (3/5)    Very similar to juvenile but some uniform blue-grey feathers on mantle and scapulars. Head and underparts less streaked and whiter. Wings and tail as juvenile but brown and blackish areas somewhat faded. Fading may produce pale subterminal spots on outer primaries, sometimes forming well-marked mirrors.

2w (5/7)    Mantle and scapulars uniform blue-grey, similar to adult. Head and body as 1st-winter but dark markings or streaking less extensive. Black on primaries more extensive, extending to p4 or p5 and along leading edge into blackish-brown greater- and median-coverts and alula. Only small amounts of white on primary tips and much smaller mirror on p9 and p10 than adult. Tail white, occasionally with dark subterminal marks. Bill blue-grey, grey-green or occasionally yellowish, with dark subterminal band. Legs bluish-grey or greyish-flesh.

3w (7/9)    Like adult, except blue-grey primary-coverts with fine blackish shaft-streaks or dark speckling on alula. Bill sometimes with dark tip.

Adult (8/10)  Head and neck white with fine dark streaking. Dusky eye-crescent. Underparts white with dark spots or streaking on breast-sides and flanks. Mantle, scapulars and back uniform blue-grey. Black outer primaries with white tips (except outermost p10). Large white mirrors on two outermost primaries. Bill yellowish. Legs yellowish, greenish or greyish.

## Spring/Summer

1s (5)     Like 1st-winter except, head and body often whiter, less streaked. The brown areas on wing and tail become very faded, often uniform greyish-white, and black areas browner, often bleached pale brown. Bill yellowish-green. Legs greenish or greenish-blue.

2s (7)     Like 2nd-winter except, head and body usually white, only lightly marked. Black areas in the wing somewhat faded and bleached. Small white areas to primary tips well worn, often absent altogether.

3s (9)     Like 3rd-winter, except head and underparts white. White primary tips reduced, sometimes abraded away completely on outermost primaries.

Adult (10)  Like adult winter, except head and underparts white. White primary tips abraded and reduced. Orbital ring red. Bill wholly yellow or yellowish-green.

## Moult

3      Partial post-juvenile moult confined to head and body, some mantle and scapular feathers, sometimes a few median-coverts, August-October (November).

5      Partial pre-breeding moult confined to head, underparts, some mantle feathers and rump, April-May. Complete post-breeding moult (April) May-September, October (November). Subsequent moults like adult but immatures likely to be slightly earlier.

Adult      Complete post-breeding moult starting mid-May or beginning of June (July) and completed by mid-November. Pre-breeding moult partial and confined to head and body, March-May.

**Geographical variation** Involves mainly colour and size. Nominate *L.c. canus* (N.W. Europe) is the palest form with light blue-grey mantle and wings. *L.c. heinei* (central Russia - wintering in parts of western Europe, including Britain) is darker above and somewhat larger. *L.c. kamtschatschensis* (NE Siberia) is the largest of the four subspecies, though somewhat intermediate in colour between *canus* and *heinei*, and *brachyrhynchus* (NW North America) the smallest.

**Biometrics**      Adult. Nominate *canus* (BWP).

| | | | | | | |
|---|---|---|---|---|---|---|
| Wing | ♂360 | (9.00;22) | 342-380 | ♀341 | (10.3;21) | 321-357 |
| Bill | 34.5 | (1.66;25) | 32.0-38.4 | 31.1 | (1.66;27) | 27.5-34.6 |
| Tarsus | 51.1 | (1.99;26) | 46.4-55.0 | 47.7 | (2.00;27) | 43.4-52.0 |
| Toe | 41.3 | (1.14;25) | 38.2-44.0 | 39.0 | (1.70;27) | 35.0-42.3 |

Adult. *L.c. heinei* (BWP).

| | | | | | | |
|---|---|---|---|---|---|---|
| Wing | ♂382 | (15.00;8) | 355-395 | ♀368 | (9.99;7) | 351-379 |
| Bill | 35.7 | (2.00;8) | 33.2-38.5 | 32.7 | (1.33;5) | 31.0-34.9 |
| Tarsus | 52.3 | (2.66;2) | 50.4-54.2 | 49.7 | (3.66;4) | 46.0-54.8 |

**References**      Coulson *et al.* (1983).

227

# LESSER BLACK-BACKED GULL *Larus fuscus*

**Identification** From Great Black-backed Gull by smaller size (wing <463mm, toe <65mm) and weaker bill (bill depth at angle of gonys <20mm). 2nd-year birds and older immatures are readily separable from Herring Gull by much darker upperwing and dark ash-grey mantle and scapulars, not clear pale grey. Juveniles up to 1st-summer are very similar to Herring Gull; primaries though are much darker - dark brown or blackish right across the feather. Sometimes the tips to inner primaries may show small pale area with grey-brown speckling; in Herring Gull the outer primaries are brown, or dark brown, and contrast with the light, heavily speckled, inner primaries.

**Sexing**

♂       Head and bill length >113mm.*

♀       Head and bill length <112mm.*

      * Measurements made in UK only.

**Autumn/Winter**

3       Mantle, scapulars and wing-coverts mottled brown with clear light margins. Rump whitish with darker streaking. Tail whitish with thin black bars on outer feathers and with conspicuous blackish subterminal band. Prominent dark markings around eye and ear-coverts. Underparts streaked dark grey-brown. Iris dark brown. Bill blackish. Legs dull flesh.

1w (3/5)       Very similar to juvenile though mantle and scapulars more uniformly dark brown, less scaly. Head and underparts often whiter.

2w (5/7)       Head and neck white with extensive dusky streaking, usually concentrated around eye though much less conspicuous than in juvenile. Dark subterminal tail band. Underparts white, with extensive dark streaking on sides of breast and flanks. Iris dark brown, sometimes with flecks of yellow. Bill blackish with light areas at tip and particularly at base. Legs flesh or yellowish-flesh.

3w (7/9)       Similar to adult with uniform ash-grey mantle, scapulars and wing-coverts, perhaps with some old brown feathers admixed. Head and neck white with extensive dusky streaking or clouding. Tail white usually with hint of a dark subterminal band. Primary tips often with white tips and sometimes outer primary (p10) with mirror. Iris pale brown or yellow-brown. Bill yellowish with dark ring at gonys.

| 4w (9/11) | Like adult but outer primary-coverts or alula with brown speckling; also sometimes with brown flecking on tail. Bill often with dark patch around gonys. |
|---|---|
| Adult (10/12) | Head and neck white with extensive dusky streaking or clouding. Wings, mantle and scapulars uniform dark ash-grey. Outer primaries black with white tips; outermost (p10) and p9 with white mirror. Tail white. Iris pale yellow with red orbital ring. Bill deep yellow with red or orange spot near gonys. Legs deep- or creamy-yellow. |

## Spring/Summer

| 1s (5) | Like 1st-winter, except head and neck whiter, wings and tail worn and faded; median- and greater-coverts especially worn and often faded to pale brown, often mixed with new, plain grey feathers; new mantle and scapular feathers plain grey-brown with pale tips. |
|---|---|
| 2s (7) | Like 2nd-winter, except head and underparts whiter or all-white. Mantle and scapulars clear dark ash-grey, often with few brown-barred feathers. Iris usually pale brownish-yellow. |
| 3s (9) | As 3rd-winter, except head and underparts white. The wing-coverts, especially median- and greater-coverts, and tertials are faded brown and worn. White primary tips much reduced or lacking through wear. |
| 4s (11) | As 4th-winter, except wings become brownish through fading; white primary tips reduced or lacking through wear. |
| Adult (12) | Like adult winter, except head and underparts white. Bill and legs bright orange-yellow. |

## Moult

| | Timing of moult varies considerably with race. In Europe 3 subspecies are recognized (see Geographical variation). Generally *L.f. graellsii* and *intermedius* moult at similar times, whereas nominate *fuscus* is much later, by five or more months. Timing as detailed below is for *graellsii* and *intermedius*. |
|---|---|
| 3 | Partial post-juvenile moult confined to head, underparts, many or some mantle feathers, and some scapulars, back and rump feathers, September-November. |
| 5 | Partial pre-breeding moult confined to head and body, January-April, followed almost immediately by complete post-breeding moult, some 2 |

months earlier than adult. Primary moult begins in late April or May and usually completed by August or September. Subsequent moults like adult but earlier: perhaps applies to birds up to 4 or 5 years of age.

Adult Complete post-breeding moult May-December (January). Body moult precedes onset of primary moult, May or June. Some begin primary moult as early as mid-May, more often July or August; wing moult suspended September or October, completing in wintering areas. Some (Fenno-Scandia) known to arrest wing moult so that pre-breeding moult includes completion of primary moult, the inner ones being replaced twice during one moulting cycle. Otherwise pre-breeding moult partial, confined to head and body.

**Geographical variation** Involves size and tone of grey on the upperparts of adults. Generally *L.f. graellsii* (Iceland, Faroes, British Isles, Brittany and north-west Spain) is larger with relatively short wings, short and heavy bill; adults with dull smoky-grey or dark ash-grey upperparts. This is the palest race (though obviously darker than Herring Gull), with obvious contrast between grey upperparts and black outer primaries. *L.f. intermedius* (southern Norway, west Sweden, Netherlands and Denmark) similar to *graellsii* in size, though with slightly longer wing and more slender bill; intermediate grey tone between *graellsii* and nominate *fuscus*, though slight contrast still with black outer primaries. *L.f. fuscus* (Baltic-White Sea area and northern Norway) is slightly longer-winged and has almost blackish upperparts showing no contrast with black primaries; rarely shows white mirror on p9.

**Biometrics** Adult. *L.f. graellsii* (Harris & Hope Jones 1969, BWP).

| | | | | | | |
|---|---|---|---|---|---|---|
| Wing | ♂430 | (6.6;26) | 417-446 | ♀409 | (9.7;35) | 394-430 |
| Bill | 55.6 | (2.3;30) | 49.0-60.0 | 50.0 | (2.2;50) | 45.5-54.9 |
| Tarsus | 65 | (2.9;26) | 56-70 | 60 | (3.0;33) | 55-68 |
| Toe | 56.3 | (1.99;29) | 51.9-60.2 | 52.5 | (2.00;29) | 48.0-57.9 |

Adult. *L.f. intermedius* (Barth 1967).

| | | | | | | |
|---|---|---|---|---|---|---|
| Wing | ♂433 | (10.6;73) | 410-458 | ♀410 | (10.4;74) | 385-435 |
| Bill | 54.4 | (1.9;73) | 50.2-58.4 | 49.4 | (1.8;74) | 46.0-53.5 |
| Tarsus | 64.7 | (2.2;62) | 60.0-69.5 | 59.7 | (1.9;68) | 54.0-64.0 |

Adult. *L.f. fuscus* (Barth 1967).

| | | | | | | |
|---|---|---|---|---|---|---|
| Wing | ♂433 | (9.4;54) | 416-462 | ♀412 | (8.4;71) | 395-430 |
| Bill | 52.1 | (1.5;54) | 49.4-55.3 | 47.5 | (1.6;71) | 44.4-52.2 |
| Tarsus | 63.4 | (1.6;49) | 60.0-67.3 | 58.8 | (1.8;64) | 55.0-63.3 |

**References** Barth (1967), Harris & Hope Jones (1969), Coulson *et al.* (1983).

# HERRING GULL *Larus argentatus*

**Identification** From Great Black-backed Gull (immatures) by smaller size, wing <485mm (but some overlap), and weaker bill, bill depth <20mm (angle on gonys). Otherwise following plumage characteristics may help: head and neck darker and same colour as rest of underparts, not paler and contrasting with rest of body; distinctly blacker ear-coverts; broader subterminal tail band - 30-40mm on outermost tail feather (t6), usually 15-25mm wide in Greater Black-backed. From immature Lesser Black-backed Gull by paler primaries, the outers brown contrasting with the light, heavily speckled, inner ones; in Lesser Black-backed Gull primaries are dark brown or blackish right across the feather, though sometimes tips of inner primaries may show small pale area with grey-brown speckling.

### Inner primaries

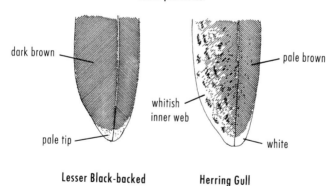

Lesser Black-backed          Herring Gull

The southern or *cachinnans* group (see Geographical variation), *L.a. cachinnans, atlantis* and *michahellis*, are considered by some to be a separate species *L. cachinnans.*

231

## Sexing

♂            Head and bill length >118mm.*

♀            Head and bill length <117mm.*

            * Measurements made in UK only.

## Autumn/Winter

3            Mantle, scapulars, wing-coverts and rump grey-brown with pale margin. Tail grey-brown with broad subterminal bar. Head, neck and underparts mottled and streaked grey-brown; more heavily mottled around eye and ear-coverts. Iris dark brown. Bill black, sometimes with small light areas on tip or at base. Legs dull flesh.

1w (3/5)    Like juvenile but head and sometimes underparts whiter. Mantle and scapulars with more complex pattern of dark bars with yellowish-brown feather margins.

2w (5/7)    Mantle and scapulars with variable number of clear grey feathers admixed with brown-barred feathers. Body feathers basically white, but with dark streaks around the neck. Subterminal tail band narrow or broken on outer tail feathers. Outer primaries black, white mirror on p10 absent or possibly showing as a greyish smudge; inner 3 or 4 primaries and their coverts mainly clear grey. Iris yellowish-brown. Bill light with obvious dark band at gonys.

3w (7/9)    Similar to adult. Mantle and scapulars uniform pale grey. Head and body white with extensive dusky streaking especially around eye and on crown, and nape. Tail white with variable amounts of brown mottling, sometimes extensive. Wing-coverts pale grey except outer primary- and greater-coverts and alula which are usually mottled, freckled or streaked with variable amount of dark brown, sometimes all-brown with pale tips, sometimes blue-grey with dark shaft-streaks. Outer primary (p10) black with small area of white on tip (sometimes speckled with brown) and small white mirror; p9 generally without mirror.*

            * Many birds in their 4th year show all the plumage characteristics of full adult birds. However, others (unknown proportion) still show signs of immaturity. This appears as brown speckling on the alula or outer primary-coverts, and possibly brown speckling on the tail too. The bill may still be black at the gonys. These features however are not reliable ageing characters since five- or six-year-old birds sometimes show these markings.

| Adult (8/10) | Head and neck variably spotted or finely streaked, especially prominent around eye and hindneck; some streaking on sides of breast and flanks. Wings and mantle uniform pale grey. Tail white. Iris yellow. Orbital ring yellow to red. Bill rich or pale yellow, with orange or red spot at gonys. Legs bright or pale flesh. |

## Spring/Summer

| 1s (5) | Like 1st-winter but dark areas on wing and tail faded to pale brown, and somewhat abraded. Perhaps with some new, clear grey scapulars. Bill pale at base. |
| 2s (7) | Like 2nd-winter, except head and underparts mainly white. Dark areas on wing and tail faded and worn, the pale areas often faded to whitish (often contrasting with grey mantle and scapulars). Bill yellowish, sometimes with reddish spot on gonys or with dark band. |
| 3s (9) | Like 3rd-winter, except head and body are white. White primary tips often much reduced, even absent through wear. |
| Adult (10) | Like adult winter, except head and underparts pure white. White primary tips abraded and much reduced, even absent through wear. |

## Moult

| | The timing of moult between races varies considerably. Subspecies fall into three groups (see Geographical variation). Timings given below are for the *argentatus* group (northern group). The *cachinnans* group (southern group) moult on average slightly earlier. *L.a. armenicus* (one subspecies) moults much later than *cachinnans*, by 1 to 2 months on average. |
| 3 | Partial moult confined to head and much of the body, August, completed by November (December). In some individuals moult may be delayed and take place in the spring. |
| 5 | Partial pre-breeding moult confined to head and body, January-April. First complete post-breeding moult begins April, completed by August or September (October). Subsequent moults like adult but generally start earlier. |
| Adult | Complete post-breeding moult April to July, completing by September-November (December). Primary moult usually end of April through to |

July. Pre-breeding moult partial and confined to head and body, January-April.

**Geographical variation** Complex, involving mainly size and colour. Subspecies can be divided into three distinct groups: the northern, or *argentatus* group, *L.a. smithsonianus* (N. America), *argenteus* (W. Europe, Iceland), nominate *argentatus* (Scandinavia, Baltic), and *vegae* (N. USSR); the southern or *cachinnans* group, *L.a. atlantis* (Azores, Madeira, Canary Islands), *michahellis* (France, Iberia, Mediterranean, Morocco), *cachinnans* (Black & Caspian Seas), *omissus* (eastern Baltic, Estonia, Finland, and north-west Russia), *barabensis* and *mongolicus* (central Asia); and the *armenicus* group, *L.a. armenicus* (Armeniya, E. Turkey, Iran). The northern races (except omissus) are characterized by pale mantle, pale flesh legs, yellow eye-ring, profuse winter-streaking, and complex juvenile patterning. The southern races show slightly darker mantle, more extensive and blacker wing tips, vermilion eye-ring, yellow legs, reduced winter head streaking and more even juvenile plumage-pattern. The *armenicus* group averages smaller than *cachinnans* group, with shorter bill, more extensive black on wing tips, dark iris, and much later moults.

**Biometrics** Adult. *L.a. argenteus* (Coulson *et al* 1983, BWP).

| | | | | | | |
|---|---|---|---|---|---|---|
| Wing | ♂433 | (10.4;261) | 391-461 | ♀413 | (9.2;219) | 387-422 |
| Bill | 54.1 | (2.2;261) | 46-60 | 49.5 | (2.0;219) | 45-56 |
| Tarsus | 65.2 | (2.99;25) | 57.0-71.2 | 60.5 | (2.00;30) | 56.6-65.7 |
| Toe | 61.6 | (2.99;25) | 51.4-66.0 | 56.7 | (2.25;30) | 52.1-60.8 |

Adult. *L.a. michahellis* (Isenmann 1973).

| | | | | | | |
|---|---|---|---|---|---|---|
| Wing | ♂465 | (8.8;80) | 445-485 | ♀440 | (8.4;80) | 418-462 |
| Bill | 61 | (1.8;80) | 56-65 | 56 | (2.5;80) | 50-61(65) |
| Tarsus | 72 | (3.4;80) | 65-80 | 67 | (2.7;80) | 60-75 |

Adult & sub-adult. *L.a. armenicus* (BWP).

| | | | | | | |
|---|---|---|---|---|---|---|
| Wing | ♂445 | (8.00;8) | 429-453 | ♀413 | (10.14;11) | 390-427 |
| Bill | 48.0 | (1.99;7) | 45.4-51.4 | 44.7 | (1.66;11) | 42.0-46.9 |
| Tarsus | 67.4 | (3.12;8) | 62.8-72.7 | 62.0 | (2.00;11) | 60.1-66.5 |

**References** Harris & Hope Jones (1969), Coulson *et al.* (1983) Isenmann (1973).

234

# GREAT BLACK-BACKED GULL *Larus marinus*

**Identification** 3rd-year birds and older readily separable from Herring Gull by much darker upper wing and blackish, not grey, mantle and scapulars. Juveniles usually distinguishable by size but some continental Herring Gulls may be as large as smaller Great Black-backed Gulls. However wing >480mm and bill depth >20mm (at angle of gonys) indicates Great Black-backed. Otherwise, following plumage characteristics may help: head and neck whiter, more sparsely and more distinctly streaked; subterminal tail band narrower (15-25mm wide on t6, outermost, 30-40mm in Herring Gull). From Lesser Black-backed Gull by larger size: wing >463mm (some overlap), toe >65mm, bill depth >20mm.

## Sexing

♂            Head and bill length >142mm.*

♀            Head and bill length <141mm.*

            * Measurements made in UK only.

## Autumn/Winter

3            Mantle, scapulars and wing-coverts mottled brown with broadly cream or yellowish-brown margin. Rump white. Head, neck and breast mottled grey. Tail white with complex wavy barring ending with narrow blackish-brown subterminal bar and broad white terminal fringe. Bill black, sometimes with whitish spot at extreme tip. Iris dark brown. Legs dull flesh.

1w (3/5)    Very similar to juvenile but head and neck whiter, less mottled with grey. Tips of mantle feathers less clearly yellowish-brown than wing-coverts giving slight contrast between the two areas. Bill sometimes pale at base.

2w (5/7)    Head and breast white, sometimes with faint dark streaking around the eye and on lower hindneck. Some slate-grey feathers present on mantle admixed with juvenile-type feathers. Tail mottled, mainly black but with white tips. Underparts whitish with coarse dark streaking on sides of breast and flanks. Bill pale at base with extensive dark subterminal ring (pattern highly variable). Iris pale with dull orange orbital ring.

3w (7/9)    Appearance like adult; some faint grey streaks around eye and lower hindneck. Tail white but with faint subterminal band of variable extent and pattern. Outer primary and/or 2nd outermost (p10/9) with a white central wedge separated from white tip by narrow black bar (Fig). Bill whitish or fleshy-yellow with dark subterminal ring, and often with some reddish on gonys. Iris pale with orange or red orbital ring.

4w (9/11)    As adult but outer primary-coverts with pale brown streaks.

Adult (10/12)    Head and neck as 1st-winter. Tail completely white. Upperwing uniform blackish-grey except for narrow white leading edge and somewhat broader white trailing edge. Outer primary (p10) black except for white tip (Fig). Primary-coverts uniform blackish-grey, as rest of upperwing. Iris pale yellow. Bill pale yellow or flesh-yellow with orange or red spot on gonys. Red orbital ring.

Outer primary      2nd outermost pr.      Outer primary      2nd outermost pr.

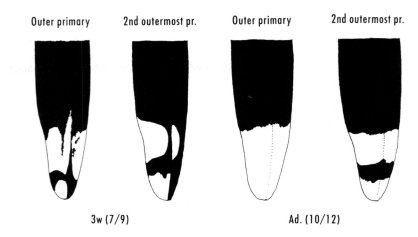

3w (7/9)                    Ad. (10/12)

## Spring/Summer

1s (5)    Like 1st-winter except head and breast nearly white; flanks and belly still with some faint dark patches. Wing and tail somewhat worn and abraded. Upperparts and wing-coverts faded and worn.

2s (7)    Like 2nd-winter except head and underparts mainly white, mantle and scapulars mainly uniform blackish, perhaps with some worn juvenile-type feathers admixed. Bill yellowish with black tip. Reddish orbital ring.

3s (9)    Like 3rd-winter except wings faded patchy brown-and-black. Shows much abrasion, especially on tail and outer primary tips - the white tips being much reduced, often broken off or shattered.

| 4s (11) | As for 4th-winter but showing faded and abraded flight feathers. |

| Adult (12) | As adult Autumn/Winter, except head and body pure white. Upperwings acquiring brownish tone due to exposure to light; white primary tips abraded and much reduced. |

## Moult

| 3 | Partial post-juvenile moult confined to head and body August-November (December). |

| 5 | Probably continuation of post-juvenile moult through to April and onset of first post-breeding wing moult (including all body feathers); p1 or p2 shed late April and usually completed October or November. |

| 7 | Partial pre-breeding moult confined to head and body, December-March, followed by complete post-breeding moult (April) May, completed by November. Timing of successive moults appears to be as adult though possibly birds up to 4 or 5 years of age may moult slightly earlier. |

| Adult | Complete post-breeding moult (April) May through to December (January). |

**Biometrics** Adult (BWP).

| | | | | | | |
|---|---|---|---|---|---|---|
| Wing | ♂500 | (8.99;24) | 481-521 | ♀472 | (9.66;23) | 453-491 |
| Bill | 64.0 | (2.00;34) | 57.8-71.2 | 57.6 | (2.26;31) | 53.7-64.5 |
| Tarsus | 78.4 | (2.42;29) | 73.6-84.4 | 71.6 | (3.33;24) | 66.6-76.8 |

**References** Coulson *et al.* (1983).


# KITTIWAKE *Rissa tridactyla*

**Identification** Larger than Little Gull, wing >275mm. Slightly forked tail, depth 5-25mm.

## Sexing

| ♂ | Bill and head length >89mm.* |

♀              Bill and head length <88mm.*

              * Measurements made in UK only.

## Autumn/Winter

3             Blackish diagonal bar on upper wing-coverts running from base of wing to carpal joint, continuing along leading edge of wing, forms bold W-pattern across wings when open (Fig). Black nape band. Black terminal tail band. Bill black.

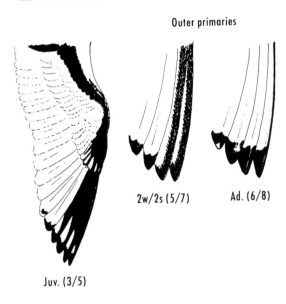

**Outer primaries**

2w/2s (5/7)       Ad. (6/8)

Juv. (3/5)

1w (3/5)       Like juvenile but back of head and nape are bluish-grey, making a dark shading from the ear-coverts over the head. Nape band somewhat faded (frequently almost absent). Diagonal carpal bar of upper wing faded to brown. Faded blackish terminal tail band. Bill blackish with some greenish-yellow. Legs usually grey.

2w (5/7)       Like adult but 50-150mm of outer web on p9 black. (Fig). Black streaks on some primary-coverts, and sometimes on other wing-coverts and tertials.

Adult (6/8)     Head basically white but with dusky markings on crown and ear-coverts.
                Tail wholly white. Bill uniform greenish-yellow.


## Spring/Summer

1s (5)          Similar to 1st-winter but head is whiter and retains dusky head markings.
                The blackish carpal bar even more faded to pale brown, and the wing-
                coverts worn and abraded. Tail abraded with much reduced brown
                terminal band. Some new tail or wing feathers visible by early summer
                with some dark markings near tips. Bill greenish-yellow. Legs usually
                grey.

2s (7)          Like adult but 50-150mm of outer web on p9 black (Fig). Head has
                dusky smudges on crown and around ear-coverts.

Adult (8)       Head white. Otherwise as Autumn/Winter. Bill yellow.

## Moult

3               Partial moult limited to head and body, August-November.

5               Partial and probably limited pre-breeding moult of head and body (more
                information required). Complete post-breeding moult earlier than adult,
                (May) June, finishing (August) September-October (November).

Adult           Complete post-breeding moult starting late May and early June and
                completed by October or November (December).

**Biometrics**  Adult (BWP, Coulson *et al.* 1983).

| | | | | | | |
|---|---|---|---|---|---|---|
| Wing | ♂312 | (4.7;24) | 290-326 | ♀302 | (6.7;21) | 279-318 |
| Bill | 34.2 | (1.57;23) | 30.9-38.0 | 33.7 | (1.66;25) | 31.0-36.0 |
| Tarsus | 34.2 | (0.99;23) | 31.9-36.1 | 32.9 | (0.85;24) | 31.0-34.5 |

**References**  Coulson *et al.* (1983), Smith (1988).

# Terns *Sternidae*

Small to moderately large seabirds. Body slim and elongated. Wings long, narrow and pointed. Normally pale grey above and white below, often with contrasting black cap. Non-breeding plumage of adults differs only in reduction of black on crown.

## Feather structure
Primaries = 11 (p10 longest, p11 minute)
Secondaries = 15-19 (20-24)
Tail = 12

## Sexes
Similar in plumage.

## Moult
Strategy: primaries serially descendant. Secondaries ascendant and descendant. Suspends/arrests. Tail mostly centrifugal.
Sequence: primaries moult from 2, sometimes 3 centres. Secondaries in 2 groups, s1-13 ascendantly and sequentially, innermost to s14 ascendant and descendant from centre of group.
Frequency: twice annually; SC, Wp. Protracted in wing. Rectrices replaced at each moult cycle.
Timing: starts summer often finishing in winter quarters late winter-early spring; partial late winter finishing early spring.

# SANDWICH TERN *Sterna sandvicensis*

**Identification** From Gull-billed Tern *Gelochelidon nilotica* by longer bill, >48mm, Gull-billed Tern <43mm; and by shorter tarsus, <29mm, compared to > 30mm in Gull-billed.

## Autumn

3      Mantle, scapulars and tertials pale grey, fading to white at tips with black-brown subterminal band. Median- and lesser-coverts greyish with bold blackish subterminal bands. Tail white with blackish subterminal band.

1w (3)      Mantle, scapulars and tertials change to grey, like adult non-breeding. Some juvenile feathers usually retained on the upperparts. Primary-coverts dull grey with ill-defined off-white borders. Tail usually with dark markings on outer feathers (some inner ones may already have moulted). Primaries show only one age-series.

2w (5)      Like adult non-breeding, with white forehead, dark blotches on crown, and dark lesser-coverts forming rather indistinct carpal bar across fore-wing. Primaries usually in active moult with 2nd series starting at p1 (June-July), likely to have advanced to p3-p4 by autumn. 1st series normally completed with p10 earlier (May-July) though some birds could still show 2 active moult series in August-September.

Adult (6)      Mantle, scapulars, tertials and upper wing-coverts uniformly pale grey; longer scapulars and tertials with white tips. Forehead with variable amounts of white speckling or blotching, often extensive or completely white (non-breeding). New silvery-grey inner primaries (up to p4 or p5) contrasting with old dark grey or dull black outer primaries (2 ages).

## Spring/Summer

1s (5)      Like 2nd-winter in appearance. Primary moult likely to show 2 active moult centres, with inner primary replacement (2nd series) starting from June-July, and old outer juvenile feathers replaced by 1st series (see Moult).

2s (7)      Similar to adult breeding but white feathers on lores and crown; forehead white as in adult non-breeding. Primary moult likely to be in progress from June onwards, earlier than adults. Moult score by late summer therefore higher, 10-20 (25) by late July, compared to 0-10 (15) in adult.

However, timing highly variable, and use of primary scores to judge age should be used in addition to plumage features.

Adult (8)  Mantle, scapulars, tertials and all upper wing-coverts pale grey, the longer scapulars and tertials often tipped white. Crown and nape black with elongated black feathers on rear of crown forming distinct crest. Bill black with 8-12mm of tip yellow. Usually in wing moult by late summer with up to 2 (3) replaced inner primaries by late July and up to 5 or 6 by September, when suspended.

## Moult

3/5  Complete post-juvenile moult starting soon after fledging, August-September. Much of the body, head and median-coverts and some of tail and tertials are replaced by adult-type non-breeding plumage. Body moult suspended prior to migration. Wing moult starts December-January and normally completed by May-July but 2nd series starts at p1 from June-July of second year and probably completes late winter (but details sketchy). 1st non-breeding is replaced directly by 2nd non-breeding plumage. Subsequent moult in 3rd calendar year probably starts slightly earlier in summer than in adults; thus moult scores at time of suspension normally higher.

Adult  Complete post-breeding moult starting with head and body during incubation, (May) June-July (August). Head usually in full non-breeding plumage by late August to late September. Flight feathers begin mid-July to late August. Wing moult is suspended just prior to migration when 5-6 inner primaries replaced. Some finish this moult by late October, others not until winter. A 2nd series in the primaries normally starts November-December, arresting in late January or February with 2-6 new inner primaries. A 3rd series found in some birds, possibly early post-breeding moulters. Partial pre-breeding moult February-late March, not always completed before return to breeding grounds.

**Geographical variation** Slight; involving mostly colour of bill. *S.s. eurygnatha* (South America) with all-yellow bill instead of mostly black. *S.s. acuflavida* (N. C. America) slightly smaller in wing and bill (wing ♂ av. 298mm, ♀ 295mm; bill ♂ av. 53.3mm, ♀ 51.4).

**Biometrics**  Nominate *sandvicensis* (BWP).

| | | Wing ♂ | | | ♀ | | |
|---|---|---|---|---|---|---|---|
| Wing | *ad.* ♂ | 309 | (4.61;21) | 302-317 | ♀ 304 | (6.03;16) | 294-320 |
| | *juv.* | 302 | (3.96;5) | 297-307 | 296 | (4.43;11) | 290-307 |
| Fork | *ad.* | 73.1 | (6.43;12) | 65-84 | 68.9 | (6.17;10) | 58-76 |
| | *juv.* | 39.0 | (4.20;6) | 34-45 | 39.5 | (3.82;13) | 34-45 |

|       |      |           |       |      |           |       |
|-------|------|-----------|-------|------|-----------|-------|
| Bill  | 55.5 | (1.78;21) | 53-58 | 53.1 | (2.19;16) | 49-56 |
| Tarsus | 26.9 | (0.70;21) | 26-28 | 25.9 | (0.86;16) | 24-27 |

# COMMON TERN *Sterna hirundo*

**Identification** From Arctic Tern by longer tarsus, >18mm; Arctic Tern <18mm. Width of black on inner web of outermost primary (p10) at tip of p6 >4.5mm; in Arctic <4.5mm (Fig).

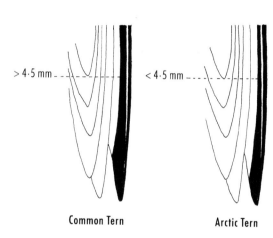

Common Tern          Arctic Tern

## Autumn

3          Back, mantle, scapulars and wing-coverts grey with brown terminal fringes. Lesser-coverts black with pale terminal fringe.

1w (3)     Many of the brown feathers on the upperparts are lost, but some retained, together with tertials which show characteristic dark crescents contrasting with greyer new feathers. Lesser-coverts blackish or dark brown. Flight feathers uniform (one age), though rather worn and brown by September-November.

2w (5)        Crown black with white forehead; underparts white - similar in appearance to adult non-breeding. Dark carpal bar. Bill black. Legs dull orange-brown. Primaries fresh but sometimes outermost 1-2 feathers unmoulted heavily abraded. Inner p1-p3 often new and pale grey, so in some individuals three ages of primaries may be discernible, though usually only two (see Moult).

Adult (6)    Upperparts and all wing-coverts uniform slate-grey, but some birds moulting into winter plumage may already show blackish lesser-coverts. Flight feathers in active moult or suspended. Usually two age-groups of primaries (new inners and old outers), sometimes three.

## Spring/Summer

1s (5)        Some birds are intermediate between juvenile plumage and adult-type non-breeding. Any old juvenile feathers will be patterned as tertials or scapulars, i.e. brown with dark crescents, though very worn and faded. Some birds may be in wing or tail moult; outer primaries abraded and faded, contrasting with new grey inner ones. Some show 3 age-groups of primaries with one or two outermost being very worn, original juvenile feathers (see Moult and Fig).

2s (7)        Outer primary-coverts brownish-grey, contrasting with greyer neighbouring coverts. Wear is a great deal more pronounced than would be expected in an adult at this time of year. Birds showing these characteristics are rarely in full breeding plumage, usually with white flecking on forehead and traces of dark feathering on carpal area. Primaries show two age-groups, and often three.

Adult (8)    Wing-coverts uniform bluish-grey, with perhaps the odd unmoulted blackish-grey lesser-covert. Usually two age-groups of primaries, sometimes three.

               Note: most 1st-summer birds remain in Africa. A few may return to spend some time in the northern hemisphere.

## Moult

3         Often no moult until in winter quarters. Some (very few) start head and body before migration, August-September.

3/5       A complete moult in winter quarters begins November/December (head, body, tail and most wing-coverts) completing March. Primaries from (December) January/February, completing June-August; a few suspend at p6-p9. Before completion of this series, 2nd series starts with p1, May-

Example 1

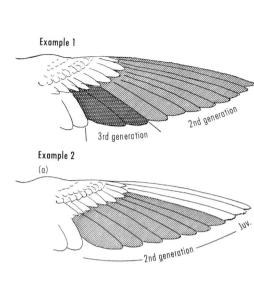

Is (5) June/August. 2nd calendar year. Complete replacement of primaries starting in winter quarters. Suspends before migration, completing on summer grounds. New wave starts at p1 in late summer.

Example 2

(a)

Is (5) April/May. 2nd calendar year. Replacement of inner 6–9 primaries. Suspends about March before migration, leaving worn unmoulted juvenile outer primaries. Onset of moult in summer will start at both p1 and p8 in this example (see below).

(b)

Is (5) May/June of 2nd calendar year. Example as above but serially descendant moult in progress involving 2 centres of active moult.

(c)

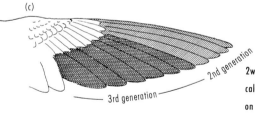

2w (7) December–February of 3rd calendar year. Sequence follows on from (b) above.

Two variations in moult strategy in immature Common Tern.
Figures 2a through to 2e is an example of immature moult sequence over the course of 3 calendar years.

245

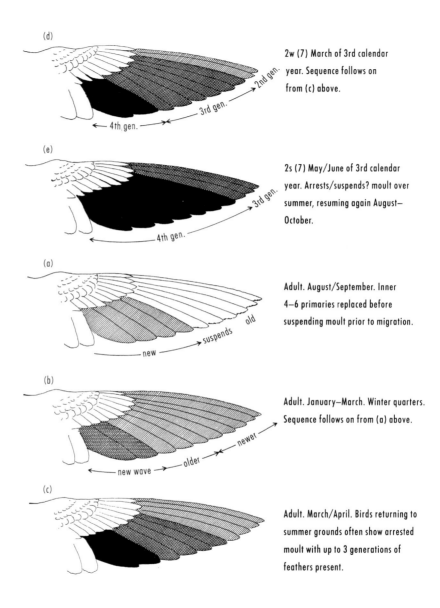

(d)

2nd gen.

3rd gen.

4th gen.

2w (7) March of 3rd calendar year. Sequence follows on from (c) above.

(e)

3rd gen.

4th gen.

2s (7) May/June of 3rd calendar year. Arrests/suspends? moult over summer, resuming again August–October.

(a)

old

suspends

new

Adult. August/September. Inner 4–6 primaries replaced before suspending moult prior to migration.

(b)

newer

older

new wave

Adult. January–March. Winter quarters. Sequence follows on from (a) above.

(c)

Adult. March/April. Birds returning to summer grounds often show arrested moult with up to 3 generations of feathers present.

July of 2nd calendar year (three ages of primaries therefore can be present) but is slow (and sometimes suspends with only p1-p2 new), completing March-June of 3rd calendar year. During late summer of 2nd calendar year (July-August) head, body and tail feathers replaced, followed in December-February by start of wing moult; this suspends in May-June, and is usually completed by August-October. Thereafter timing much as adult (Fig).

Adult        Complete post-breeding moult starting with body shortly after young fledge. Wing moult not until July or August with up to 4 (6) inner primaries replaced before suspending prior to migration, resuming in winter quarters, completed January to early March; a few birds appear to arrest moult before migration, starting a 2nd series at p1 - such birds can, therefore, exhibit three age-groups of primaries. Innermost secondaries moulted twice (at the onset of primary moult and again at the finish), as also is the tail. Partial pre-breeding moult, confined to head, body, tail, upper wing-coverts, outer secondaries and inner primaries, begins with p1 and tail December-February; all but wing feathers completed by March-April when primaries are arrested (up to p4 or p5, rarely p7 new); also start another series from p1 in late winter, then arrest before spring migration at p1 or p2 (Fig).

**Geographical variation** Slight; involving mostly colour of bill and legs, also colour of body. Darker and longer-winged from west to east. *S.h. longipennis* (E. Siberia) has darker grey upperparts, all-black bill and dark red-brown legs in breeding season. Nominate *hirundo* from America slightly shorter in wing (av.265mm - USA).

**Biometrics**    Nominate *hirundo* (Netherlands) (BWP).

| | | | | | | | | |
|---|---|---|---|---|---|---|---|---|
| Wing | ad. | ♂272 | (7.01;73) | 257-287 | ♀270 | (6.52;39) | 259-290 | |
| | juv. | 255 | (8.84;19) | 248-270 | 256 | (8.37;21) | 244-268 | |
| Fork | ad. | 76.9 | (7.42;46) | 64-94 | 78.4 | (7.20;27) | 66-92 | |
| | juv. | 43.0 | (5.47;20) | 36-54 | 42.5 | (3.68;21) | 37-48 | |
| Bill | | 37.1 | (1.40;66) | 35-40 | 35.2 | (1.24;36) | 32-37 | |
| Tarsus | | 20.2 | (0.77;45) | 19-22 | 19.8 | (0.52;36) | 19-21 | |

**References**    Baker (1983*b*), Walters (1987*a*, 1987*b*).

# ARCTIC TERN *Sterna paradisaea*

**Identification** From Common Tern by shorter tarsus, <18mm; Common Tern >18mm. Width of black on inner web of outermost primary (p10) at tip of p6 <4.5mm; in Common >4.5mm (see fig under Common Tern).

## Autumn

**3**  Back, mantle, scapulars and wing-coverts grey or yellowish-brown with dark brown subterminal band giving distinct scaly pattern (highly variable, but generally less scaly than Common Tern). Tertials light grey with off-white tips with dusky grey or blackish subterminal marks or freckling.

**1w (3)**  Many of the dark yellowish-brown feathers replaced by uniform blue-grey adult-type feathers, but most juvenile feathers retained until in winter quarters.

**2w (5)**  Like adult non-breeding plumage; white forehead, white underparts, dark slate carpal bar (lesser-coverts) which contrast with grey wing-coverts, and blackish bill and legs. No adults assume full non-breeding plumage on breeding grounds; a few (probably failed or non-breeders) show limited body moult, but breeding plumage largely retained and unmoulted until in winter quarters.

**Adult (6)**  Mantle, scapulars and wing-coverts uniformly bluish-grey. Rump white. Black forehead and crown. Bill red, although late in season there may be some black. Legs coral red.

## Spring/Summer

**1s (5)**  As 2w. 1st-summer birds rarely return to breeding grounds; but northward movements do occur in spring from the wintering quarters resulting in small percentage reaching breeding areas.

**Adult (6)**  As adult Autumn.

## Moult

**3/5**  Complete post-juvenile moult usually starting in winter quarters, but can be October when first signs of body moult show. Body moult and tail mostly completed by February/March. Wing feathers start from December or January, completed April, sometimes May. Thereafter timing much as adult.

248

Complete post-breeding moult takes place in winter quarters. A few non-breeding or failed breeding birds often start body moult before migration. Most start wing moult late September to early November, and complete early February to early March. Partial pre-breeding moult involves head, body, tail and upper wing-coverts. Wings, therefore, only moulted once - unlike those of Common Tern.

**Biometrics**     Netherlands & Scandinavia (BWP).

| | | | | | | | |
|---|---|---|---|---|---|---|---|
| Wing | ad. | ♂279 | (5.44;20) | 270-290 | ♀274 | (10.1;16) | 261-288 |
| | juv. | 246 | (2.68;5) | 244-250 | 244 | (4.42;15) | 238-253 |
| Fork | ad. | 111 | (10.6;19) | 96-130 | 97.8 | (13.1;18) | 72-118 |
| | juv. | 46.8 | (4.66;5) | 41-52 | 50.3 | (4.96;14) | 44-59 |
| Bill | | 33.0 | (1.40;19) | 31-35 | 30.8 | (1.16;20) | 29-33 |
| Tarsus | | 15.9 | (0.49;20) | 15.0-17.0 | 15.6 | (0.45;19) | 14.8-16.5 |

# LITTLE TERN *Sterna albifrons*

## Autumn

**3**

Mantle, scapulars, tertials and wing-coverts pale buff with broad off-white fringe and black subterminal band (Fig). Upper wing-coverts and primary-coverts greyish-black. Central tail with dark central wedges. Bill black. Primaries all one age.

**1w (3)**

Like adult non-breeding except most scapulars and tertials show dark subterminal bar (Fig). Lesser-coverts and primary-coverts dark grey-brown. Tail with dark central wedges. Inner primaries (p1-p3) possibly moulting; wing moult suspended prior to migration.

**2w (5)**

Like adult non-breeding, i.e. forehead and crown white with black patch in front of eye and black streaks over and behind eye, widening towards black nape; lesser wing-coverts slate-grey forming dark carpal bar. Primaries likely to show 3 moult series, similar to adult but less advanced, with moult score of 5-15 (p1-p3) for inner new feathers (3rd series), 25-35 (p2-p8) for next generation (2nd series), leaving old outermost 1 or 2 feathers (p9-p10); in adults likely to be 10-20 (p2-p4) in 3rd series and 20-25 (p3-p7) in 2nd series, leaving old 3 outermost.

**3w (7)**

Some outer upper median primary-coverts (the small feathers on the leading edge of wing proximal to primary-coverts) brown. There may only be one or two, sometimes only on one wing, but they stand out from adult-type pure grey feathers. Primary series as adult.

Adult (8)     Mantle, scapulars, tertials and all upper wing-coverts light bluish-grey. Outer upper median primary-coverts uniform grey. Primaries likely to show 3 series of feathers, and sometimes 4. Transition from breeding to non-breeding plumage occurs typically in autumn before birds migrate. Thus in autumn most birds likely to show white feather streaking in the crown and some darkening of the lesser-coverts. The bill is often less yellow, and frequently horn-black.

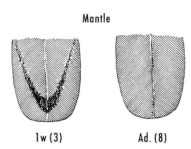

**Mantle**

1w (3)          Ad. (8)

## Spring/Summer

1s (5)        Like 2nd-winter though perhaps with less advanced primary score (especially early in season) but timing highly variable (see Moult). Most 1st-summer birds remain in Africa. A few return in spring/summer to the northern hemisphere, sometimes visiting breeding colonies.

2s (7)        Some outer upper median primary-coverts (the small feathers on the leading edge of the wing proximal to primary-coverts) brown; contrasting with pure grey adult-type feathers.

Adult (8)     Mantle, scapulars, tertials and all upper wing-coverts uniform light bluish-grey. Black eye-stripe joining black nape and crown. Forehead white. Bill yellow, usually with black tip. Upper median primary-coverts uniform grey.

## Moult

3/5           Complete post-juvenile moult from early August to late September starting with mantle and scapulars, followed by head and wing-coverts; some inner secondaries may be moulted at this time. Rest of flight feathers not until late September to early December and normally in winter quarters. This series normally complete by April-May; a 2nd series begins at p1 from February-March progressing to p4-p6 by May; some birds begin a 3rd series late May and June at p1 again. This 3rd series is usually arrested, probably starting a new series at p1 in July without continuing previous series but details as yet unresolved.

7          Timing and strategy probably as adult.

Adult      Complete post-breeding moult beginning in June (when feeding young) with primaries; up to 7 inner primaries can be replaced before suspending moult just prior to migration, more usually 3-5 (6) replaced (p1-p6). Body, head, upperparts and tail begin shortly after p1 dropped. Wing moult and body resumed in winter quarters, a 2nd series of primaries begins when 1st series has reached p7 (mid-October/December). Body, head, wing-coverts, tail and a 3rd primary series normally starts February to mid-March, when 1st series is nearing completion (p8-p9), but may arrest before finishing. Birds returning to breeding grounds therefore often show 3 ages in primaries. By June-August with onset of post-breeding moult 4 different ages of primaries may be present for a short period though determining these age differences in the later series may prove difficult.

**Geographical variation** Slight; in nominate *albifrons* (Europe, N.Africa, east and central Asia, Egypt to northern Pakistan and India) involves mostly timing and strategy of moult and also size. Birds from southern Europe and Middle East slightly smaller, bill more slender. Moult series usually more advanced in southern and eastern regions than western European populations.

**Biometrics**   Nominate *albifrons* (BWP).

| | | | | | | |
|---|---|---|---|---|---|---|
| Wing *ad.* | ♂181 | (3.27;16) | 176-187 | ♀175 | (3.31;19) | 167-180 |
| *juv.* | 168 | (3.35;4) | 164-172 | 171 | (3.76;11) | 166-177 |
| Fork *ad.* | 42.8 | (4.90;6) | 36-49 | 36.1 | (3.15;10) | 29-41 |
| *juv.* | 14.3 | (1.96;5) | 12-17 | 15.4 | (1.56;11) | 13-18 |
| Bill | 30.2 | (1.72;13) | 27.8-33.1 | 28.7 | (1.13;17) | 26.7-30.8 |
| Tarsus | 16.8 | (0.67;13) | 15.6-17.8 | 16.6 | (0.72;18) | 15.1-17.8 |

**References**   Baker (1983*b*).

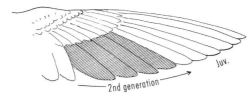

1w (3/5) October. 1st calendar year.
Primary moult normally begins in
winter quarters about September–December.
Progresses conventionally but 2nd
wave 3rd generation primaries may
begin at p1 before completion
of 1st moult.

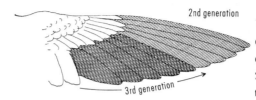

1s (5) April–May. 2nd
calendar year. 1st series
complete at this time while
2nd series about half way
through wing.

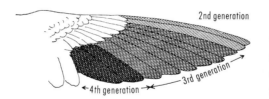

1s (5) May–June. 2nd
calendar year. 2nd series
progresses to about p8 or 9
and then arrests; also new
3rd series starts at this time
and arrests at same time
as 2nd series.

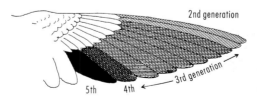

1s (5) July. 2nd calendar
year. New 4th series starts
at p1 and progresses
descendantly, normally suspending
at p5/6 prior to migration.

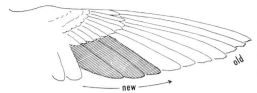

Adult. June. Descendant primary moult begins in late breeding period. Outer old primaries faded and abraded.

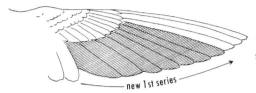

Adult. August–September. Primaries moult up to 7 inner ones before suspending prior to migration.

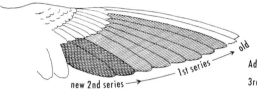

Adult. October–December. New 3rd series starts at this time, usually in winter quarters.

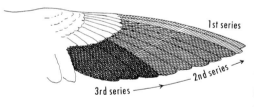

Adult. February–March. A new 3rd series starts at this time when 1st series is nearing completion. Often arrests, thus birds returning to summer grounds often show 3 generations of primaries.

Adult. July. Post-breeding moult begins with a new series starting at p1 when 4 generations of primaries may be present.

# BLACK TERN *Chlidonias niger*

**Identification** From White-winged Black Tern *C. leucopterus* by shallower incisions on web (Fig), and by shorter tarsus <18mm, (18-22mm in White-winged), and by deeper fork in tail (adult) >13mm (5-13mm in White- winged). Outer web of outermost tail feather (t6) is grey, not pure white. Pale margin on inner web of p7 diffuse and unclear; in White-winged the margin is well-defined and sharp.

Black Tern    White-winged Black Tern

| | |
|---|---|
| **Sexing** | Adults in breeding plumage only: |
| ♂ | Head and neck jet-black with faint green gloss on crown and nape. Mantle black, contrasting with slate-grey wing-coverts, rump and scapulars. |
| ♀ | Head, neck and mantle slate-grey, similar in tone to rest of upperparts, instead of distinctly darker. |

**Autumn**

| | |
|---|---|
| 3 | Mantle and scapulars variably grey-brown to dull black towards tip, fringed black-brown or buff. Lesser-coverts blackish. Median-coverts dark grey with deep brown tips, sometimes pale brown or even off-white. Scapulars and tertials broadly fringed white (Fig). |
| 1w (3) | In juvenile plumage for most of the autumn period; some start body moult in September, but generally moult begins in winter quarters (see Moult). A small percentage of birds may show some new grey feathers on the back, mantle or scapulars. |
| 2w (5) | Similar in appearance to adult non-breeding. Plumage variable but usually |

underparts white, sometimes with a few feathers tipped dark. Primaries moderately fresh and usually only one age-group discernible but sometimes inner primary replacement started (see Moult) (Fig).

Adult (6)    In full non-breeding plumage blackish skull-cap and dark patch on side of the neck. Upperparts and upper wing light grey, except for slightly darker grey mantle. Scapulars and tertials uniformly light grey. Primaries often show three age-groups of feathers; inner primaries usually in moult.

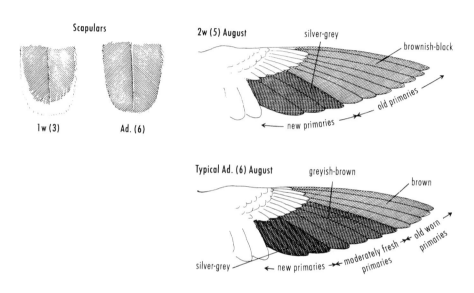

Scapulars

1w (3)    Ad. (6)

2w (5) August    silver-grey    brownish-black
old primaries
← new primaries

Typical Ad. (6) August    greyish-brown    brown
old worn primaries
silver-grey    ← new primaries →← moderately fresh primaries

**Spring/Summer**

1s (5)    Like adult non-breeding, but perhaps whitish underparts with some dark grey feather tips giving blotchy effect. Two ages of primaries discernible, the outers being well worn and brown, compared to the newer inner ones. 1st-summer birds may remain in winter quarters or move north, rarely reaching breeding grounds; some stragglers may visit breeding colonies.

Adult (6)    Upperparts and underparts black or slate-grey, apart from white vent and underside of the tail.

## Moult

3          Complete, but rarely started before arrival in winter quarters. Starts at the earliest in September, more usually October-November, with head, mantle and scapulars. Wing moult starts December-January; some may not finish wing moult until June or even August of 2nd calendar year, by which time the inner primaries have usually started moulting again.

5          Complete post-breeding moult starting as early as May, more usually June or July; timing slightly earlier or similar to adult. Sequence and timing thereafter as adult.

Adult      Complete post-breeding moult, starting with head in late May or early June. Tail and wings from about early July to mid-August; moult suspended prior to autumn migration with up to p4, sometimes up to p5 or p6 (p7) new; moult resumed after reaching winter quarters, usually completing January-February. Pre-breeding moult partial, confined to head, body, tail, inner primaries and some wing-coverts. The 2nd series of inner primaries starts moulting from p1 as early as November which is often before completion of 1st (post-breeding) series, but more usually from February, completed by March or early April; moult arrested just prior to spring migration with 1-5 (6) inner primaries replaced.

**Biometrics**   Nominate *niger* (BWP).

| Wing | *ad.* | ♂218 | (4.03;56) | 210-226 | ♀213 | (5.17;38) | 204-224 |
|------|-------|------|-----------|---------|------|-----------|---------|
|      | *juv.* | 208 | (4.17;12) | 202-215 | 206 | (3.36;18) | 201-211 |
| Fork | *ad.* | 18.8 | (2.18;38) | 15-25 | 17.2 | (2.45;31) | 13-21 |
|      | *juv.* | 13.2 | (1.31;14) | 11-16 | 12.2 | (1.17;11) | 10-14 |
| Bill |       | 27.8 | (1.21;47) | 26-30 | 26.5 | (0.82;36) | 25-28 |
| Tarsus |     | 16.4 | (0.60;39) | 15-18 | 16.3 | (0.51;38) | 15-17 |

**References**   Walters (1987*a*).

# Auks *Alcidae*

Small to medium-large, highly aquatic, diving seabirds. Body elongated. Wings short and narrow. Plumage dark brown above, white below with a few exceptions. Seasonal changes normally involve increase in white areas.

## Feather structure
Primaries = 11 (p10 longest, p11 minute)
Secondaries = 16-21
Tail = 12-16

## Sexes
Similar in plumage.

## Moult
Strategy: simultaneous.
Sequence: simultaneously.
Frequency: twice annually; SC, Wp.
Timing: midsummer finishing early winter; late winter finishing early spring.

# GUILLEMOT *Uria aalge*

**Identification** From Brünnich's Guillemot *U. lomvia* by much longer gonys (bill tip to gonydeal angle), 27-34mm, compared to Brünnich's 20-23mm.

## Autumn/Winter

3            Plumage similar to winter adult but smaller overall with underdeveloped bill (shorter by 50% in some cases) and flight feathers. Often hairy filaments still visible in very loosely structured and fluffy-looking plumage.

1w (3/5)     A variable number of outer greater-coverts retained, contrasting with blacker inner new ones. Where all greater-coverts are moulted these contrast markedly against much browner and worn-looking primary-coverts. Bill usually shorter, <41mm and mostly <39mm. Measurements similar to adult by late winter or early spring.

Adult (4/6)  Greater- and primary-coverts uniformly dark blackish-brown showing no contrast in feather age with rest of wing-coverts. Bill >43mm.

## Spring/Summer

1s (5)       Chin and throat chocolate-brown (as in adult) but normally with some white feathers. Wing-coverts, especially lesser-coverts, faded brown, worn and paler towards tip giving slightly marbled effect; old coverts contrasting with darker and uniform back and mantle. Primaries and primary-coverts bleached, the former being particularly abraded towards tips.

Adult (6)    Back, mantle, wing-coverts and flight feathers uniformly dark blackish-brown, showing no contrast.

## Moult

3            Partial post-juvenile moult August/September-October confined to body and variable number of wing-coverts; some lesser- and median- and inner greater-coverts replaced though most retained until over 1 year old when first complete moult takes place.

5            Breeding plumage attained by partial pre-breeding body moult (head, neck, throat, underparts and mantle), January to late April or early May. Complete post-breeding moult from mid-June onwards, usually completed by late October.

| | | | | | | |
|---|---|---|---|---|---|---|
| Adult | | Complete post-breeding moult: females and failed breeding males start head and neck moult mid-July onwards, others by late July. Flight feathers from early August when primaries shed almost simultaneously rendering birds flightless for 45-50 days. Moult completed by October/November but timing highly variable. Up to 5% of adults retain slight traces of winter plumage on neck, throat, and head during the breeding season. Partial pre-breeding moult, confined to head and neck, October, completed by early December. | | | | |

**Geographical variation** Slight and predominantly clinal. *U.a. albionis* (Ireland, south Britain, Channel Isles, France, W. Iberia) distinctly paler than nominate *aalge* (W. Atlantic, Iceland, Baltic, southern Norway, Britain north of Farne Islands (55° 38'N)) more greyish above and less heavily streaked on flanks and pure white, not spotted, underwing-coverts. *U.a. hyperborea* (N. Norway, Spitsbergen, Bear Island, N. Russia) similar to nominate race but with longer wing and stouter bill. Some individuals in Atlantic and Arctic Oceans have narrow white eye-ring, prolonged posteriorly as a white narrow line; the frequency of these 'bridled' individuals increases from south to north.

**Biometrics** Breeding adults. *U.a. albionis* (BWP).

| | | | | | | |
|---|---|---|---|---|---|---|
| Wing | ♂196 | (4.63;8) | 191-203 | ♀195 | (3.88;6) | 190-200 |
| Bill | 47.0 | (1.83;8) | 44-50 | 46.3 | (1.63;6) | 44-48 |
| Depth* | 12.9 | (0.54;8) | 12.0-13.8 | 12.7 | (0.67;7) | 12.1-14.0 |
| Tarsus | 37.4 | (0.52;8) | 37-38 | 37.4 | (0.79;7) | 37-39 |

Breeding adults. Nominate *aalge* (BWP).

| | | | | | | |
|---|---|---|---|---|---|---|
| Wing | ♂204 | (3.47;16) | 194-209 | ♀206 | (4.94;20) | 198-218 |
| Bill | 47.7 | (2.14;13) | 44-51 | 46.0 | (2.14;20) | 43-51 |
| Depth* | 13.2 | (0.47;16) | 12.2-13.9 | 12.8 | (0.51;19) | 12-13.7 |
| Tarsus | 38.4 | (1.09;16) | 36.5-41.0 | 38.2 | (1.38;20) | 36-42 |

* Bill depth measured at angle of gonys.

**References** Harris & Wanless (1988, 1990).

# RAZORBILL *Alca torda*

## Autumn/Winter

3          Smaller and blacker than adult. Small bulbous bill lacks pale lines or transverse grooves. Flight feathers poorly developed. Loose structure to feathers.

1w (3/5)      Like winter adult but with thinner white tips to secondaries and usually different shape of dark areas (Fig). Bill smaller and without bill grooves.

2w (5)       Birds moulting in early autumn (August-September) and birds with traces of first bill grooves are likely to be over a year old.

Adult (6/8)    Dark brownish-black upperparts. Well-developed bill with pale transverse lines (less marked in winter) and one or more bill grooves. Broader white tips to secondaries with generally characteristic shape of dark areas (Fig).

### Secondaries

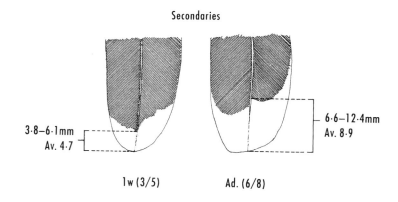

3·8–6·1mm
Av. 4·7

6·6–12·4mm
Av. 8·9

1w (3/5)         Ad. (6/8)

## Spring/Summer

1s (5)       Similar in appearance to adult but throat generally with some white feathers. Thinner white tips to secondaries (Fig) and worn, paler brown secondaries. Usually without bill grooves, possibly first one developing.

Adult (6)     Uniform black or blackish throat. Broader white tips to secondaries. Comparatively fresh and blackish primaries. Bill grooves (one, usually two, sometimes three) and pale transverse lines well-developed.

## Moult

| 3 | Partial post-juvenile moult, July-October (November) confined to body and some wing-coverts; some upper and primary wing-coverts retained. |

3      Partial post-juvenile moult, July-October (November) confined to body and some wing-coverts; some upper and primary wing-coverts retained.

5      Partial pre-breeding moult confined to body and remainder of unmoulted wing-coverts, February to late April (May). Complete post-breeding moult into winter plumage earlier than adult, mid-June to September.

Adult      Complete post-breeding moult starting with body and lesser-coverts. Remainder of wing-coverts and all flight feathers including tail moulted simultaneously, late July probably completed by October. Partial pre-breeding moult confined to head and neck (sometimes whole body), mid-January, probably completing March (April).

**Geographical variation** Nominate *torda* (N. America, Greenland, Norway, Sweden, Finland, N. Russia) larger than southern race *islandica* (Iceland, Faroes, British Isles, Brittany).

**Biometrics**      Full-grown. *A.t. islandica* (BWP).

| | | | | |
|---|---|---|---|---|
| Wing | ♂193.6 (4.48;13) | 187-200 | ♀196.8 (2.39;5) | 194-200 |
| Bill | 34.2 (1.79;13) | 31.3-38.5 | 32.3 (1.18;5) | 30.7-33.6 |
| Depth* | 20.7 (0.96;11) | 19.1-22.4 | 20.2 (0.78;5) | 19-21 |
| Tarsus | 30.7 (1.44;13) | 28-33.2 | 29.5 (1.60;5) | 27.6-31.2 |

Nominate *torda* (BWP).

| | | | | |
|---|---|---|---|---|
| Wing | ♂209.7 (5.05;21) | 201-216 | ♀207.6 (4.33;24) | 201-216 |
| Bill | 35.7 (1.65;26) | 32-39 | 34.5 (1.42;26) | 32-37 |
| Depth* | 24.7 (1.15;25) | 23-2 | 23.7 (0.78;26) | 22-25 |

* Bill depth from angle of gonys.

**References**      Hope Jones (1988), Harris & Wanless (1990).


# BLACK GUILLEMOT *Cepphus grylle*

## Autumn/Winter

3      Most underpart feathers white with grey-brown tips. Upper wing-coverts

tipped dark brown, giving mottled appearance to the wing-patch. Mouth orange. Legs reddish-brown.

1w (3/5)    Underparts white, although often a few juvenile feathers retained. Upper wing-coverts as juvenile. Mouth orange. Legs reddish-brown.

Adult (4/6)    Underparts white. Upper wing-patch appears pure white (rarely one or two greater-coverts are finely tipped brown). Mouth vermilion. Legs bright red.

## Spring/Summer

1s (5)    Upper wing-coverts as juvenile. Most moult all body feathers, giving a matt brown summer plumage. A few retain up to half the white feathers. Primaries already very worn in early summer.

Adult (6)    Adults have pure white wing-patch. Full breeding plumage dark brownish-black with metallic sheen in good light. A few white feathers are occasionally retained, especially on the belly.

## Moult

3/5    Partial post-juvenile moult confined to head and body starting 1 month after fledging through into November (December). A partial spring moult into first pre-breeding plumage usually occurs (March) April-May (June). Complete moult into winter plumage takes place before adults, July-September.

Adult    Partial pre-breeding moult of head and body from late December onwards, usually taking about 2 months, so completed February to April. Post-breeding moult complete; flight feathers shed simultaneously, mid-August. Some head and neck feathers may be moulted whilst still feeding young. Most are in winter plumage by September-October.

**Geographical variation** Predominantly clinal but subspecific assignment complex and in need of review (see BWP). Probably five races involved.

**Biometrics**    Adult. *C.g. arcticus* (BWP).

| | | | | | | |
|---|---|---|---|---|---|---|
| Wing | ♂164 | (3.8;13) | 157-171 | ♀163 | (2.8;7) | 159-166 |
| Bill | 31.9 | (1.5;13) | 29.7-34.5 | 30.9 | (1.6;6) | 29.1-33.6 |
| Tarsus | 31.3 | (0.6;13) | 30.1-32.6 | 30.4 | (1.0;7) | 28.7-31.8 |

**References**    Ewins (1984, 1988).

# PUFFIN *Fratercula arctica*

**Ageing**   Depends on number of grooves on the outer part of the upper beak anterior to pale diagonal ridge.

### Autumn/Winter

1w (3/5)   Smaller than adult, beak all dark and ungrooved. Feathers in front of eye black.

Full-grown (4/6)   Immature birds have fewer than two complete grooves.

Adult (8)   Two or more bill grooves; but care is needed as these are often indistinct, and ridge separating outer and inner bill is often dark (Fig). Do not count the groove posterior to this.

### Spring/Summer

1s (5)   Bill triangular, no complete groove or even ridge on beak. Face sometimes dusky. Eye ornaments undeveloped. Few visit colonies but many on sea nearby.

Full-grown immature (6)   Bill larger but still rather triangular and usually with a kink on upper edge near cere. Fewer than two complete bill grooves. At colony, plumage is blacker than adult at the same season.

Adult (8)   Upper edge of bill rounded and usually smooth. Two or more complete grooves. Plumage often bleached by end of summer and bill sheath flaked off. A few retain trace of black winter face.

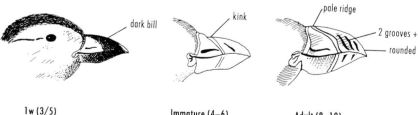

1w (3/5)            Immature (4–6)            Adult (8–10)

263

## Moult

5 Main moult mid-summer before return to colony; birds subsequently in immaculate plumage.

6 Immatures complete moult early summer before return to colony; upperparts then black.

8 Timing of adult moult variable and flightless birds seen all months. Most have main moult in late winter. Plumage becomes worn by end of breeding season and bill sheath flakes off.

**Geographical variation** Clinal, involving size only: size increases from south to north but racial distinction is arbitrary because adjacent populations show much overlap. *F.a. grabae* (Faroes, British Isles, South Norway, Brittany) is smallest. Nominate *arctica* (Iceland, Greenland, Norway, E. Canada) is intermediate with average wing 167mm (sexes combined). Largest race is *naumanni* (high arctic Greenland, Spitsbergen) with average wing 181.5mm (sexes combined).

**Biometrics** Adult. *F.a. grabae*, Isle of May (Harris 1979).

| | | | | |
|---|---|---|---|---|
| Wing | ♂161.8 (3.44;29) | 152-172 | ♀161.7 (2.66;19) | 154-170 |
| Bill | 46.5 (1.42;30) | 42.2-50.8 | 44.2 (1.41;22) | 40.0-48.5 |

Adult. St Kilda (Harris 1979).

| | | | | |
|---|---|---|---|---|
| Wing | ♂157.1 (5.77;20) | 140-174 | ♀156.0 (3.04;20) | 147-165 |
| Bill | 44.2 (1.14;21) | 40.8-47.6 | 42.1 (1.34;20) | 38.0-46.1 |

**References** Corkhill (1972), Harris (1979, 1984).

# Pigeons *Columbidae*

Small to medium-large arboreal and terrestrial birds. Body plump and compact, head rather small. Wings rather short, broad and rounded. Plumage predominantly soft browns, greys, or vinaceous, often with iridescent white or black patches on sides of neck.

## Feather structure

Primaries = 11 (p8/9 or p9 longest, p11 minute)
Secondaries = 11-12 (10-15)
Tail = 12

## Sexes

Similar or only slightly different in plumage.

## Moult

Strategy: primaries descendant or serially descendant. Secondaries ascendant and ascendant/descendant. Some species arrest/suspend. Tail mostly centrifugal.
Sequence: primaries sequentially, sometimes from 2 centres. Secondaries sequentially, sometimes 2 centres, ascendantly and sequentially from s1, and ascendantly and descendantly from centre of innermost group.
Frequency: once annually; SC. Slow and protracted.
Timing: spring-summer finishing early winter-spring.

# STOCK DOVE *Columba oenas*

**Sexing**      Adults only (not possible when birds are in worn plumage):

♂           Tertials and scapulars bluish-grey.

♀           Tertials and scapulars brownish-grey.

## Autumn/Winter

3           Median- and lesser-coverts, tertials and much of back matt light brown, sometimes admixed with ash-grey adult-type feathers. No iridescence on neck or nape.

1w (3/5)    Some brown juvenile feathers or unmoulted light brown tertials often visible among ash-grey adult-type feathers. Beware of confusion with late-moulting adults whose feathers may look very worn and faded. Check outermost primary-coverts if in doubt: these are light brownish in young birds while adults' are dark greyish-black.

Adult (4/6) Uniform ash-grey feathers on mantle, back, lesser- and median-coverts, though some birds (before or during moult) show worn brownish old feathers. Outer primary-coverts greyish-black.

## Spring/Summer

1s (5)      Birds whose moult has been arrested can be aged on colour of outer primary-coverts, these being lightish brown instead of adults' greyish-black colour.

Adult (6)   Only birds in arrested wing moult are ageable. Outer primary-coverts greyish-black.

**Moult**     Timing varies considerably, especially in juveniles (the breeding season is particularly prolonged in this species). An understanding of moult is imperative for successful ageing.

3/5         Young birds undergo a complete moult, beginning soon after leaving the nest. Apparently a good percentage of them suspend wing moult in October or November, recommencing sometime in spring. However, many birds complete the moult without interruption, finishing December or January. When moult has been completed, 1st-winters not distinguishable from adults.

Adult

Primary moult begins May-July (individually variable): normally complete by December (sometimes January). Some birds suspend wing moult in late autumn or early winter (usually outer 1-3 primaries unmoulted), and begin again in spring.

**Geographical variation** *C.o. yarkandensis* (Central Asia) is marginally paler on head, rump, and underparts than nominate form, being light ash-grey rather than medium bluish-grey. Wing averages slightly longer (7mm).

**Biometrics**     Adult. Nominate *oenas* (BWP).

| | | | | | | |
|---|---|---|---|---|---|---|
| Wing | ♂222 | (3.15;30) | 216-228 | ♀216 | (4.68;20) | 208-223 |
| Bill | 19.6 | (0.95;23) | 18.0-21.2 | 19.1 | (0.72;16) | 17.8-20.0 |
| Tarsus | 29.6 | (0.96;25) | 28.0-31.2 | 29.2 | (1.11;16) | 27.8-31.4 |

**References**     Baker (1982).


# WOODPIGEON *Columba palumbus*

## Autumn/Winter

3

Primary-, median- and lesser-coverts pale grey-brown with buff tips. White neck-patch absent.

1w (3/5)

Brown/buff feathers on outer lesser-coverts; one centre of primary moult only.

2w (5)

Only a small proportion of birds are separable. Post-juvenile moult incomplete (2 moulting centres in primaries, indicating serially descendant moult - check both wings), and/or buff tips present on outer lesser-coverts (usually found last on underwing distal to carpal joint).

Adult (4)

Primary-coverts uniform dark slate-grey. Lesser-coverts ash-grey to grey-brown, lacking buff tips.

1s (5)   Outer primary- and lesser-coverts with buff tips. Two moulting centres in primaries (as in 2nd-winter).

Adult (6)   As for Autumn/Winter. Beware confusion of adult completing moult of outer two primaries in March to June (no buff tips present) with 1st-summer birds.

**Moult**   Birds in active or suspended/arrested moult can be found in every month of the year. The prolonged breeding season should always be borne in mind.

3/5   Complete post-juvenile moult starts about 6 weeks after fledging. In almost all birds moult is arrested in November or December, recommencing in March or April; about 5% are still actively moulting in January-February. The stage at which birds arrest depends on fledging date; birds from early broods may complete without arresting; others (5-10%, presumably from late broods) may not start post-juvenile moult until following spring. On recommencement, primary moult occurs at two points: the next feather in sequence from the point of arrestment, followed shortly by innermost primary (thus a serially descendant moult strategy). Both moult cycles progress at about 1 feather per 4 weeks; once the post-juvenile moult is completed (June-October, dependent on the stage reached before arresting), it is generally impossible to distinguish between 1st-summer and adult moult.

Adult   Primary moult commences mid-April to mid-May. A few complete by mid-November, and about half by the end of the year; remainder either suspend with one or two primaries unmoulted (usually recommencing March or April), or complete slowly, finishing by late January.

**Geographical variation** Slight in European populations, involving mostly subtle differences in plumage colour. Size constant over much of Europe and western Siberia. Size and colour become distinctive in extralimital race *C.p. casiotis* (central Asia). 3 other races recognized.

**Biometrics**   Nominate *palumbus* (BWP).

| | | | | | | |
|---|---|---|---|---|---|---|
| Wing *ad.* | ♂252 | (4.93;44) | 243-263 | ♀250 | (5.98;30) | 240-260 |
| *juv.* | 242 | (4.51;29) | 235-251 | 243 | (5.14;22) | 234-251 |
| Bill | 21.4 | (1.15;40) | 19.3-23.6 | 21.1 | (1.25;29) | 19.3-23.4 |
| Tarsus | 32.8 | (0.86;37) | 31.4-34.6 | 32.7 | (1.28;26) | 30.2-34.5 |

**References**   Murton, Westwood & Isaacson (1974), Baker (1979).

# COLLARED DOVE *Streptopelia decaocto*

**Sexing**     Adults only:

♂     Crown and nape greyish-pink or vinous-grey; narrow feather-tips (if any) in black half-collar are white.

♀     Crown and nape drab (pale olive-brown); narrow feather-tips (if any) in black half-collar drab-grey.

Note: ♂♂ generally have brighter vinous-pink underparts, particularly on breast and belly but the feature is obviously a subjective judgement and probably requires birds in good condition or large sample sizes to achieve proper assessment. Beware also of attempting to sex birds in well-worn plumage; ♂♂ generally retain relatively pure vinous-grey crown and nape.

**Ageing**     The breeding period for this species is protracted and nesting birds can be found at any time between March and November. For this reason the seasonal headings under which ageing characteristics are given should only be used as a rough guide. Juvenile birds are as likely in the spring as in the autumn or winter.

Since juveniles undergo a complete moult, commencing roughly four weeks after leaving the nest, and may also be moulting at the same time as adults, a thorough understanding of moult sequences is necessary in this species for accurate ageing.

3     Upperparts and wing-coverts with pale cream fringes giving scalloped effect. Poorly-defined black collar. Iris brown. Legs grey-mauve or purple-red.

1w & 1s (3/5)     May show similar features to juvenile - depending on breeding state; the more advanced birds will look like adults. Those showing active wing moult or arrested moult can be aged accordingly; this character can be used to age young birds into the new year (5) as late as the end of April. However, in March and April only birds with a primary score greater than 15 should be aged as 5 owing to possible confusion with early moulting adults.

## Summer/Autumn

Adult (4)     Upperparts uniform greyish-fawn. Clear black collar with (in ♂♂) white edges top and bottom. Iris ruby-red. Legs bright red.

**Autumn/Winter**

FG (2/4)  Adults with completed primary moult after end of October are unageable (2 and 4 in the new year) since many young birds will also have completed their moult at this time making them inseparable from adults.

**Moult**

3/5  Complete post-juvenile moult. Timing highly variable depending on time of hatching. Commences primary moult some four weeks after leaving the nest. Early-hatched birds start from March or April and have usually completed moult by August; later birds in July start in August and moult more rapidly, completing early December. Late-hatching birds may start September or October but moult at slow rate or suspend between late November and mid-March.

Adult  Complete post-nuptial moult beginning (April) late May to early July, mainly completed by end of October; some moult later, starting August and completing early December.

**Geographical variation** Little in Europe. More marked elsewhere, involving mostly size and colour, becoming smaller and darker from west to east. Birds from southern India and Sri Lanka do not overlap in size with European birds also of nominate form: wing of adult ♂ 165mm (5.7;27), 152-178mm; adult ♀ 162mm (3.8;15) 155-168mm.

**Biometrics**  Adult. Nominate *decaocto* (BWP).

| | | | | | | |
|---|---|---|---|---|---|---|
| Wing | ♂182 | (2.85;32) | 177-188 | ♀177 | (2.64;28) | 173-182 |
| Bill | 16.9 | (0.71;22) | 16.0-18.1 | 16.6 | (1.02;18) | 15.2-18.4 |
| Tarsus | 25.4 | (0.74;24) | 24.1-26.7 | 24.7 | (0.66;19) | 23.6-25.8 |

**References**  Insley & Young (1979).

# TURTLE DOVE *Streptopelia turtur*

**Sexing**  Adults only:

♂  Crown, nape and forehead bluish-grey. Breast salmon-pink.

♀          Crown grey, tipped sandy-brown. Forehead buff-grey or isabelline. Nape olive-brown like mantle.

## Autumn

3          Lesser- and median-coverts rufous-grey with white terminal fringes. Tips of primaries rufous. Iris grey-brown or light brown.

1w (3)        Mantle and wing-coverts should have some old juvenile feathers which are easily distinguished from new (adult-type) ones by tips which are abraded and fringed off-white. Iris yellow-brown or orange-yellow.

Adult (6)      Breast and throat with pinkish hue. Lesser- and median-coverts with black centre fringed rufous, i.e. no white tips. Outer median primary-coverts (small feathers near the leading edge of the wing next to large alula feather) uniform grey. Iris orange-red.

## Spring/Summer

1s (5)        Outer median primary-coverts (small feathers near leading edge of the wing, beside large alula feather) grey, tipped brown or rufous. Sometimes juvenile middle secondaries retained (narrower and shorter than neighbouring ones). Also possibly old outer primaries and corresponding primary-coverts retained, latter with traces of rufous fringes.

Adult (6)      As Autumn.

## Moult

3          Complete post-juvenile moult starting with body in July (though highly variable, some earlier, some later). Wing and tail moult August or September and suspended (arrested?) before migration (1-4 inner ones new), completing in winter quarters.

Adult        Complete post-breeding moult starting June or July with body and followed by wing and tail in August but suspended by September or October. Some begin much later and not until in winter quarters. Suspended birds finish in winter quarters, January-March.

**Geographical variation** Slight: larger birds are found in northern parts of Asian range. *S.t. arenicola* (N.W. Africa, Balearic Islands, S.E. Turkey and central Asia) smaller than nominate (av.175mm in ♂, 167mm in ♀) and paler in colour. 2 other African races recognized.

**Biometrics**    Full-grown. Nominate *turtur* (BWP).

| | | | | | | |
|---|---|---|---|---|---|---|
| Wing | ♂179 | (2.53;37) | 174-185 | ♀172 | (2.73;16) | 167-177 |
| Bill | 16.8 | (0.92;38) | 15.4-18.7 | 16.0 | (0.68;16) | 14.9-16.6 |
| Tarsus | 23.6 | (0.88;20) | 22.4-24.9 | 22.9 | (0.62;14) | 22.1-23.8 |

**References**    Baker (1980*b*).

# Cuckoos *Cuculidae*

Small to fairly large birds with elongated bodies. Wings moderately long and rounded or long and pointed. Plumage highly variable though often grey, brown or rufous upperparts and buff or white underparts, frequently barred.

## Feather structure
Primaries = 10 (p8 longest)
Secondaries = 9
Tail = 10

## Sexes
Mostly similar in plumage. ♂♂ average larger.

## Moult
Strategy: primaries descendant and ascendant. Secondaries ascendant and centripetal from s1 and s9. Occasionally suspends. Tail irregular.
Sequence: primaries in 2 series, p1-p4 descendant, p5-p10 ascendant and alternate. Secondaries in 2 series, s6-s9 ascendant and alternate, s1-s5 centripetally.
Frequency: twice annually; Sp, WC.
Timing: summer/late winter finishing early spring.


# CUCKOO *Cuculus canorus*

**Identification**  In structure and appearance bears close resemblance to Oriental Cuckoo *Cuculus saturatus*. That species is, on average, slightly shorter winged (Adult ♂ av. 210mm, 198-221mm; Adult ♀ av. 198mm, 191-209mm. Juvenile ♂ av. 201mm, 190-212mm; Juvenile ♀ av. 190mm, 179-201mm - taken from European USSR); no single reliable plumage features discovered. Beware of small southern race *bangsi* (adult wing 192-221mm); occasional spring birds in Britain may measure as little as 194mm.

**Sexing**

♂  In 1st-summer birds and adult, slate-grey nape, chin and throat extending well down breast. Demarcation line of grey against barring is well-defined.

♀  There are two colour morphs: in grey morphs appearance is similar to adult ♂ (10% indistinguishable from ♂♂) but usually differs in having rufous or pink-buff background to barring on chest and sides of neck, and sometimes small rufous spots on grey median- and greater-coverts and on outer webs of secondaries. In rufous morphs (rare) the upperparts are rich rufous-cinnamon with well-spaced greyish-black bars. Similar to rufous-coloured juveniles but black bars on upperparts are narrower (1-4mm) than rufous bars, not broader as in juvenile. White fringes on primary tips extend only to p6-p7, not p10.

## Autumn

3

Plumage pattern and colouration varies considerably from heavily barred chestnut upperparts in some individuals to almost uniform grey. Rufous-chestnut birds are heavily barred on all upperparts with some feathers fringed creamy-white. Grey birds have upperparts fringed pure white giving scalloped effect. All birds show whitish fringes on upper wing-coverts and flight feathers. Secondaries and greater-coverts barred or spotted chestnut. Most birds have some exposed white feathers on forehead or nape present up to 3 months after fledging.

Adult (4)

Upperparts uniformly slate-grey, or in the case of rufous-morph ♀ barring on upperparts 1-4mm, and narrower than rufous bars. Lacks white tips on outer primaries (only to p6 or p7), and usually those on upper wing-coverts.

## Spring/Summer

1s (5)

Some barred juvenile secondaries and often wing-coverts retained. Usually 1-2 secondaries retained, but can be up to five. In birds that were less distinct as juveniles, these secondaries can sometimes be overlooked. Moulted coverts frequently have ill-defined rufous dots on feather edges (more marked in ♀ than ♂).

Adult (6)

Some birds may have two age-groups of secondaries distinguishable by abrasion (but beware of 1st-summer birds which often retain a number of old juvenile secondaries). Such birds can be aged as 6. Otherwise birds showing uniform age of secondaries must be aged 4.

## Moult

3

Moult of body feathers begins soon after leaving the nest. Moult of wings and tail takes place during and after migration, though some individuals begin before migration and suspend (September-January, completing February-July). Primaries are moulted irregularly, while secondaries moult from outer and inner ends, usually suspending before completion.

Wings do not always moult synchronously, so both wings should be examined. Tail moult is irregular.

Adult          Some adults examined also showed asynchronous moult in wings. Most appear to have a complete moult annually: starts in winter quarters, (September) October-November, completed February-March, sometimes suspends.

**Geographical variation** Considerable: mostly clinal and involving width of dark barring on underparts, and size. Within Europe less marked though *bangsi* (Iberia, N.W. Africa) is smaller with wing of adult ♂ averaging 210mm (-;14) 203-221mm, adult ♀ 204mm (7.39;14) 192-213mm.

**Biometrics**     Nominate *canorus* (BWP).

| | | | | | | |
|---|---|---|---|---|---|---|
| Wing | *ad.* ♂221 | (4.32;52) | 213-230 | ♀210 | (3.86;35) | 204-216 |
| | *juv.* 208 | (5.94;24) | 203-219 | 201 | (3.84;20) | 195-208 |
| Bill | 27.7 | (15.1;44) | 25.5-31.2 | 26.8 | (1.01;32) | 25.2-28.6 |
| Tail | *ad.* 177 | (4.14;48) | 170-186 | 167 | (5.46;33) | 158-177 |
| | *juv.* 172 | (6.03;22) | 164-180 | 163 | (4.10;18) | 157-171 |

**References**     Stresemann & Stresemann (1961), Baker (1980*b*), Kennerley & Leader (1991).

# Barn Owls *Tytonidae*

Medium-sized, mainly nocturnal predators. Body elongated with large, round head. Wings large with rounded tips. Plumage predominantly white in *Tyto alba* with golden-brown upperparts and variably speckled dark brown and grey.

## Feather structure
Primaries = 10 (p9 longest)
Secondaries = 12 (+ 4 small)
Tail = 12

## Sexes
Mostly similar in plumage.

## Moult
Strategy: primaries serially descendant and ascendant. Secondaries ascendant and descendant. Suspends. Tail irregular.

Sequence: primaries start at p6 and thereafter ascendant and descendant. In later years 2-3 series active, each replacing only a few feathers in single season. Pattern becomes increasingly complicated. Secondaries in 3 groups, s1-s4 and s5-s7 ascendant, s12-s8 descendant.

Frequency: almost continuous. Body slow and protracted. Flight feathers can take several years to replace.

Timing: body throughout year. Flight feathers late summer-autumn finishing early winter.

# BARN OWL *Tyto alba*

**Sexing**
Barn Owls develop a raised growth (flange), running along the edge of the third, innermost talon, after about 7 months after fledging. Young birds with fully developed flanges can be sexed using this feature.

♂
Uniform white underparts. Tiny specks confined only to flanks. Flange on third, innermost talon 1.5mm (nominate *alba*); in overall darker *T.a. guttata* underparts buff, usually spotted all over.

♀
Yellowish hue to underparts and mostly completely speckled with spots 1-2mm across. Flange on third, innermost talon 2.0mm (nominate *alba*). In *guttata* underparts rufous-buff, spotted all over.

**Autumn/Winter**

3
Recently fledged birds have characteristic down around nape, thighs and legs. After loss of down, plumage is indistinguishable from that of adults. However, comparatively unabraded outer primaries are a useful guide and also tail pattern (Fig) (extent and pattern highly variable - use caution!). Insignificant or no development of flange on third, innermost talon (Fig).

### Outermost primary

Juv./1w (3/5)        Ad. (8/10)

| 1w (3/5) | Primaries and secondaries evenly worn and of a similar age. Primary shape useful guide (Fig). Distinguishable linear ridge along inner edge of third talon, about 0.5mm wide (Fig). |
|---|---|

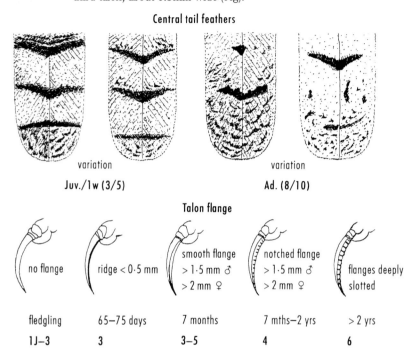

**Central tail feathers**

Juv./1w (3/5)          variation

Ad. (8/10)          variation

**Talon flange**

| no flange | ridge < 0·5 mm | smooth flange > 1·5 mm ♂ > 2 mm ♀ | notched flange > 1·5 mm ♂ > 2 mm ♀ | flanges deeply slotted |
|---|---|---|---|---|
| fledgling | 65–75 days | 7 months | 7 mths–2 yrs | > 2 yrs |
| 1J–3 | 3 | 3–5 | 4 | 6 |

| 2w (5/7) | Primaries showing just one active moult centre, and usually with no more than 3 new feathers replaced (p6 usually, sometimes p7, rarely p5). New feather pattern and extent of speckling often different from retained juvenile primaries which generally show a dusky grey rim towards the tip. Secondaries with one moult centre, generally replacing 3 or 4 inner feathers (s9-12) - like new primaries in pattern; extent of speckling usually different from pattern of juvenile secondaries. |
|---|---|

| 3w (7/9) | Often 3 generations of feathers in the wing; in primaries new feather replacement both outward and inward from 1st moult centre (p6, p7), sometimes advances only as far as p8 or p9, leaving 1 or 2 unmoulted juvenile outer primaries which are heavily worn and show distinct grey rim at tips. Secondaries rarely, if ever, all moulted out into adult-type feathers; inner series with retained juvenile feather(s), s1-4, maybe only 1 retained, more often 2, rarely 3. Flange on edge of third, innermost talon well-developed, 1.5-2.0mm, and notched (Fig). |
|---|---|

278

| Adult (8/10) | Old, unmoulted primaries, abraded, sometimes markedly so due to moult strategy (see Moult), and usually showing 2 or even 3 active moult series. |

## Spring/Summer

| 1s (5) | Primaries and secondaries evenly worn and patterned and of the same age. |

| 2s (7) | As for 2nd-winter; feather condition slightly more abraded though the new feathers (p6 and/or p7, rarely p5) comparatively fresh. |

| 3s (9) | As for 3rd-winter. |

| Adult (8) | Even patterning and colour of primaries and secondaries; several (usually single) feathers replaced in primary or secondary tracts (normally single or a pair in primaries and 3 or 4 throughout secondaries). |

## Moult

| 3 | Partial post-juvenile moult confined to body starting in nest; some feathers still growing October-November. All flight feathers, tertials and greater-coverts retained. |

| 5 | Partial post-breeding moult starting mid-July to mid-August replacing just 1-2 (3) primaries (p6, p7, rarely p5), and 2 or 3 inner secondaries (s12-13, s11-14, sometimes s10), before suspending. |

| 7/9/11 | Subsequent moult in 3rd calendar year slightly later; feather replacement through the wing continues with 2-7 further primaries shed, usually p4-5 and p7-8, and 6-10 secondaries. In 4th calendar year 2-6 primaries replaced, mostly p3 (p2-4) and p9 (p10); some birds start new moult series with p6 as well. In 5th calendar year 0-4 primaries of 1st series and 1-4 of 2nd series shed. |

| Adult | Partial post-breeding moult starting (July) August-September. Primary moult serially descendant and ascendant from centre at p6. Pattern irregular and somewhat complicated; usually involves 2-3 active moult centres of the primaries, and with 3 groups of secondaries active. Replacement protracted, replacing only a few feathers in single season. Body moult also protracted and slow, almost throughout the year. |

**Geographical variation** Marked and complex, mostly clinal involving size and colour. In Europe 4 races separable mainly on size; rather large nominate *alba* and *guttata* (Europe, except some Mediterranean islands) with short and slender tarsus and toes and with tarsus largely feathered. In *alba*, population from Britain is the palest; ♂ ♂ have mostly yellow upperparts and fully white underparts except for occasional yellowish wash to breast; ♀ ♀ as ♂ but upperparts with equal amounts of pale yellow and grey, underparts with slight yellow tinge, usually with small black spots on breast, belly and flanks; flight feathers generally pale yellowish-white with reduced barring and no grey on tips. Iberian birds with more spots on underparts than those of Britain. Birds from western France vary in colour between British and Iberian types; those from northern and eastern France are more heavily spotted. In *guttata*, upperparts dark grey with limited golden-rufous of feather bases showing, flight feathers and tail well-marked uniform rufous-cinnamon, and facial disc and underparts rufous-cinnamon or rufous-yellow with numerous black spots 1-3mm across. Populations highly variable in colour, especially in southern Netherlands, Belgium, German Rhine valley, central Switzerland, and central Yugoslavia. Larger *erlangeri* (N. Africa, Crete, Cyprus, and Middle East), and *ernesti* (Corsica, Sardinia), are paler above and purer white below than nominate *alba*, and with no spots below or only a few small ones in ♀ ♀; long and partly bare tarsus, and heavy bare toes.

**Biometrics**   Full-grown. Nominate *alba* (BWP).

| | | | | | | |
|---|---|---|---|---|---|---|
| Wing | ♂289 | (6.18;18) | 279-299 | ♀290 | (6.19;13) | 280-300 |
| Tail | 115 | (3.64;18) | 110-122 | 115 | (5.46;13) | 109-124 |
| Bill | 30.8 | (0.79;9) | 30-32 | 32.4 | (1.05;4) | 31-33 |
| Tarsus | 57.0 | (2.90;8) | 54-60 | 56.8 | (2.45;5) | 54-60 |

*T.a. guttata* (BWP).

| | | | | | | |
|---|---|---|---|---|---|---|
| Wing | ♂286 | (5.44;54) | 275-297 | ♀287 | (5.44;66) | 273-298 |
| Tail | 115 | (4.21;23) | 108-121 | 114 | (5.20;22) | 107-123 |
| Bill | 31.2 | (1.73;17) | 29-33 | 30.8 | (1.43;18) | 29-33 |
| Tarsus | 56.6 | (1.88;49) | 53-59 | 56.0 | (1.96;61) | 52-60 |

*T.a. erlangeri*, Crete, Cyprus & Middle East, sexes combined (BWP).

| | | | |
|---|---|---|---|
| Wing | 299 | (8.54;11) | 286-310 |
| Tail | 118 | (3.97;11) | 112-124 |

**References**   Baker (1981*a*), Johnson (1991).

# Owls *Strigidae*

Small to large predators, mostly nocturnal. Body elongated with large round head. Wings variable, mostly rather short, broad and rounded. Plumage variable, usually cryptic, brown, grey, cream, or buff and often vermiculated or with dark streaks.

## Feather structure
Primaries = 10 (longest varies with species p6/7, p7/8 or p9)
Secondaries = 12-14 (19)
Tail = 12 (10)

## Sexes
Mostly similar in plumage. ♀♀ average larger.

## Moult
Strategy: primaries descendant and serially descendant, but somewhat irregular. Secondaries ascendant and descendant. Suspends. Tail centripetal but irregular, almost simultaneous.
Sequence: primaries sequential or in 2 or 3 series often starting from p4 or p5, sometimes p2. Secondaries from up to 3 centres.
Frequency: in small owls once annually; SC. In larger owls nearly continuous. Body slow and protracted. Flight feathers can take several years to replace completely.
Timing: summer/late autumn finishing early winter.

# LITTLE OWL *Athene noctua*

## Autumn/Winter

3 — Head and upperparts brown with few distinctive white markings. Feathers on body loose and fluffy (2nd down, mesoptile), often with white 1st down (neoptile) on tips, retained longest on crown, flanks and thighs.

1w (3/5) — Appearance similar to adults but mesoptile down often present on innermost tertials. White spots on head generally bolder, especially on nape, and more rounded (Fig). Outer primary (p10) pointed at tip due to steep angle on inner web; white tip extends to inner web (Fig).

Adult (4/6) — Upperparts and head dark brown. White spots on crown much reduced and thinner than 1st-winter (Fig). Innermost tertials fresh (after moult) with broad and squarer-tipped ends. Outer primary (p10) with broad, strongly curved inner web making shape very rounded (Fig).

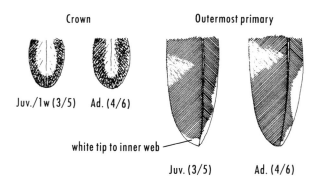

Crown — Outermost primary

Juv./1w (3/5) — Ad. (4/6)

white tip to inner web

Juv. (3/5) — Ad. (4/6)

## Spring/Summer

1s (5) — Separation is sometimes difficult and not recommended after May. Most useful character is abrasion on tertials. Some feathers on crown and nape may show broad white pattern. Primary shape should be used with caution as abrasion reduces differences in shape between age-groups.

Adult (6) — Tertial abrasion is a useful guide, together with primary shape (see cautionary note above under 1s). White on head narrower.

282

## Moult

3     Partial post-juvenile moult, starting soon after fledging, confined to head, body and lesser- and median-coverts; July, completed by September, October (November).

Adult    Complete post-breeding moult starting as early as (May) June-July and completed by September or early November. Secondaries moult from 3 centres, usually around s12, s5, and s1. Tail shed almost simultaneously.

**Geographical variation** Marked and complex. Generally paler from west to east and south, accompanied by slight cline of increasing size. *A.n. vidalii* (Britain, Iberia, Netherlands, east through Denmark, Germany, Poland to Baltic States) is the darkest race being dark fuscous-brown (no russet-brown or sandy) conspicuously spotted white above. 2 other European races recognized and a further 9 elsewhere.

**Biometrics** *A.n. vidalii* (BWP).

| | | | | | | | |
|---|---|---|---|---|---|---|---|
| Wing | *ad.* ♂ | 163 | (3.66;13) | 158-169 | ♀166 | (3.90;13) | 161-173 |
| | *juv.* | 160 | (2.98;35) | 155-166 | 163 | (4.12;39) | 157-171 |
| Tail | *ad.* | 75.9 | (2.00;11) | 74-79 | 79.6 | (2.06;9) | 77-83 |
| | *juv.* | 73.1 | (2.86;29) | 69-78 | 74.1 | (2.70;27) | 71-80 |
| Bill (C) | | 14.0 | (0.49;20) | 13.3-14.7 | 13.9 | (0.78;21) | 13.0-15.2 |
| Tarsus | | 34.8 | (1.19;21) | 33.4-36.3 | 35.6 | (1.09;20) | 34.0-36.8 |

**References** Baker (1980*b*).

# TAWNY OWL *Strix aluco*

**Sexing**          *S.a. sylvatica*

♂          Wing <255mm; Weight <400g.

♀          Wing >268mm; Weight >434g.

Alternatively, use discriminant function D=17.46 – (0.057 x wing length) – (0.005 x body weight). If D >0 then classify as ♂.

## Autumn/Winter

3          Some advanced juveniles may appear similar to adults but traces of down (2nd, mesoptile down) often visible on nape, mantle or rump.

1w (3/5)          After down has been lost, plumage is very similar to that of adult; but pattern of vermiculation on primaries and secondaries distinct, showing a broken or thin terminal band (Fig).

2w (5/7)          Most primaries and secondaries still juvenile-type, with as few as 1 or 2 primaries replaced, starting at p5 and p6 and progressing both ascendantly and descendantly; these new feathers are broader and more rounded and show a much broader, usually unbroken terminal band (Fig). Only small number of secondaries replaced, usually from moult centre at s10 but also at s1 and s5. New secondaries also show a much broader terminal band than neighbouring juvenile secondaries. This moult pattern is typical of birds in northern Britain: other populations may replace more feathers.

3w (7/9)          Many birds have replaced all their juvenile primaries, but a small proportion may suspend at p9 or p10. Any old outer feathers are very faded and abraded. In one study 76% of 3rd-winter birds retained at least 1, often 2 or more, juvenile secondaries, usually s4 (s3) and s7 (s8). These too show up as pale and abraded feathers with thin or broken terminal bands and contrasting sharply with newer and darker replaced secondaries (check both wings as pattern is typically asymmetrical). In birds that have replaced all primaries and most of the secondaries, ageing can be made easier by looking at the white area at the base of the underside of the primary and secondary feathers. Blow or move the underwing-coverts to one side. To distinguish 1 generation of adult feathers (2w 5/7) from 2 generations (3w 7/9), those feathers replaced on the last moult have a pinkish-brown wash to this white area, while feathers replaced on the last-but-one moult do not. Therefore, birds with a mixture of white and brown-washed feather bases are 3rd-winter (7/9), while 2nd-winter birds have brown-washed bases only. Distinguishing these two feather-types requires conditions which are not too bright (not direct sunshine).

Adult (8/10)  All primaries and secondaries adult-type (Fig). Adult feathers can be retained through 3 or more annual moult cycles: beware of misclassifying very worn feathers as juvenile plumage.

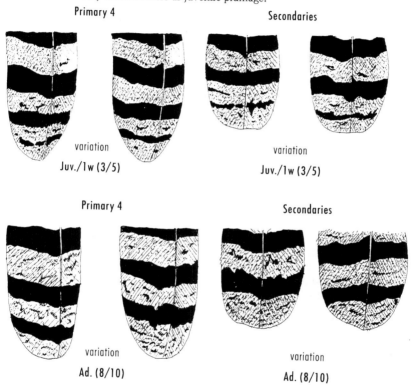

Primary 4

Secondaries

variation
Juv./1w (3/5)

variation
Juv./1w (3/5)

Primary 4

Secondaries

variation
Ad. (8/10)

variation
Ad. (8/10)

## Spring/Summer

1s (5)  Primaries and secondaries may all be juvenile-type, depending on stage of moult. P5 and p6 are usually the first to be replaced by adult feathers (Fig). Some secondaries are also replaced by adult feathers commencing at s10 and sometimes s5 and s1.

2s (7)  Like 3rd-winter but not as advanced. Since most birds will be in active moult, it is more likely that some outer juvenile primaries will be present, especially in spring or early summer.

3s (9)    Most will be impossible to age, especially if moult has started. Some may still have retained juvenile secondaries (1-5), though these old feathers are the first to be replaced when moult commences.

Adult (8)    As adult Autumn/Winter.

**Moult**

3    Partial post-juvenile moult involving head, body and some wing-coverts, May-October. All flight feathers, tertials, primaries, wing-coverts and tail feathers retained.

5    Moult starts in April to June usually at p5/p6 and progresses outwards and inwards. Secondary moult usually starts at centres at s10, s5 and s1. Number of flight feathers replaced highly variable and dependent on food availability and the breeding success of individual birds. Wing moult suspended September-October. Body moult slightly later than wings and continues to about December.

7/8/9    Subsequent moults in 3rd calendar year probably slightly later but this depends on breeding status; replacement of flight feathers continues from point of suspension. Typically (5) 6-8 primaries replaced, so in some birds primaries now all adult-type. Secondaries moult from 3 centres and usually all but 1 or 2 juvenile feathers are replaced, although one study showed that 24% of birds had lost all their juvenile feathers at this stage. In 4th calendar year any remaining juvenile flight feathers are replaced, otherwise the replacement of primaries and secondaries follows the same sequence in which juvenile feathers were replaced.

Adult    Post-breeding moult starts in May or June and may be earlier in non-breeding birds. Primary moult follows the initial moult sequence of the juvenile feathers. Usually only 3 or 4 primaries replaced each year but this is highly variable. Adult flight feathers can be retained through 3, sometimes 4, annual moult cycles. Secondaries moult from 3 centres, s1-4 and s5-7 ascendantly, s13-8 descendantly. Tail feathers shed and grown almost simultaneously once every two years. In some birds not all tail feathers are moulted in the same year. Body moult starts shortly after wing, finishing December.

**Geographical variation** Marked and complex: involves both size and colour. Colour also subject to large individual variation. *S.a. sylvatica* (Britain, France, Iberia, Asia Minor) smallest race (see Biometrics). Nominate *aluco* from

286

central and northern Europe clinally larger towards east. Northern group from Britain, France, Norway, and northern Italy variable in colour but lacking distinct colour morphs - usually deep rufous to dark grey birds occur in west of range, while pale grey predominates in east. Southern group from Iberia through to Asia Minor has 2 morphs, rufous and grey, and is characterized by close dark barring on crown, hindneck and underparts and by heavily vermiculated and speckled mantle and wing-coverts.

**Biometrics**    Full-grown. *S.a. sylvatica*, Britain (Hardy *et al.* 1981).

Wing    ♂259.4 (4.5;20)    250-268   ♀273.6 (6.9;22)    257-281

Nominate *aluco* (BWP).

| | | | | | | | |
|---|---|---|---|---|---|---|---|
| Wing | *ad.* ♂267 | (5.12;35) | 259-275 | ♀278 | (5.48;30) | 269-287 |
| | *juv.* 262 | (6.23;14) | 253-270 | 271 | (5.63;14) | 263-282 |
| Tail | *ad.* 155 | (6.36;24) | 148-166 | 162 | (5.06;19) | 154-171 |
| | *juv.* 151 | (4.19;13) | 146-158 | 160 | (5.88;12) | 150-167 |
| Bill (C) | 19.6 | (0.88;34) | 18.4-21.1 | 20.6 | (0.92;26) | 19.4-22.4 |
| Tarsus | 46.5 | (1.14;36) | 44.8-48.3 | 48.3 | (2.14;23) | 46.2-52.8 |

**References**    Baker (1981*a*), Hardy, Hirons, Stanley & Huson (1981), Pictiäinen, Ahola, Forsman, Haapala, Korpimäki, Lagerström & Niiranen (1988), Petty (1991).

# LONG-EARED OWL *Asio otus*

**Identification**    From Short-eared Owl by typically orange-yellow or orange-red iris. Ear-tufts up to 45mm long (up to 25mm in Short-eared Owl), and by shorter wing (see Biometrics).

**Sexing**    All ages.

♂    Generally paler and less strongly vermiculated than ♀; inner web of secondaries (particularly towards the outer portion) white. Under-parts streaked dark brown but ground colour white with some light buff

tinges. Tips of feathers of lower mantle and scapulars heavily vermiculated black and deep buff, not pale grey as in ♀.

♀                Generally darker golden-buff ground colour, especially on underparts
and underwing; inner web of secondaries buff. Underparts streaked as
♂ but buff ground colour, especially on breast and upper belly, with
some white especially on thigh region. Tips of lower mantle feathers and
scapulars sparsely vermiculated blackish and pale grey, not deep buff as
in ♂.

## Autumn/Winter

3                General feather structure very loose and downy (2nd down, mesoptile),
often with white 1st down (neoptile) on tips. Underparts, head,
nape and rump with variable amounts of mesoptile down, usually retained longest on nape or back of head - as late as November;
sometimes necessary to brush back adult-type feathers to uncover
hidden down.

1w (3/5)       Pattern of vermiculations in wing and general ground colour uniform.
Vermiculated bars on inner secondaries thinner and more densely
bunched than on adult feathers -usually 7 or 8 bars on outer web as
opposed to 5 or 6 in adults. Tail broadly barred (Fig).

2w (5/7)       Many can be aged after completion of moult by retention of old juvenile
secondaries, which are usually of a contrasting colour (less grey, more
buffy) and with narrower and more closely bunched vermiculated bars
(Fig). Open the wing and look at the pattern as a whole - the odd 2 or 3
old secondaries will stand out.

Adult (6/8)    Some birds show evidence of suspended secondary moult. New and old
feathers show similar pattern of vermiculated bars, i.e. broad and well
spaced, though old feathers are slightly different in colour and show
comparatively more wear. Tail less heavily barred and more vermiculated
than juvenile (Fig). Birds whose secondaries are evenly coloured and
worn cannot be aged beyond 2+ calendar years (4).

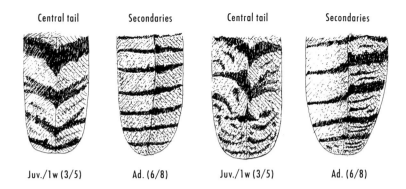

| Central tail | Secondaries | Central tail | Secondaries |
|:---:|:---:|:---:|:---:|
| Juv./1w (3/5) | Ad. (6/8) | Juv./1w (3/5) | Ad. (6/8) |

## Spring/Summer

1s (5)  Like 1st-winter. More worn condition of flight feathers helpful, particularly outer primaries.

2s (7)  Like 2nd-winter but beware of moulting birds as the old juvenile secondaries are usually the first feathers to be moulted out.

Adult (8)  As adult winter but beware of moulting birds as the old retained adult secondaries are the first to be moulted out. Birds with evenly coloured and worn secondaries (before moult) cannot be aged beyond 3+ calendar years (6).

## Moult

3  Partial post-juvenile moult with almost continuous moult of body in 1st year of life. Also involves head and upper wing-coverts, but not flight feathers, greater- or primary-coverts or tail.

5  Like adult post-breeding, but moult of secondaries and tail starts some 2-3 weeks later relative to primaries. Degree of moult interruption and suspension similar to adult.

Adult  Complete or partial post-nuptial moult starting with p1 June-July in ♂, slightly later in breeding ♀. Inner primaries replaced rapidly. Secondaries moulted from 3 centres, s11 or s12, s5, and s1; often suspended. Tail feathers shed and grown simultaneously. Body moult usually (July) August-September.

**Biometrics**        Nominate *otus* (BWP).

| | | | | | | | |
|---|---|---|---|---|---|---|---|
| Wing | *ad. ♂* 294 | (6.04;57) | 282-310 | ♀ 299 | (5.95;64) | 287-309 |
| | *juv.* 290 | (5.80;41) | 279-302 | 299 | (5.72;50) | 286-316 |
| Tail | *ad.* 137 | (3.71;35) | 130-144 | 141 | (4.49;52) | 132-149 |
| | *juv.* 139 | (4.24;38) | 130-147 | 143 | (3.52;41) | 136-148 |
| Bill (C) | 16.1 | (0.96;20) | 14.5-17.5 | 17.6 | (1.27;14) | 15.7-19.3 |
| Tarsus | 38.2 | (0.95;20) | 36.9-40.0 | 39.9 | (1.19;16) | 38.4-42.3 |

**References**        Baker (1983*b*), Haapala & Niiranen (1987).


# SHORT-EARED OWL *Asio flammeus*

**Identification**    From Long-eared Owl by typically yellow iris. Ear-tufts up to 25mm. Generally longer wing (see Biometrics).

**Sexing**            Colour morphs in Short-eared Owl vary greatly, from very pale ♀ ♀, resembling ♂ ♂, to brown ♂ ♂, resembling ♀ ♀. Colour alone should not be used for sexing, but rather a combination of patterning on the inner web of secondaries and streaking on the abdominal region:

♂                     Inner web of outer secondaries white with hardly any barring - perhaps a few smudges. Streaking on lower part of abdomen and thighs very narrow - 1mm. General colour in this region whitish-buff.

♀                     Inner web of outer secondaries whitish-buff with well-defined barring. Streaking on lower part of abdomen and thighs broad (2-3mm). General colour in this region buff.

### Autumn/Winter

3                     General feather structure very loose and downy (2nd down, mesoptile), often with white 1st down (neoptile) on tips. Underparts, head, nape and scapulars with varying amounts of mesoptile down. Usually retained longest on nape or back of head.

1w (3/5)      Once mesoptile down worn away, plumage is very like adult. Pattern on
              tail (t1) different from adult; broad buff or buff-white tip (10-15mm)
              with blackish-brown shaft-streak like inverted V (Fig).

Adult (4/6)   Pattern on tail highly variable but rarely with such a broad buff or
              whitish-buff tip as 1st-winter; usually t1 completely dark or with narrow
              pale terminal margin. Some, however, may have comparatively broad
              buff tip but this is always heavily mottled brown and rarely with dark
              inverted-V shaft-streak; if shaft-streak present it does not taper to a point,
              nor does it reach tip (Fig).

### Central tail feather

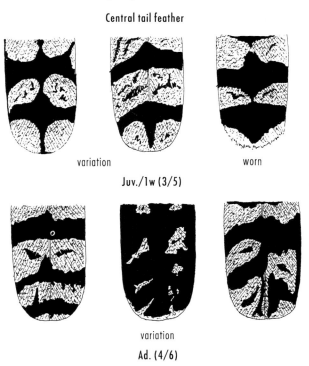

variation                              worn

### Juv./1w (3/5)

variation

### Ad. (4/6)

**Spring/Summer**

1s (5)        Possible to age before tail feathers moulted out (see 1st-winter), but tail
              may show much abrasion which reduces the definition of patterning as
              found in fresh feathers. However, even if the pale tip of t1 is reduced to
              as little as 5mm the dark inverted-V shaft-streak is still evident (Fig).
              After loss of juvenile tail feathers, cannot be distinguished from adult.

| Adult (6) | As adult Autumn/Winter. After moult cannot be aged beyond 2+ calendar years (4). |

**Moult**

| 3 | Partial post-juvenile moult confined to head, body and some wing-coverts. Starts in nest, often not finished until October. |

| 5 | Much as adult, though perhaps commences slightly earlier. More details are needed. |

| Adult | Complete post-breeding moult commencing June or July with p1. Secondaries moulted from 3 centres, descendantly from s12 and ascendantly from s1 and s5. Tail shed simultaneously when p6-p8 dropped. Body moults about 1 month after flight feathers start. Completed by October or November. A small percentage of birds retain 1 or 2 secondaries until following moult. |

**Biometrics**    Full-grown. Nominate *flammeus* (BWP).

| | | | | | | |
|---|---|---|---|---|---|---|
| Wing | ♂315 | (6.29;39) | 304-326 | ♀319 | (6.38;28) | 309-331 |
| Tail | 142 | (5.65;39) | 134-152 | 144 | (4.27;32) | 137-154 |
| Bill (C) | 16.7 | (0.72;16) | 16.0-17.5 | 16.9 | (0.60;12) | 16.2-18.0 |
| Tarsus | 44.5 | (1.01;16) | 42.8-46.0 | 46.2 | (1.31;14) | 44.5-48.1 |

**References**    Baker (1983*b*).

# Nightjars *Caprimulgidae*

Small to medium-sized aerial insect-feeders, mostly nocturnal. Bodies mainly round. Wings usually long, narrow and pointed. Cryptic plumage, mostly brown and grey, blackish vermiculations and often with white patches on wing and tail.

## Feather structure
Primaries = 10 (p8 or p9 longest)
Secondaries = 13
Tail = 10

## Sexes
Similar in plumage.

## Moult
Strategy: primaries descendant. Secondaries ascendant and descendant. Suspends/arrests. Tail centrifugal.
Sequence: primaries sequentially. Secondaries from 2 centres, ascendantly from s1 and descendantly from s12-s13.
Frequency: once annually; SC.
Timing: summer-early autumn finishing winter-early spring.

# NIGHTJAR *Caprimulgus europaeus*

**Identification** Plumage colour and pattern can be similar to Common Nighthawk *Chordeiles minor* (USA, Canada), but that species shows distinctive forked tail (11-23mm - longest to shortest tail feather) and tail is also shorter (102-115mm); white primary patches (both sexes) on outer 5 primaries, whereas ♂ Nightjar only on 3. Red-necked Nightjar *Caprimulgus ruficollis* has generally paler and more rufous upperparts; rufous half-collar on nape, and longer tail (148-168mm). Egyptian Nightjar *C. aegyptius* is much paler overall; lacks white primary patches and white tips to outer tail feathers.

**Sexing** Post-juveniles only (5-6):

♂ Two outermost tail-feathers tipped pure white (20-38mm). Inner web of three outermost primaries with white spot.

♀ Two outermost tail feathers and primaries without white patches. However, tips of tail feathers may form small white or buff band rarely exceeding 3-4mm.


**Spring/Autumn**

1w (3) Similar to adult but paler overall owing to finer and less extensive vermiculations. Primaries, secondaries and tail all show arrow-heads to varying degrees on the tips; white or pale grey margins to tips of primaries, especially pronounced on inners. These should not be confused with the pale grey areas found on adult ♀♀, on which the colouring is far more diffuse, paler and longer in extent (10-15mm) (Fig).

1s/2w (5) Some individuals may show a number of unmoulted secondaries or greater-coverts. Ageing is only possible where juvenile secondaries lie alongside new adult feathers, since adults too sometimes retain old feathers. Juvenile feathers have more buff streaking near the tip, and markings are more clearly defined than those of adults which tend to be diffuse. If there is a distinct difference of pattern within secondaries (particularly in respect of sharpness of barring) then this represents old against new feathers and thus a bird in its 2nd calendar year. Rarely unmoulted primaries (1 or perhaps 2) also recorded (arrested moult).

Note: in ♂♂ the breadth of white on tip of second outermost tail feather (t4) is dependent on age: <27mm in 1s, 28-35mm in 2- and 3- year-olds and probably >37mm when older.

Adult (6)    Some birds may show two age-groups of secondaries, as in 1st-summers, but the old retained feathers show much the same pattern as the new ones (Fig).

Adult (4)    Uniform wear and pattern of secondaries.

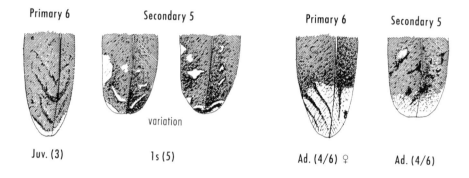

| Primary 6 | Secondary 5 | Primary 6 | Secondary 5 |
| --- | --- | --- | --- |
| | variation | | |
| Juv. (3) | 1s (5) | Ad. (4/6) ♀ | Ad. (4/6) |

## Moult

3    Body moult commences July or August. A complete moult takes place in winter quarters, November-March (April). Primaries seem to moult descendantly. Secondaries appear to have at least two moult centres, starting from inners and outers; perhaps sometimes suspends or arrests. Usually only 1 or 2 (4) secondaries are unmoulted. Arrested primary moult recorded too (rare).

Adult    Variable. Most appear to start body moult July/August, replacing head, body and (sometimes) tertials, rarely p1 replaced on breeding grounds: others may depart with all plumage unmoulted and worn. Moult arrested or suspended during migration, resumed in winter quarters late September to October (November), usually complete January to late March. Occasionally secondaries (arrested or suspended?) of birds returning to summer breeding grounds show two age-groups of feathers.

**Geographical variation** Clinal, involving size, colour and amount of white in outer primaries of ♂. Largest are nominate *europaeus* from northern part of range, gradually decreasing in size towards south. Smallest are *meridionalis* (N. Africa, Greece, Turkey), wing 183mm (;26) 175-192mm in adult ♂, and 185mm (;12) 176-189mm in adult ♀, and extralimital *unwini* (Iraq to Pakistan), wing 184mm (4.90;10) 178-192mm (unsexed). Colour variation marked and complex but generally dark in humid areas and pale in deserts.

**Biometrics**   Nominate *europaeus* (BWP).

| | | | | | | |
|---|---|---|---|---|---|---|
| Wing *ad.* | ♂192 | (5.50;33) | 184-201 | ♀195 | (6.38;19) | 184-202 |
| *juv.* | 190 | (2.90;8) | 185-194 | 190 | (4.90;9) | 183-197 |
| Bill | 8.8 | (0.56;12) | 8.0-9.5 | 8.9 | (0.69;16) | 7.5-9.7 |
| Tarsus | 16.8 | (0.67;10) | 16.1-17.8 | 17.2 | (0.72;12) | 16.3-18.2 |
| Tail | 137 | (5.03;34) | 129-146 | 136 | (4.63;23) | 129-144 |

**References**   Baker (1980*b*).

# Swifts *Apodidae*

Small to medium-sized aerial insect-feeders. Body compact. Wings long and pointed. Plumage mostly black or blackish-brown, sometimes with white patches.

### Feather structure
Primaries = 10 (p9 longest)
Secondaries = 8 (9/10 reduced)
Tail = 10

### Sexes
Similar in plumage.

### Moult
Strategy: primaries descendant (serially descendant). Secondaries ascendant. Suspends/arrests. Tail centripetal.
Sequence: primaries mostly sequentially.
Frequency: once annually; SC.
Timing: late summer-autumn finishing winter-early spring.

## SWIFT *Apus apus*

**Identification** Similar to Pallid Swift *Apus pallidus* but tail generally more deeply forked. Tail difference between outermost and 2nd outermost (t5-t4) in Swift is 7.5-11.5mm, av. 9.5; in Pallid 3-8mm, av. 5. Head of Pallid Swift broader than that of Swift: measured across crown between ridges above eye, Swift is 11-17mm, av. 14.5; in Pallid 15-20.5mm, av. 17.5.

### Spring/Summer

3
Brown body feathers fringed white giving markedly scalloped effect. All flight feathers and wing-coverts along leading edge of wing narrowly fringed white. Tips of tail feathers and outer web of t5 narrowly margined white; inner web of t5 wider and more curving towards rounded tip than in adult. Beware in late summer/early autumn that white fringes (scalloping) may be much reduced giving similar appearance to non-breeding adult - always check t5 for narrow white margin of juvenile.

1s (5)
Resembles adult. 9th primary shape may be useful. Tips of primaries 1-6 or 1-7 appear sharp and pointed due to wear of white fringes (Fig). Outermost tail feather rounded but not curved as in juvenile.

2s (7)
Those birds showing extremely abraded 10th primary, usually showing only as bare shaft, can be aged thus (see Moult).

Adult (6)
Plumage very largely uniform brown, lacking distinctive scalloping of juvenile. Primary tips broader and more rounded than in 1st-summer birds (Fig). Outermost tail feather pointed and without white margin to outer web. Often shows abraded outermost primary (p10) though wear comparatively moderate compared to 2nd-summer unmoulted juvenile primary.

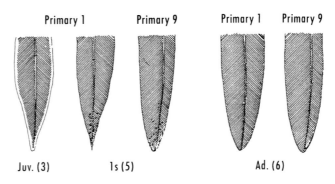

| Primary 1 | Primary 9 | | Primary 1 | Primary 9 |

Juv. (3)          1s (5)                    Ad. (6)

## Moult

3/5

Wing moult does not occur in the first winter, so those birds that return to Europe in the spring have carried the same feathers since leaving the nest. In second winter, moult apparently as adult with evidence also of arrested moult of primaries at p9, leaving juvenile p10 unmoulted until 3rd-winter.

Adult

Complete post-breeding moult takes place September-March in winter quarters. Many adults of varying ages show signs of arrested wing moult, usually at 9th primary. Birds returning to breed in this state will have worn outermost 10th primary.

**Geographical variation** Slight and involving colour only. *A.a. pekinensis* (S & Eastern Asia) is distinctly paler with paler grey-brown forehead, browner upper-parts and whiter and larger throat-patch; paler inner primaries, secondaries and greater-coverts.

**Biometrics** Nominate *apus* (BWP).

| | | | | | | | |
|---|---|---|---|---|---|---|---|
| Wing | *ad.* ♂ | 173 | (3.22;85) | 167-179 | ♀ 173 | (3.64;81) | 164-180 |
| | *juv.* | 166 | (5.88;14) | 157-174 | 168 | (3.15;13) | 162-173 |
| Tail | *ad.* | 75.8 | (2.72;50) | 71-82 | 74.3 | (3.06;35) | 69-79 |
| | *juv.* | 69.1 | (2.57;7) | 65-73 | 67.2 | (2.15;11) | 64-70 |
| Fork | *ad.* | 31.6 | (2.15;48) | 28-36 | 29.7 | (3.10;34) | 25-34 |
| | *juv.* | 27.6 | (3.17;7) | 24-32 | 24.5 | (1.62;11) | 22-27 |
| Bill | | 6.6 | (0.42;10) | 6.0-7.2 | 6.6 | (0.31;10) | 6.2-7.2 |

Fork is measured from tip of t1 to tip of t5. Bill is exposed culmen.

**References** De Roo (1966), Baker (1979).

# Kingfishers *Alcedinidae*

Very small to medium-sized perching birds with large heads and long bills. Wings rather short, rounded. Plumage often colourful with brilliant blues and greens.

### Feather structure
Primaries = 10 (p8 or p9 longest)
Secondaries = 11-14 (12 in most, 13/14 reduced)
Tail = 12 (13/15)

### Sexes
Similar in plumage.

### Moult
Strategy: primaries descendant. Secondaries ascendant and descendant. Arrest/suspend. Tail irregular.
Sequence: primaries sequentially from 2 synchronized groups. Secondaries from 2 centres, ascendantly and descendantly from s10, ascendantly from s1.
Frequency: once annually; SC.
Timing: summer finishing early winter.

# KINGFISHER *Alcedo atthis*

## Sexing

Pull, Juv(1/3J)  With practice young birds can be sexed on colour of crown, lower back and rump. ♂♂ are predominantly blue or blue-green, ♀♀ are green or green-blue. Pulli can be sexed too providing that some crown or back feathers have emerged from pin. There are, inevitably, a few intermediates which must remain unsexed.

Adult

♂  At least two-thirds of lower mandible black, sometimes becoming pale orange at base.

♀  Two-thirds of lower mandible orange, becoming dark brown or black towards distal third.

## Autumn/Winter

3  Front of tarsus and upper foot dark brown or blackish. Breast feathers orange with brown smudges often forming dark breast-band. Moustachial stripe dark greeny-brown admixed with blue.

1w (3/5)  In autumn feet and front of tarsus brown, sometimes with orange patches; breast feathers tipped with greenish or grey hue, but sometimes clear orange as in adult. All flight feathers fresh and unabraded - no moult. By early to late winter (November-March) tarsus and feet are unreliable ageing features as adults can also show dark patches on their legs. Primaries and secondaries alike (no age difference) (Fig).

Adult (4/6)  In autumn (August-October) tarsus and feet orange though brown patches may appear late on in the season. Breast orange. Primaries abraded in early autumn and in many moult has started. In replaced primaries and secondaries, shape and condition are a useful guide (Fig).

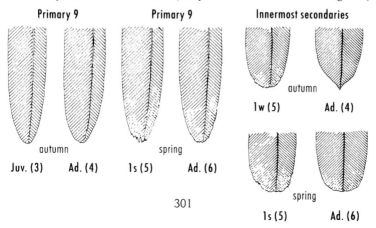

Primary 9        Primary 9        Innermost secondaries

autumn

1w (5)        Ad. (4)

autumn                    spring

Juv. (3)    Ad. (4)    1s (5)    Ad. (6)

spring

1s (5)        Ad. (6)

## Spring

1s (5)  Outermost primaries and inner secondaries moderately worn and abraded at tips (Fig) though beware of adults in suspended moult.

Adult (4/6)  Primaries and secondaries moderately fresh showing only slight abrasion towards tip of feathers. Some birds suspend moult in winter; such birds will therefore have two ages of feather in the wing, the outer primaries being very abraded and pale in colour compared to comparatively new inner ones.

## Moult

3/5  Partial post-juvenile moult confined to head and body and variable number of tail feathers, sometimes all, July or August. Usually complete by December.

Adult  Complete post-breeding moult July-November (December), but may be completed by October. Primaries moulted in two groups, p1-6 and p7-10 both descendant and concurrently, from end of June to mid-August. Late moult or onset of cold weather can result in suspended moult; thus sometimes p6, and more rarely p10, retained. These feathers replaced from May-June of following season. Secondaries moult from 2 centres; ascendantly and descendantly from s10, and ascendantly only from s1.

**Geographical variation**: *A.a. ispida* (W. Europe) averages darker and larger than nominate *atthis* (Mediterranean and central European USSR eastwards), also has whiter chin and heavier, stouter bill. 5-6 other extralimital races recognized.

**Biometrics**  Full-grown & adult. *A.a. ispida* (BWP).

| | | | | | | |
|---|---|---|---|---|---|---|
| Wing | ♂78.3 | (1.35;51) | 76-81 | ♀78.2 | (1.38;63) | 76-81 |
| Bill | 44.6 | (2.53;24) | 40-47 | 42.9 | (1.82;33) | 40-46 |
| Tarsus | 10.2 | (0.58;12) | 9.4-10.9 | 10.2 | (0.40;23) | 9.6-11.2 |

*A.a. atthis* (BWP).

| | | | | | | |
|---|---|---|---|---|---|---|
| Wing | ♂76.8 | (1.72;12) | 74-79 | ♀77.5 | (1.72;13) | 75-80 |

**References**  Doucet (1971), Baker (1980a), Bunzel (1987).

# Bee-eaters *Meropidae*

Small to medium-sized perching birds, with long, slightly decurved bills. Body elongated. Wings moderately long and pointed. Plumage generally brilliant green or blue, bright reds to yellows common on throat.

## Feather structure
Primaries = 10 (p9 longest, p10 much reduced)
Secondaries = 14
Tail = 12

## Sexes
Mostly similar in plumage.

## Moult
Strategy: Primaries descendant. Secondaries ascendant and descendant. Suspends. Tail irregular.
Sequence: primaries sequentially. Secondaries from 2 centres, s13 ascendantly and descendantly, s1 ascendantly.
Frequency: twice annually; SC, Wp.
Timing: summer finishing late winter; winter finishing early spring.

## BEE-EATER *Merops apiaster*

**Sexing**        Adults and birds older than 1s (5):

♂        Outer web of greater-coverts uniform rufous-chestnut. Median-coverts rufous-chestnut.

♀        Outer web of greater-coverts dull rufous-chestnut with greenish-blue leading edge (Fig). Median-coverts similar to ♂ but mostly admixed with green.

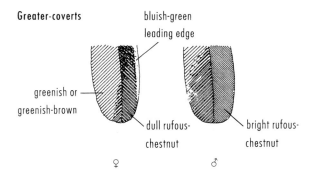

Greater-coverts          bluish-green
                          leading edge

greenish or
greenish-brown

dull rufous-
chestnut

bright rufous-
chestnut

♀                ♂

**Autumn**

1w (3)        Nape, mantle and upper wing-coverts dull green (hardly any chestnut). Lower back and rump green or dull yellowish-green, rarely golden-yellow or golden-green as in adult. Central tail lacks elongated feather tips. Iris dark brown to red-brown.

2w (5)        As 1st-summer but plumage generally more worn. Primary-coverts very abraded and brown, or with faint blue fringes, contrasting markedly with blue or bluish-green fringes on primaries and alula. In some birds primary-coverts may show mixed ages of feathers i.e. old brown or brownish-blue ones contrasting with fresh unabraded greenish-blue new ones.

Adult (6)        Rear crown, nape, mantle and upper back rufous-chestnut. Lower back and rump golden-yellow, sometimes streaked green. Well-developed elongation to tips of central pair of tail feathers. Primary-coverts greenish-blue, same colour as surrounding feathers (primary fringes and alula) (Fig). Iris greyish-red to bright red, rarely brown.

### Primary-coverts

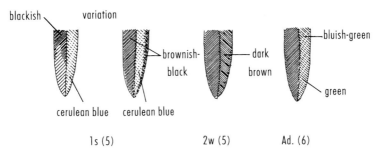

**Spring/Summer**

1s (5)     Similar to adult in appearance but fringes of primary-coverts cerulean-blue, or blue (mottled black), not greenish-blue as in adult. Colour contrasts with greenish-blue fringes to surrounding primaries and alula (best seen when wing is closed rather than fully spread). Elongated tips to central pair of tail feathers.

Adult (6)   As for Autumn.

General plumage coloration related to ageing appears variable; even eye colour can vary between ages. Primary-covert feature is the most reliable ageing character and should override all other features mentioned.

**Moult**

3     Complete post-juvenile moult, some starting August, others not until October. Those starting in winter quarters moult straight into pre-breeding plumage. Wing moult usually starts October or November and is finished by February-March.

5     Partial, head and body, some wing-coverts, but only in birds which moulted post-juvenile plumage early; later moulters go straight into pre-breeding plumage.

Adult   Complete post-breeding moult starting mid-June or July with head and body. Wings start August in some and are suspended just before autumn migration: others do not start wing or tail moult until in winter quarters.

Suspended moult resumed in winter quarters from October or November, finishing February. Partial pre-breeding moult confined to head, body and wing-coverts.

**Biometrics**    Full-grown & adult (BWP).

| | | | | | | |
|---|---|---|---|---|---|---|
| Wing ad. | ♂152 | (2.93;30) | 148-159 | ♀146 | (2.89;18) | 140-151 |
| juv. | 144 | (3.37;11) | 139-149 | 141 | (3.55;5) | 137-145 |
| Bill | 43.1 | (2.95;26) | 37-47 | 41.2 | (2.98;17) | 34-45 |
| Tarsus | 12.8 | (0.68;25) | 11.7-13.8 | 12.6 | (0.55;15) | 11.6-13.5 |
| Tail tip* | 23.0 | (2.37;29) | 19-28 | 17.2 | (1.95;17) | 14-20 |

*From longest (tip) t1 to 2nd longest (t2).

**References**    Lessells & Krebs (1989).

# Hoopoes *Upupidae*

Medium-sized perching birds with long decurved bill and crest. Wings broad and rounded. Pinkish-brown plumage with black and white wings, tail and tips to crest.

**Feather structure**

Primaries = 10 (p7 longest)
Secondaries = 10 (11 reduced)
Tail = 10

**Sexes**

Similar in plumage.

**Moult**

Strategy: primaries descendant. Secondaries ascendantly and descendantly. Suspend/arrest. Tail irregular.
Sequence: primaries sequentially. Secondaries from 2 centres, ascendantly from s1, ascendantly and descendantly from s7.
Frequency: uncertain - probably once only; (Sp), WC.
Timing: summer-early autumn finishing late winter.

# HOOPOE *Upupa epops*

Adults only:

Note: adults in worn plumage can be very difficult to sex - usually only possible when pair examined together for comparison.

♂        Deep vinaceous-pink chin and breast.

♀        Cinnamon-rufous breast and chin, latter partially tinged white; more extensively streaked black on sides of belly and breast.

## Autumn/Winter

3        Plumage generally 'fluffy', loose in texture. Breast brownish-pink and lacks vinous tinge of adults.

1w (3/5)        Once body moult completed birds like adults except for pattern and shape of outermost tail feather (t5) and shape of primary (Fig); primaries brown, not black as in newly moulted adults (but beware of unmoulted adult whose feathers will also be brown but will show a degree of abrasion to tips of outer primaries, whereas young birds will be comparatively fresh).

Adult (4/6)        Tail with well-defined boundaries between black and white areas; tips broad (almost square-ended). Tip of p9 broad and rounded (Fig). Primaries black and fresh (after moult).

## Spring/Summer

1s (5)        Tail pattern, shape and abrasion helpful; if tail retained (see Moult) outermost feather (t5) has tip well abraded; boundary between distal margin of black and white diffuse and speckled (Fig). Otherwise, primary shape and condition useful guide; pointed tip to p9 (Fig) and heavily abraded tips to outer primaries.

Adult (4)        Tail pattern (outermost, t5) with well-defined border between black and white markings (Fig). Outer primaries rounded and broad but shape less obvious in worn condition.

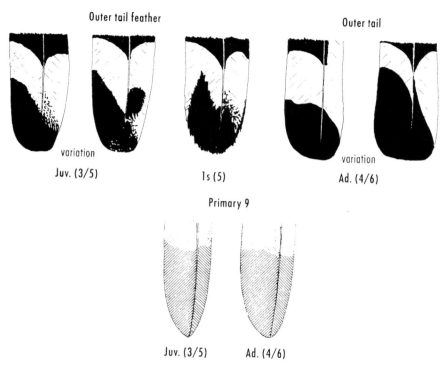

Outer tail feather

Outer tail

variation

Juv. (3/5)

1s (5)

variation

Ad. (4/6)

Primary 9

Juv. (3/5)

Ad. (4/6)

## Moult

3/5      Partial moult can start shortly after fledging in resident populations (S. Iberia & Africa), though in migratory birds probably not until in winter quarters; confined to body and sometimes part or all of tail and tertials. Wing and tail (except as above) moulted in 2nd calendar year (resident birds) or 3rd calendar year (migratory populations) at much the same time as adults.

Adult      Resident birds undertake complete post-breeding moult starting in July or August, completing October or November: in some, wing apparently suspends or arrests, or replacement is irregular. In migratory birds, moult may start July or August (including some inner primaries) and suspend prior to migration, completed December-late February; alternatively onset of moult may not be until in winter quarters, late September, October to mid-November, completed by February or March. Secondaries moult from 2 centres; ascendant from s1, ascendant and descendant from s7. Pre-breeding moult requires further investigation; probably partial and confined to head, neck and some body, January-February.

**Geographical variation** Considerable: involves size and colour of underparts, and pattern of black and white on wings and tail. Size smaller and colour deeper in tropical races, rather more uniform in European populations. Nine races recognized.

**Biometrics** Nominate *epops* (BWP).

| | | | | | | |
|---|---|---|---|---|---|---|
| Wing *ad.* | ♂151 | (2.20;23) | 147-153 | ♀146 | (3.21;12) | 142-151 |
| *juv.* | 146 | (3.42;34) | 141-152 | 142 | (3.85;34) | 135-149 |
| Bill* | 50.2 | (3.32;46) | 45-57 | 45.1 | (2.66;39) | 41-49 |
| Tarsus | 23.3 | (1.01;16) | 22-25 | 21.7 | (1.26;13) | 20-23 |

* measured from distal corner of nostril to tip.

# Wrynecks and Woodpeckers *Picidae*

Very small to large perching or climbing birds with zygodactyl feet. Wings short and rounded. Plumage cryptic, brown with blackish vermiculations, or predominantly black and white, or greenish.

## Feather structure
Primaries = 10 (p6, p7 or p8 longest, p1 much reduced in adult, larger in juvenile).
Secondaries = 10-12
Tail = 12 (but outermost pair short and soft)

## Sexes
Sexually dimorphic (not *Jynx torquilla*).

## Moult
Strategy: juveniles undergo 'complete' moult shortly after fledging except for secondaries, primary and greater-coverts. Otherwise, primaries descendant. Secondaries ascendant and descendant. Occasionally suspends. Tail centrifugal.
Sequence: primaries sequentially. Secondaries from 2 centres, ascendantly from s1, ascendantly and descendantly from s8.
Frequency: once annually (twice in *J. torquilla* SC, Wp); SC. Timing: summer finishing early winter;early spring (*J. torquilla*).

# WRYNECK *Jynx torquilla*

### Summer/Autumn

3          Fledged birds become similar in appearance to adults very quickly (see Moult). Before wing moult, juveniles have long outermost (10th) primary - half length of 9th, while those of adult are minute. Iris grey-brown or hazel-brown.

1w (3)      Primary-coverts narrow and sharply pointed; poorly-defined cinnamon spots with inverted cinnamon V on tip (Fig). Iris grey-brown.

Adult (4)     Outermost primaries and tertials abraded. After moult look for primary-coverts which are broader and rounded at tips, with well-defined deep rufous spots, mostly confined to outer web (but sometimes one or possibly two on inner which is otherwise completely black) and without inverted V on tip (Fig). Iris mahogany or rich hazel-brown, sometimes reddish-brown.

### Spring

1s (5)      Some birds retain some old unmoulted secondaries or tertials from juvenile plumage. These will be more abraded than surrounding flight feathers. Primary-coverts often worn at pale tip (inverted V), this pattern sometimes being absent altogether (see Fig). May also have contrastingly new (adult-type) outer one or two primary-coverts. Iris may still show grey-brown tone to outer rim of eye.

Adult (6)     Secondaries uniformly worn. Primary-coverts as Summer/Autumn but pale rufous spots towards tips often worn, reducing prominence (Fig).

Primary-coverts

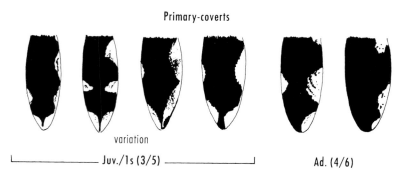

variation

Juv./1s (3/5)                 Ad. (4/6)

## Moult

3          Partial post-juvenile moult involving primaries, tail, and body. Does not moult secondaries, primary-coverts or tertials, sometimes central tail feathers. Moult usually starts in the nest shortly before fledging, mid-June to mid-July. Usually complete by July or August, sometimes early September. Many start secondary moult mid-July, but suspend before migration. Further replacement in winter quarters, though rarely all secondaries replaced, and none of tertials.

Adult        Complete post-breeding moult mid-June to mid-July and usually finished by August to mid-September. Occasionally some secondaries retained, probably suspended just before migration and replaced in winter quarters. Pre-breeding moult in February or March involves body, wing-coverts, and part or all of tail.

**Geographical variation** Often difficult to ascertain due to marked individual variation but *J. t. sarudnyi* (W. Siberia) is paler and greyer above, less vermiculated and with paler throat; underparts more white and less spotted. *J.t. tschusii* (Corsica, Sardinia, Italy and Yugoslavia) is distinctly darker than other races, especially on underparts; black markings on upperparts more marked, especially on crown, mantle and scapulars; bars on chest broader, up to 1mm; wing more rounded and shorter (av. 84, 79-86mm). Extralimital *J.t. mauretanica* (Algeria) is smaller (av. 81.5, 78-84mm) than west European populations; similar to *tschusii* in colour but upperparts darker and throat and chest paler cream and less heavily marked. Other races occur in central Asia, eastwards to Japan, becoming progressively darker and smaller further east.

**Biometrics**      Full-grown & adult. Nominate *torquilla* (BWP).

| | | | | | | |
|---|---|---|---|---|---|---|
| Wing | ♂89.6 | (2.06; 45) | 86-93 | ♀89.0 | (2.03; 23) | 86-93 |
| Bill | 16.1 | (0.90; 21) | 14.8-17.4 | 15.8 | (0.89; 12) | 14.9-17.1 |
| Tarsus | 19.5 | (0.49; 18) | 18.8-20.5 | 19.2 | (0.49; 10) | 18.7-19.7 |

**References**     Baker (1981 *a*).

# GREEN WOODPECKER *Picus viridis*

**Identification** From Grey-headed Woodpecker *P. canus* by black lores and facial mask. Yellowish, not grey, underparts. Wing >152mm, tarsus >27mm. In Grey-headed, wing <151mm, tarsus <27mm.

## Sexing

♂      Red malar stripe bordered black below and behind. Juveniles should show signs of red in black malar stripe sometimes by early June, usually July and August.

♀      Black malar stripe - no red. Juveniles that lack red should not be sexed as female until body moult is well under way in late July or August.

## Autumn/Winter

3      Underparts white or greenish-white and heavily mottled or barred dark brown. Iris grey-brown.

1w (3/5)      After moult, similar to adult but tertials show pale barring, most prominent on inner web and extending to tip (Fig). Primary-coverts more pointed than adult at tip; more-or-less uniform grey-brown with white barring, sometimes with faint dull green leading edge.

Adult (4/6)      Tertials uniform yellowish-green except for basal part of inner web which is browner and has whitish barring, but this does not extend towards tip (Fig). Primary-coverts broader and more rounded at tip; black with white barring and with diffuse but distinctive yellowish-green leading edge, similar in colour to rest of green upperparts. Iris white with pinkish tinge or pink outer ring.

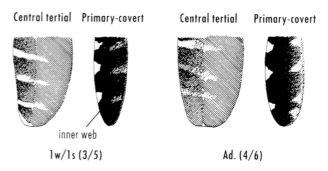

Central tertial    Primary-covert      Central tertial    Primary-covert

inner web

1w/1s (3/5)           Ad. (4/6)

## Spring/Summer

1s (5)　　　Tertials usually retained and like 1st-winter. Primary-coverts also as in 1st-winter.

Adult (6)　　As for Autumn/Winter.

## Moult

3　　　　　Partial post-juvenile moult involving primaries, tail, and body. Does not moult secondaries, primary-coverts or tertials though sometimes one or even two tertials may be replaced; occasionally outer primary-coverts replaced too, leaving old and contrasting inners unmoulted. Primary moult starts in nest, early June to July (earlier in Mediterranean regions), and is usually complete by October or November.

Adult　　　Complete post-breeding moult beginning with wing in late May to mid-July (earlier in Mediterranean regions), followed by body in July. Complete by mid-October, sometimes as late as end of November.

**Geographical variation** Slight and mostly clinal. *P.v. karelini* (central-southern Europe) has upperparts duller green than nominate race, dull grey-green when worn; colour of cheeks and underparts less saturated, only feather tips green. *P. v. innominatus* (S.Iran) like *karelini* except cheeks, throat and chest almost white; barring on tail more contrasting and sharper. *P.v. sharpei* (Spain and Portugal) is like *karelini* on upperparts, but black on side of face is confined to malar stripe and lores. Red malar stripe in males only narrowly bordered by black below and behind.

**Biometrics**　Adult. Nominate *viridis* (BWP).

| | | | | | | |
|---|---|---|---|---|---|---|
| Wing | ♂164 | (3.28;23) | 158-170 | ♀164 | (2.85;23) | 159-169 |
| Bill | 45.5 | (2.00;24) | 42-48 | 45.5 | (2.42;22) | 42-49 |
| Tarsus | 29.7 | (0.97;15) | 28-31 | 29.9 | (0.85;16) | 28-31 |

**References**　Baker (1981*a*), Miettinen, Pusa & Nikander (1986).

# GREAT SPOTTED WOODPECKER *Dendrocopos major*

## Sexing

♂          Crimson nape patch.

♀          Nape uniformly bluish-black.

Juveniles cannot be sexed until nape begins body moult; in British birds *D.m. anglicus* this is about July, but can be as late as October in eruptive north European birds of nominate race. Any sign of red on nape indicates ♂.

## Autumn/Winter

3          Crown dull crimson, edged black. Primaries tipped white. Vent dull red.

1w (3/5)   After body and primary moult, similar to adult but contrast is apparent between new black mantle feathers or replaced lesser- and median-coverts and old greater- and primary-coverts. Sometimes outer primary-coverts are replaced and contrast with abraded, browner inner ones (Fig).

Adult (4/6) All wing-coverts uniform glossy-black. There is typically no contrast in the wing, though beware of any unmoulted, and therefore browner, primary-coverts, often retained after moult. Usually such feathers are only one or a few scattered among the new ones (not sequential - see Fig). Note also that any bird in secondary moult must be adult.

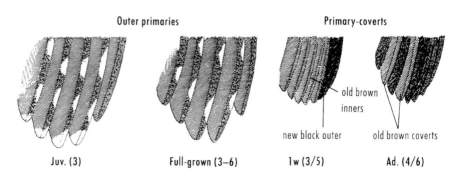

|  Outer primaries |  | Primary-coverts |  |
| :---: | :---: | :---: | :---: |
| Juv. (3) | Full-grown (3–6) | 1w (3/5) | Ad. (4/6) |

old brown inners

new black outer

old brown coverts

## Spring/Summer

1s (5)        Contrast is evident between old and brown unmoulted wing-coverts and newer glossy-black ones. Often inner greater-coverts may be replaced leaving old outers. Also outer primary-coverts sometimes replaced, contrasting with more abraded and browner inner ones.

Adult (6)     Wing-coverts uniform glossy-black. Beware of odd old retained primary-covert (see Moult).

## Moult

3        Partial post-juvenile moult including body, primaries, some or all upper wing-coverts, and tail; secondaries, tertials, and most or all of greater- and primary-coverts retained. Occasionally some inner greater-coverts and outer primary-coverts replaced. Primary moult begins in or just after fledging period; timing varies with latitude; usually May, completed by September to late November but likely to be later in continental nominate *major*, especially if erupting, as late as December or even January. During eruptions in nominate *major* primary moult is slowed down and often suspended.

Adult      Complete post-breeding moult June to mid-July, finishing mid-September to late October in temperate regions, later in northern latitudes; early August in Iberian race. Erupting populations slow moult down but do not suspend like post-juveniles. Sometimes odd one or two retained primary-coverts can be found anywhere in the tract.

**Geographical variation** Marked and strongly clinal involving mainly size and colour of underparts. About 24 races have been described. Northern birds are large with short but thick bill and white underparts; in south smaller with longer and more slender bill, underparts greyer or browner. Nominate *major* (Scandinavia, European USSR) greyish or creamy-white below, short but broad and deep-based bill. *D.m. pinetorum* (continental Europe - south of nominate *major*) smaller with longer and thinner bill, and pale grey-brown underparts and forehead. *D.m anglicus* similar to *pinetorum* but is slightly smaller and with more slender bill, upperparts darker and browner, and cheeks more buffy, scapulars less white. *D.m. italiae* (Italy and S. Alps) like *anglicus* but slightly paler below and whiter or pale parts of head.

317

**Biometrics**     Full-grown, sexes combined. *D.m. anglicus* (JKB).

| | | | |
|---|---|---|---|
| Wing | 130.2 | (2.6; 28) | 126-134 |
| Bill | 29.9 | (1.40; 22) | 27-33 |
| Bill (D)* | 8.7 | (;16) | 8-9 |
| Tarsus | 23.1 | (;15) | 21-25 |

*D.m. major* (BWP).

| | | | | | | | |
|---|---|---|---|---|---|---|---|
| Wing | ♂142 | (2.76;17) | 138-147 | ♀141 | (1.58;10) | 138-144 | |
| Bill | 28.9 | (0.98;18) | 28-31 | 27.4 | (1.04;10) | 26-29 | |
| Bill (D)* | 9.7 | (20) | 9-10 | (sexes combined) | | | |

* at gonys

**References**     Baker (1980*a*), Miettinen, Pusa & Nikander (1986).

# LESSER SPOTTED WOODPECKER *Dendrocopos minor*

## Sexing

Juvenile

♂ Forehead buff, tipped black, with crimson feathering on rear of crown. Extent of red depends on progress of juvenile moult, becoming more extensive and thus similar to adult by late autumn.

♀ Similar to ♂, but crimson feathering much reduced, almost to the extent of being difficult to see.

Adult

♂ Crown crimson.

♀ Crown buffish-white, sometimes with feathers tipped pink or red especially towards rear of crown. Black of nape extends much further onto crown than in ♂.

## Autumn/Winter

3 Tips to outer primaries white. Nape brownish-black. Rear of crown buff, streaked brownish-black.

1w (3/5) Brownish-black feathers on nape, contrasting with glossy black adult-type feathers. Any old outer primaries may still show white tips, though much abraded. If primary moult almost complete, measure small outermost, unmoulted primary from tip to longest primary: 1st-winter <46mm, adult >50mm. After moult very similar to adult. Contrast in colour may be apparent between retained juvenile primary-coverts and rest of wing-coverts. Sometimes some greater-coverts retained also, contrasting with new, blacker, adult-type neighbouring wing-coverts.

Adult (4/6) Wing-coverts uniformly black, showing no contrast in colour.

## Spring/Summer

1s (5) Primary-coverts mostly retained, but sometimes 1-3 outer ones replaced thus showing contrast against older inners; occasionally, greater-coverts retained which also show contrast with blacker neighbouring wing-coverts.

| Adult (6) | As Autumn/Winter. After moult cannot be aged beyond 2nd calendar year (4). |

**Moult**

| 3 | Partial post-juvenile moult starting soon after leaving the nest (sometimes while in the nest); primaries moult at this time, but not secondaries, tertials, primary-coverts (except occasionally 1-3 outers) or greater-coverts; completed (August, September) October-November, depending on subspecies. |

| Adult | Complete post-breeding moult starting in June or July, completed by September (October-November). Secondaries moult from 2 centres, ascendant from s1, ascendant and descendant from s8. |

**Geographical variation** Great and complex: involves mostly size (indicated by wing and tail and, to a lesser degree, bill) and colour, becoming darker and smaller from north to south, and larger and paler from west to east. The palest form, *kamtschatkensis* (Siberia) is virtually white on forehead, ear-coverts and underparts; shows much white on mantle, back and rump and broad white bars on scapulars, tertials, wing-coverts and flight feathers. *D.m. quadrifasciatus* (S.W. Caspian) is darkest and smallest form with brown forehead, ear-coverts, and underparts; upperparts and flight feathers mainly black. In Europe 3 groups separable on size. 1. *D.m. buturlini* (southern France, northern Spain, Italy, western and southern Yugoslavia, Bulgaria, northern Greece), *danfordi* (Greece, Turkey), and *comminutus* (Britain) are small in wing (ca. 86-87mm) with average or long bill. 2. *D.m. hortorum* (northern France, Netherlands, east to Poland and Rumania, south to Swiss Alps, Austria and northern Yugoslavia) is intermediate in wing (ca. 90mm) and bill. 3. Nominate *minor* (Fenno-Scandia, north-east Poland, and western Russia) is long in wing (ca. 94mm) and bill.

**Biometrics** Adult. *D.m. comminutus*, sexes combined (BWP).

| Wing | 87.1 | (1.20;34) | 84-90 |
| Bill | 12.7 | (0.56;35) | 11.5-13.8 |

Adult *D.m. hortorum* (BWP).

| Wing | ♂89.9 | (1.52;22) | 87-92 | ♀90.5 | (2.04;13) | 88-94 |
| Bill | 17.4 | (0.72;22) | 16.4-18.5 | 17.2 | (0.79;12) | 16.3-18.3 |
| Tarsus | 14.3 | (0.65;16) | 13.5-15.4 | 14.4 | (0.69;10) | 13.4-15.1 |

**References** Baker (1980*a*), Miettinen, Pusa & Nikander (1986).

# REFERENCES

Aebischer, N.J. (1985) Aspects of the biology of the Shag. Ph.D. Thesis. Durham.

Ainley, D.G., Lewis, T.J. & Morrell, S. (1976) Moult in Leach's and Ashy Storm-petrels. Wilson Bulletin, 88: 76-95.

Allaine, D. & Lebreton, J.D. (1990) The influence of age and sex on wing-tip pattern in adult Black-headed Gull Larus ridibundus. Ibis, 132: 560-567.

Alström, P. (1985) Artbestämning av storskarv Phalacrocorax carbo och toppskarv Ph. aristotelis. Vår Fågelvärld, 44: 325-350.

Anderson, A. (1975) A method of sexing Moorhens. Wildfowl, 26: 77-82.

Appleby, R.H., Madge, S.C. & Mullarney, K. (1986) Identification of divers in immature and winter plumages. British Birds, 79: 365-391.

Baker, J.K. (1979) A guide to ageing & sexing non-passerines (part 1). Ringers' Bulletin, 5: 82-86.

Baker, J.K. (1980a) A guide to ageing & sexing non-passerines (part 2). Ringers' Bulletin, 5: 91-94.

Baker, J.K. (1980b) A guide to ageing & sexing non-passerines (part 3). Ringers' Bulletin, 5: 104-107.

Baker, J.K. (1981a) A guide to ageing & sexing non-passerines (part 4). Ringers' Bulletin, 5: 117-119.

Baker, J.K. (1981b) A guide to ageing & sexing non-passerines (part 5). Ringers' Bulletin, 5: 133-135.

Baker, J.K. (1982) A guide to ageing & sexing non-passerines (part 6). Ringers' Bulletin, 6: 17-18.

Baker, J.K. (1983a) A guide to ageing & sexing non-passerines (part 7). Ringers' Bulletin, 6: 32-33.

Baker, J.K. (1983b) A guide to ageing & sexing non-passerines (part 8). Ringers' Bulletin, 6: 43-46.

Baker, J.K. (1984) A guide to ageing & sexing non-passerines (part 9). Ringers' Bulletin, 6: 70-71.

Barth, E.K. (1967) Standard body measurements in Larus argentatus, L. fuscus, L. canus, and L. marinus. Nytt. Mag. Zool. 14: 7-83.

Beer, J.V. & Boyd, H. (1962) Measurements of White-fronted Geese wintering at Slimbridge. Wildfowl Trust 14th Ann. Report, 114-119.

Berthold, P. (1967) On adherent colours of the plumage. Bull Br. Orn. Club 87: 89-90.

Bourne, W.R.P., Mackrill, E.J., Paterson, A.M. & Yésou, P. (1988) The Yelkouan Shearwater. British Birds, 81: 306-319.

Boyd, H., Harrison, J. & Allison, A. (1975) Duck Wings. WAGBI.

British Ornithologists' Union (1992) Checklist of Birds of Britain and Ireland. 6th edition. Tring, Herts: BOU.

Bunzel, M. (1987) The Kingfisher in Mittelwestfalen. Inaugural dissertation. Münster University.

Burn, D.M. & Mather, J.R. (1974) The White-billed Diver in Britain. British Birds, 67: 257-296.

Busching, W.D. (1987) Fund eines Geldschnabel-tistauchers (*Gavia adamsii*) im Kreis Stralsund und Kennzeichen der Seetaucher. Orn. Mitt. 39. Jahrg Nr.10: 256-284.

Corkhill, P. (1972) Measurements of Puffins as criteria of sex and age. Bird Study, 19: 193-201.

Coulson, J.C., Thomas, C.S., Butterfield, J.E.L., Duncan, N., Monaghan, P. & Shedden, C. (1983) The use of head and bill length to sex live gulls, *Laridae*. Ibis, 125: 549-557.

Cramp, S. (ed) (1985) Handbook of the birds of Europe, the Middle East, and North Africa: the birds of the Western Palearctic. Vol IV. Oxford University Press. Oxford.

Cramp, S. & Simmons, K.E.L. (eds) (1977, 1980, 1983) Handbook of the birds of Europe, the Middle East, and North Africa: the birds of the Western Palearctic. Vols I, II, III. Oxford University Press. Oxford.

de Kroon, G.H.J. (1979) Method and provisional results of trapping Water Rail in the Netherlands. Ringing & Migration, 2: 132-136.

De Roo, A. (1966) Age characteristics in adult and subadult Swift *Apus apus* (L.) based on interrupted and delayed wing-moult. Gerfaut 56: 113-134.

Doucet, J. (1971) The moult of remiges and rectrices in the Kingfisher (*Alcedo atthis*). Gerfaut, 61: 14-42.

Dunnet, G.M. & Anderson, A. (1961) A method for sexing living Fulmars in the hand. Bird Study, 8: 119-127.

Edelstam, C. (1984) Patterns of moult in large birds of prey. Ann. Zool. Fennici, 21: 271-276.

Evans, M.E. & Kear, J. (1978) Weights and measurements of Bewick's Swans during winter. Wildfowl, 29: 118-122.

Ewins, P.J. (1984) Ageing Black Guillemot. Ringers' Bulletin, 6: 73.

Ewins, P.J. (1988) The timing of moult in Black Guillemot *Cepphus grylle* in Shetland. Ringing & Migration, 9: 5-10.

Fjeldså, J. (1973) Distribution and geographical variation of the Horned Grebe *Podiceps auritus*. Ornis Scandinavica, 4: 55-86.

Flegg, J.J.M. & Glue, D.E. (1973) A Water Rail study. Bird Study, 20: 69-79.

Forsman, D. (1984) Roufågelsguiden. Lintutieto.

Ginn, H.B. & Melville, D.S. (1983) Moult in Birds. BTO Guide 19.

Göhringer, R. (1951) Vergleichude Untersuchungen über das Juvenil- und Adult-kleid bei der Amsel (*Turdus merula L.*) und beim Star (*Sturnus vulgaris L.*). Revue Suisse Zool., 58: 279-358.

Grant, C.H.B. (1911) The moults and plumages of the Common Moorhen. Ibis, 2: 298-304.

Grant, P.J. (1982) Gulls: a guide to identification. T. & A.D. Poyser, Calton.

Haapala, J. & Niiranen, S. (1987) Sarvipöllön iän Määrittäminen. Lintumies, 22: 160-162.

Hardy, A.R., Hirons, G.J.M., Stanley, P.I. & Huson, L.W. (1981) Sexual dimorphism in size of Tawny Owl: a method for sexing in field studies. Ardea, 69: 181-184.

Hario, M. (1986) Itämeren Iokkilinnut. Lintutieto.

Harper, D.G.C. (1984) Moult interruptions in passerines resident in Britain. Ringing & Migration, 5: 101-104.

Harris, M.P. (1966*a*) Breeding biology of the Manx Shearwater *Puffinus puffinus*. Ibis, 108: 17-33.

Harris, M.P. (1966*b*) Age of return to the colony, age of breeding and adult survival of Manx Shearwater. Bird Study, 13: 84-95.

Harris, M.P. (1979) Measurements and weights of British puffins. Bird Study, 26: 179-186.

Harris M.P. (1984) Ageing Puffins. Ringers' Bulletin, 6: 73-74.

Harris, M.P. & Hope Jones, P. (1969) Sexual differences in measurements of Herring and Lesser Black-backed gulls. British Birds, 62: 129-133.

Harris, M.P. & Wanless, S. (1988) Measurements and seasonal changes in weight of Guillemot *Uria aalge* at a breeding colony. Ringing & Migration, 9: 32-36.

Harris, M.P. & Wanless, S. (1990) Moult and autumn colony attendance of auks. British Birds, 83: 55-66.

Hope Jones, P. (1988) Post-fledging wing and bill development in the Razorbill *Alca torda islandica*. Ringing & Migration, 9: 11-17.

Insley, H. & Young, L. (1979) Ageing Collared Doves. Ringers' Bulletin, 5: 72-74.

Isenmann, P. (1973) Biometrische Untersuchungen an der Gelbfüssigen Silbermöwe (*Larus argentatus michahellis*) aus der Camargue. Vogelwarte, 27(1): 16-24.

Jenni, L. & Winkler, R. (1989) The feather-length of small passerines: a measurement for wing-length in live birds and museum skins. Bird Study, 36: 1-15.

Johnson, P.N. (1991) Development of talon flange and serrations in the Barn Owl *Tyto alba*: a guide to ageing. Ringing & Migration, 12: 126-127.

Kennerley, P.R. & Leader, P.J. (1991) Separation of Cuckoo and Oriental Cuckoo. Dutch Birding, 13: 143-145.

Kop, P.P.A.M. (1971) Some notes on the moult and age determination in the Great Crested Grebe. Ardea, 59: 1-2; 56-60.

Lessells, C.M. & Krebs, J.R. (1989) Age and breeding performance of European Bee-eaters. Auk, 106: 375-382.

Marquiss, M. (1980) Using moult and iris colour to age Sparrowhawks. Ringers' Bulletin, 5: 94-95.

Matthews, G.V.T. & Campbell, C.R.G. (1969) Weights and measurements of Greylag Geese in Scotland. Wildfowl 20: 86-93.

Miettinen, J., Pusa, J. & Nikander, P.J. (1986) Voiko Eikkojen iän määrittää ? Lintumies, 21:188-194.

Milstein, P. le S., Prestt, I. & Bell, A.A. (1970). The breeding cycle of the Grey Heron. Ardea, 58: 171-257.

Murton, R.K., Westwood, N.J. & Isaacson, A.J. (1974) Factors affecting egg-weight, body weight and moult of the Woodpigeon *Columba palumbus*. Ibis, 116: 52-73.

Newton, I. (1986) The Sparrowhawk. T & A.D. Poyser, Calton.

Newton, I. & Marquiss, M. (1982) Moult in the Sparrowhawk. Ardea, 70: 163-172.

Nieboer, E. (1973) Geographical and Ecological Differentiation in the Genus *Circus*. PhD Thesis. Amsterdam University.

Norman, S.C. (1990) Factors influencing the onset of post-nuptial moult in Willow Warblers, *Phylloscopus trochilus*. Ringing & Migration, 11: 90-100.

Norman, S.C. (1991) Suspended split-moult system - an alternative explanation for some species of Palearctic migrants. Ringing & Migration, 12: 135-138.

Okill, J.D., French, D.D. & Wanless, S. (1989) Sexing Red-throated Divers in Shetland. Ringing & Migration, 10: 26-31.

Olsen, K.M. (1989) Field identification of the smaller skuas. British Birds, 82: 143-176.

Owen, M. & Ogilvie, M.A. 1979. Wing moult and weights of barnacle geese in Spitsbergen. Condor, 81(1): 42–52.

Palmer, R.S. (1976) Handbook of North American Birds. Vol 1. Yale University Press. New Haven.

Parr, A.J. (1984) Ageing and sexing Coot. Ringers' Bulletin, 6: 72.

Petty, S.J. (1991) A guide to age determination of Tawny Owl *Strix aluco*. Ecology and Conservation of European Owls (report).

Picozzi, N. (1981 *a*) Weight, wing-length and iris colour of Hen Harriers in Orkney. Bird Study, 28: 159-161.

Picozzi, N. (1981 *b*) Growth and sex of nestling Merlins in Orkney. Ibis, 125: 377-382.

Pictiäinen, H., Ahola, K., Forsman, D., Haapala, J., Korpimäki, E., Lagerström, M. & Niiranen, S. (1988) Pöllöjen iän Määrittäminen. Helsingin yliopiston eläinmuseo. Helsinki.

Piersma, T. (1988) The annual moult cycle of Great Crested Grebes. Ardea, 76: 82-95.

Potts, G.R. (1971) Moult in the Shag *Phalacrocorax aristotelis*, and the ontogeny of the "Staffelmauser". Ibis, 113: 298-305.

Prater, A.J., Marchant, J.H. & Vuorinen, J. (1977) Guide to the Identification and Ageing of Holarctic Waders. BTO Guide 17.

Salminen, A. (1983) Suomen sorsalinnut. Lintutieto.

Scott, D.A. (1970) The breeding biology of the Storm Petrel *Hydrobates pelagicus*. D. Phil. Thesis. University of Oxford.

Scott, P. & The Wildfowl Trust. (1972) The Swans. Michael Joseph. London.

Smith, R.D. (1988) Age and sex-related differences in biometrics and moult of Kittiwakes. Ringing & Migration, 9: 44-48.

Smithe, F.B. (1975, 1981) Naturalist's Colour Guide. 3 parts. Am. Mus. Nat. Hist. New York.

Snow, D.W. (1967) A guide to moult in British Birds. BTO Guide 11.

Stegmann, B. (1956) Über die Herkunft des flüchtigen rosenroten Federpigments. J. Orn. 97: 204-205.

Stresemann, E. (1967) Inheritance and adaptation in moult. Proc. Int. Orn. Cong. 14: 75-80.

Stresemann, E. & Stresemann, V. (1966) Die Mauser der Vögel. Journal für Ornithologie, 107 Sonderheft.

Stresemann, V. & Stresemann, E. (1961) Die Handschwingen-Mauser der Kuckucke (*Cuculidae*). Journal für Ornithologie, 102: 317-352.

Svensson, L. (1992) Identification Guide to European Passerines. 4th edition. Stockholm.

Temple, S.A. (1972) Sex and age characteristics of North American Merlins. Bird Banding, 43: 191-196.

Village, A., Marquiss, M. & Cook, D.C. (1980) Moult, ageing and sexing of Kestrels. Ringing & Migration, 3: 53-59.

Voous, K. (1977) List of Recent Holarctic Bird Species. Revised edition. BOU, London.

Walters, J. (1987 *a*) Primary moult in Black Terns and Common Terns. Ringing & Migration, 8: 83-90.

Walters, J. (1987 *b*) The onset of the postnuptial moult in the Common Tern *Sterna hirundo* near Amsterdam. Ardea, 67: 62-67.

Winkler, R. (1979) Zur Pneumatisation des Schädeldaches der Vogel. Der Ornithologische Beobachter, 76: 49-118.

Winkler, R. (1987) Zur Grossgefiedermauser junger Kormorane *Phalacrocorax carbo sinensis*. Der Ornithologische Beobachter, 84: 317-323.

Wood, H.B. (1950) Growth bars in feathers. Auk, 67: 486-491.

Yésou, P., Paterson, A.M., Mackrill, E.J. & Bourne, W.R.P. (1990) Plumage variation and identification of the 'Yelkouan Shearwater'. British Birds, 83: 299-319.

Zonfrillo, B. (1987) Ageing Manx Shearwaters. Ringers' Bulletin, 7: 15.

# GLOSSARY

anterior: at or towards the front of the bird or a particular structure

arrested moult: a moult which has stopped before all the old feathers have been replaced. The old feathers, which have been retained, are then replaced in sequence at the time of the next complete moult. For example a bird which has moulted p1 to p6 and has then arrested would not replace the outer primaries until after p1 to p6 had been renewed during the next moult (see Fig. 15)

ascendant moult: moult which progresses from a point in the wing inwards (towards the bird's body)

bare parts: the areas of the body surface which are not covered by feathers: the bill, eyes, legs and feet, together with any unfeathered skin

brood patch: the bare patch (or patches) developed on the belly of most incubating birds

centrifugal: a term which describes the progress of moult in two directions from one centre i.e. inwards and outwards at the same time. For example tail moult which progresses from the central pair outwards

centripetal: the opposite of centrifugal - a moult which starts at two centres and converges. For example tail moult which starts with the outer pair and finishes at the central pair

cere: fleshy covering found at proximal portion of the upper mandible in birds of prey (see Fig. 1)

contour feathers: the outer feathers covering the head and body. Usually applied only to the small body feathers, but strictly speaking also includes all flight feathers

culmen: the central ridge of the upper mandible (see Fig. 1)

descendant: moult which progresses from a point on the wing outwards (away from the bird's body)

dimorphic: of a species, occurring in two forms. Usually applied to sexual dimorphism which is the existence of differences in appearance between male and female members of a species

distal: towards the outside, far from the bird's body

dorsal: of the back or upper surface

emargination: a step or abrupt narrowing of the web of a feather, occurring towards the tip of the outer web of the feather (see Fig. 2)

EURING: the European Union for Bird Ringing

feather tract: in most species the feathers are not distributed evenly all over the body, but in a series of groups known as tracts - e.g. dorsal, femoral. The feathers in a tract usually moult about the same time

gonys: angle formed by the junction of the two rami of the lower mandible near its tip (see Fig. 1)

nail: a horny plate-like feature, shaped like a shield, found at the tip of the upper mandible of wildfowl (see Fig. 1)

notch: an abrupt narrowing of a feather, similar to emargination, but occurring in the inner web of the feather (see Fig. 1)

326

patagium: the fold of the skin, covered with tiny feathers, which links the forepart of the wing with the body

posterior: at or towards the back of a bird or particular structure

preen gland: a gland situated immediately above the base of the tail feathers and secreting oil used in preening

proximal: towards the inside, nearer the body - the reverse of distal

rami: the two halves of the lower mandible, separated by soft tissue near the base but uniting distally in the gonys

rectrices: the main tail feathers

remiges: collective term for the primaries and secondaries

rictal bristles: bristles situated at the angle of the gape and prominent in some species e.g. Nightjar *Caprimulgus europaeus*

score: moult scores are computed for a tract by adding together the scores for individual feathers within the tract. For example the primary score of a bird with 10 primaries which are large enough to be recorded will lie between 0 (moult not started) and 50 (all feathers completely renewed). This scoring system follows that used by the BTO on its moult cards

serially descendant: when a new moult cycle starts before the preceding one has finished (reached the outermost primary) so that there are two or more active moult centres in the wing which have started at different times and are following the same sequence. This is the equivalent of the German term *Staffelmauser* - 'step-wise moult' (Stresemann & Stresemann 1966) (see Fig. 15)

simultaneous moult: all the feathers in the tract are lost at the same time (see Fig. 15)

shield: a fleshy covering on the proximal portion of the upper mandible; in some species the shield sometimes extends up the forehead e.g. Coot *Fulica atra*. In birds of prey this shield is referred to as the cere

speculum: a bar or patch of distinctive colour (usually metallic) found on secondaries in wildfowl (see Fig. 1)

suspended moult: a temporary interruption which is subsequently resumed at the point of interruption. For example, a bird which has moulted p1 to p6 and has then suspended will resume its moult at p7 (see Fig. 15)

# INDEX OF ENGLISH NAMES

# INDEX OF SCIENTIFIC NAMES